The Marshall Cavendish
ILLUSTRATED ENCYCLOPEDIA OF
PLANTS
AND
EARTH SCIENCES

The Marshall Cavendish
ILLUSTRATED ENCYCLOPEDIA OF
PLANTS
AND
EARTH SCIENCES

VOLUME NINE

EDITOR-IN-CHIEF
Professor David M. Moore

SPECIALIST SUBJECT EDITORS
Professor V. H. Heywood
Botany
Professor A. Hallam
Earth Sciences
Dr S. R. Chant
Botany

ADVISORY EDITORS
Professor W. T. Stearn
Flowering Plants
Dr I. B. K. Richardson
Flowering Plants
Dr Peter Raven
Plant Ecology
Professor Lincoln Constance
Special Consultant

EDITORIAL DIRECTOR
Dr Graham Bateman

Marshall Cavendish
New York · London · Sydney

CONTENTS

Reference Edition Published 1988

Published by:
Marshall Cavendish Corporation
147 West Merrick Road
Freeport N.Y. 11520

AN EQUINOX BOOK

Planned and produced by:
Equinox (Oxford) Ltd
Littlegate House
St Ebbe's Street
Oxford OX1 1SQ
England

Copyright © Equinox (Oxford) Ltd 1988

Library of Congress Cataloging-in-Publication Data
The Encyclopedia of plants and earth sciences.
  Bibliography: p.
  Includes index.
  1. Botany—Dictionaries. 2. Botany, Economic—Dictionaries.
3. Crops—Dictionaries. 4. Angiosperms-Dictionaries. 5. Earth
sciences—Dictionaries. 6. Ecology—Dictionaries. I. Marshall
Cavendish Corporation.
QK7.E53 1988 580′.3′21 87-23927

ISBN 0-86307-901-6 (Set)
ISBN 0-86307-910-5 (Vol 9)

Previous page
Rock profile San Sebastian, Spain (see p.1194).

coal and oil), calcium carbonate (as limestone), aluminum and iron oxides, and *evaporites.

The different types of sedimentary rock described here can be related not only to weathering processes, but also to the *climatic zone of the Earth in which they formed (for weathering is obviously greatly influenced by climate) as well as to the different parts of tectonic plates over which surface processes may be operating.

Argillaceous Rocks

By definition, argillaceous rocks contain particles less than 1/16mm in diameter and are usually even more finely grained, requiring electron-microscope techniques to study them. They form about 60% of all sedimentary rocks, and on average contain 60% *clay minerals (formed by the chemical weathering of alumino-silicate minerals), 30% *quartz, 5% *feldspar, and around 1% each of iron oxides and organic matter. Such finely disseminated organic matter can act as a source for oil – indeed it is estimated that 75% of all organic matter is buried within argillaceous deposits, rather than concentrated in materials such as *coal (see *petroleum).

When first deposited, argillaceous sediments contain considerable quantities of water, which may amount to as much as 80% of their volume. Such large amounts of water are held between the flakes of clay minerals, which become packed better together during burial by a process termed compaction. The amount of compaction plays a major role in determining the nature of the resultant argillaceous rock.

The types of clay mineral present in an argillaceous rock give some indication of the degree of chemical *weathering, and hence climatic conditions, experienced by the source region: the mineral *kaolinite, for example, indicates intense chemical weathering. The type of source rock is more difficult to interpret, save in the case of fuller's earth deposits that contain clay minerals resulting from the break-down of volcanic ash. Fuller's earth deposits may therefore result from the weathering *in situ* of falls of volcanic ash.

Argillaceous rocks are described as *siltstones, *clays, mudstones, *shales or *marls.

Clay and Mudstone

Clay is an *argillaceous rock resulting from the first stages of the compaction of mud. It is soft and easily absorbs more water, becoming plastic (see *clay minerals). Unlike clay, mudstone will not absorb water. It has lost much of the water present when the sediment was originally a mud, and breaks in a random fashion, reflecting its homogeneous internal structure.

Shale

Shales result from the compaction of mud.

mineral grains present in a sedimentary rock enables conclusions to be made about both the nature of the source rock (which contributed the rock fragments) and the *weathering processes that caused its disintegration. Such an interpretation is relatively easy for a coarse-grained sediment, such as beach pebbles, but is more difficult with a sand, in which a constituent grain may be only a part of a single crystal: thus pebbles could be matched with known exposures of probable source rocks, but a sand grain consisting wholly of the mineral quartz could have been derived from a multitude of rock types. A sandstone composed entirely of *quartz contains virtually no information about its source, but is

testament to the fact that the various surface processes (weathering, *erosion, *deposition) fractionate original crustal materials into pure deposits of, in this example, silica. The way in which the source rock has been fractionated into its various components by surface processes determines to which of the major categories the eventual sedimentary rock belongs. (Most sedimentary rocks, classified as either detrital or chemical-organic, are also classified according to their grain-size as *rudaceous rocks, *arenaceous rocks or *argillaceous rocks.) The degree of fractionation accomplished by surface processes has tremendous economic importance, producing concentrates of carbon (as

The Rocks of the Earth

Rocks are divided into three classes or types: *igneous, *sedimentary and *metamorphic. A fourth type of "rock", *soil, consists of the eroded products of true rock. Major entries on these types of rock are included in this section in the order given above. The order in which more detailed entries are arranged reflects the ways in which rocks are commonly classified. Igneous rocks are arranged in order of decreasing acidity or quartz content and, after each rock type is described, its fine-grained or volcanic equivalent is dealt with. Sedimentary rocks are arranged in order of increasing particle size, with rocks of organic origin left to the end of the section. Finally, metamorphic rocks are arranged in a sequence such that rocks in whose formation pressure is dominant are dealt with before those in which heat is a progressively more important factor.

Igneous Rocks

Whenever we see that most spectacular of natural phenomena, a volcanic eruption, we obtain direct evidence of the existence of molten rock material issuing from within the Earth. The molten material at depth is termed *magma* and when it solidifies the product is an igneous rock.

Nearly all igneous rocks are composed of silicate materials, and the magmas from which they form are derived from partial melting of the Earth's mantle and crust, layers of the Earth which are normally in a solid state. The deepest zone of the Earth, the core, is thought to be permanently molten, but this is not the source of the igneous rocks we see at the surface today (geophysical and other evidences suggest strongly that the core is composed of iron and nickel rather than silicates). Nevertheless, igneous activity in the past – and continuing to the present day – may be responsible for the distinct compositional zones of the interior of the Earth, if we assume that the planet formed originally as a homogeneous body. To support this assertion we must consider first the way in which rocks melt.

It is generally thought that when existing solid rocks begin to melt, as a result of local thermal perturbation within the Earth, the melting will be only partially completed before the magma collects together and begins to migrate away from the source region under the influence of gravity. It is thus possible to make a distinction between the molten phase (the magma) and the

remaining unmelted material (the refractory residue). If we assume the Earth originally had a composition like that of the chondritic *meteorites, it must have consisted of a mixture of metallic iron and nickel with silicate materials. Heating such a mixture first produces a melt rich in iron and nickel while leaving a refractory residue of silicates. The melt phase is in this case denser than the refractory residue and we can thus assume that it migrates downward, at the same time displacing the silicates upward. This is an attractive hypothesis to explain the formation of the core.

Subsequently, continued heating of the silicate layer induces further episodes of partial melting within it. In this case the melting behavior is more complex, but there is a general tendency for certain constituents (e.g., silicon, aluminum, sodium, potassium, water) to become concentrated in the melt while others, notably magnesium, are concentrated in the residue: thus silicate magmas tend to migrate upwards. This has resulted in the differentiation of the silicate-rich parts of the Earth into an upper layer known as the crust, rich in silica, aluminum and the alkali metals, and a lower zone, the mantle, rich in magnesium silicates, which are relatively silica-poor, and rather impoverished in aluminum and alkalis.

Hence igneous activity can be viewed as one of the most fundamental Earth processes, and probably all the rocks we see at

the surface of the Earth today owe their ultimate origins to this activity.

Igneous rocks at the surface of the Earth are of course subsequently subjected to *erosion and *weathering and give rise to sedimentary materials such as sandstones and clays. Both igneous and these *sedimentary rocks can also become reconstituted as *metamorphic rocks under the influence of heat and pressure; for example, in episodes of mountain-building. Finally, igneous activity is also effective in expelling water and carbon dioxide from the interior of the Earth, thus making a substantial contribution to the oceans and the atmosphere. Some of the carbon dioxide may become fixed again in solid rock when it combines with calcium to form *limestones.

Classification. Igneous rocks are classified in a number of ways and one of the most important distinctions, based on mode of occurrence, is into the two main groups, *extrusive* and *intrusive*.

The extrusive rocks are those which reach the surface as magma and are ejected either as streams of molten material (lavas) or as explosive ejections of droplets and already solidified particles (see *vulcanicity). The explosively ejected rocks are known as *pyroclastics*, those composed of small particles being termed *ashes* or *tuffs*, while coarser material is termed *agglommerate*.

The intrusive rocks represent magma

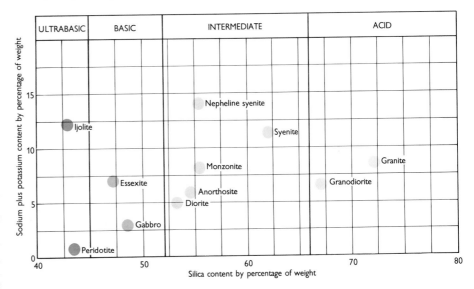

The classification of igneous rocks according to their silica and sodium-plus-potassium contents, with the positions on the table of several common plutonic igneous rocks shown (their fine-grained equivalents would be similarly placed).

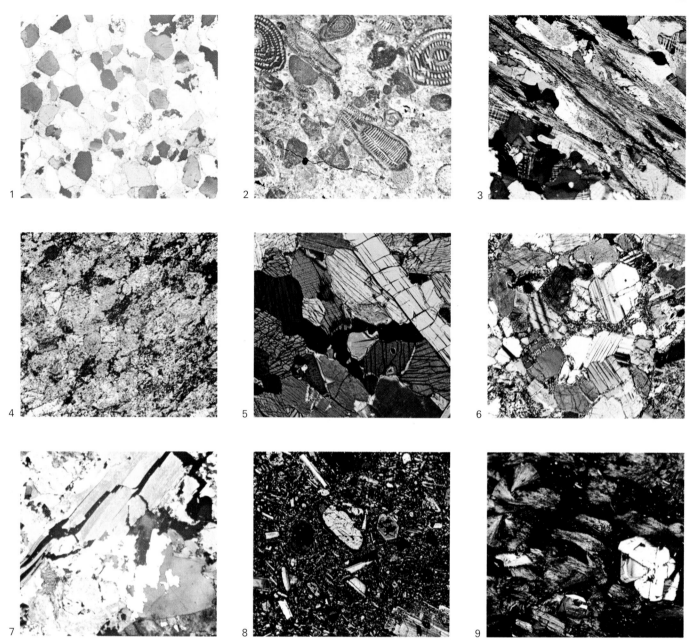

trapped below ground and solidifying there, and in order to see them we must wait until erosion has removed the overlying strata. The intrusive rocks generally cool more slowly than the extrusive and thus crystallize to a larger grain-size. The coarser-grained intrusive rocks (crystals generally greater than 0.2in (5mm) in diameter) are usually known as *plutonic* rocks.

Igneous rocks may also be classified in terms of their chemical compositions, one of the oldest divisions being based on their silica content (that is the weight per cent of SiO_2 determined by chemical analysis). The divisions are *acid rocks* ($SiO_2 > 64\%$), *intermediate rocks* ($SiO_2 = 53$–64%), *basic rocks* ($SiO_2 = 45$–53%), and *ultrabasic rocks* ($SiO_2 < 45\%$). The total content of the alkali metal oxides ($Na_2O + K_2O$) is also a useful indication of the nature of igneous rock types.

Apart from alkalis and silica, the other main chemical constituents of igneous rocks may be described quite simply. Firstly,

alumina, aluminum oxide (Al_2O_3), is a major constituent (10 to 20% by weight) of nearly all rock types, the major exception being *peridotite, which has much less than this. Consequently, those rocks such as granites and syenites which have a high total content of silica plus alkalis (75% or more), together with substantial quantities of Al_2O_3, contain only relatively small amounts of other constituents such as calcium oxide (CaO), iron oxides (FeO and Fe_2O_3) and magnesium oxide (MgO). Conversely, the content of these constituents is much higher in gabbros which have a low total of alkalis plus silica. Peridotites have relatively low silica and alumina as already noted and are very rich in magnesium, fairly rich in iron, but unlike the gabbros rather poor in calcium.

The chemical compositions discussed above have been expressed in terms of oxides, but this is a matter of convenience rather than reality. The rocks themselves consist of mixtures of minerals, most of

Thin sections of a selection of igneous, metamorphic and sedimentary rocks viewed under crossed polars: (1) and (2) are sedimentary, (3) and (4) metamorphic and the remainder igneous. (1) Quartz sandstone, a typical arenaceous rock, having particles principally of silica; (2) limestone, whose principal constituents are calcite and dolomite, shown here containing fossils; (3) gneiss, a rock formed during high-grade regional metamorphism; (4) hornfels, a result of metamorphism through heat; (5) peridotite, an igneous rock whose primary constituent is olivine; (6) gabbro, a typical basic rock; (7) granite, a typical alkaline rock; (8) basalt, the fine-grained equivalent of gabbro; and (9), rhyolite, the fine-grained equivalent of granite.

which are silicates, and it happens that silicates have compositions which can be expressed in oxide terms. For example, the chemical formula of magnesium orthosilicate (the mineral *olivine) is Mg_2SiO_4, and this can be expressed as $2MgO + SiO_2$ (magnesium oxide plus silica). In detail, rocks are classified by their mineral assemblages and by the relative proportions of the different minerals they contain. Several parameters are of importance:

Hound Tor, Dartmoor, UK, a striking formation of granite. Granite is described as a plutonic igneous rock, since it is intruded into the rocks of the crust at depth, so becoming visible at the surface only through the influence of erosion.

(*i*) The ratio of the dark-colored or ferromagnesian minerals (olivine, pyroxene, hornblende and biotite mica) to the pale-colored minerals (feldspars, feldspathoids and quartz). This ratio is often called the *color index*. A high color index implies a high content of magnesium, iron and often calcium.

(*ii*) The relative proportions of the alkali *feldspars (orthoclase, sanidine, microcline and perthites) to the calcium-bearing plagioclase feldspars (all *plagioclases that have more calcium than does albite). A high content of alkali feldspar implies richness in alkali metals, and conversely a high plagioclase content implies richness in calcium.

(*iii*) The presence or absence of *quartz or *feldspathoid minerals (nepheline, leucite, sodalite). This parameter is a reflection of the balance between alkalis and silica. An excess of silica means that the rocks contain free quartz. When alkalis and silica are balanced only feldspars will be present, while a silica deficiency is expressed by the presence of feldspathoids, compositionally similar to feldspars but poorer in silica.

A consideration of the chemical characteristics of the various groups allows some generalizations about mineralogy to be made. Granites, syenites and feldspathoidal syenites are all poor in ferromagnesian minerals and have color indices of 20 or less (i.e., less than 20% of the rock is made up of ferromagnesian minerals). Color index rises to about 50 in the gabbros and is between 20 and 50 in the diorites and syenodiorites. The peridotites have color indices approaching 100. Granites are the only rocks with enough silica to contain significant

amounts of free quartz, whereas the feldspathoidal syenites are sufficiently alkali-rich to contain significant quantities of feldspathoids, usually nepheline: most of the other igneous rocks contain neither quartz nor feldspathoids except in small quantities, their major light-colored constituent being a feldspar of one sort or another. Rocks poor in alkalis are characterized by plagioclase feldspar (except for the peridotites which contain little or no feldspar) – typical examples are gabbros and diorites. Increasing alkali content leads to rocks containing significant quantities of both plagioclase and alkali feldspar (syenodiorites, granites), while high-alkali rocks are characterized by alkali feldspar well in excess of plagioclase (e.g., syenites and feldspathoidal syenites).

Fine-grained extrusive rocks are frequently mineralogically difficult to identify, and it is often necessary to resort to chemical analysis for accurate identification. Nevertheless, many of the mineralogical criteria discussed above apply equally well to them.

Textures. Igneous rocks are normally examined by microscope in sections cut thin enough to transmit light. Polarized light is employed to produce interference colors, which make otherwise similar minerals easily distinguishable.

Plutonic rocks consist of large crystals intimately interlocking and showing a variety of textures as a result of the individual minerals beginning to crystallize in sequence, rather than simultaneously, as the magma is cooled. The typical texture of a rapidly cooled extrusive rock is rather different: here large crystals of feldspar and olivine, which formed as a response to slow cooling while the magma was still underground, are set in a fine-grained matrix which crystallized rapidly after eruption.

Magmatic Differentiation. Once magma is formed and begins its ascent towards the surface, several processes capable of modifying its composition *en route* may come into operation: these come under the general heading of magmatic differentiation.

One of the most important single processes is fractional crystallization. The textures seen in an extrusive rock illustrate how this may happen, because in general the large, early-formed crystals do not have the same overall composition as the magma from which they have crystallized. Like the refractory residues mentioned earlier, they tend to be poorer in silica and alkalis than the liquid fraction, though individual cases vary. Removal of the crystals from the liquid – for example, by gravitative settling – will give rise to a new magma richer in certain elements than was the original. Detailed studies have shown that this process has frequently operated to produce variation in magmas.

Environments of Igneous Rocks. Specific details of the occurrences of different rock types are given under the individual headings of those types. However, it is possible to make some generalizations arising from the above discussions of igneous differentiation processes.

*Peridotites, characteristic of the Earth's mantle, are highly refractory rocks having very high melting temperatures (e.g., 2700°F (1500°C)) and high densities (around 225lb/ft³ (3.5g/cm³)). Less refractory rocks, such as *basalts, with melting temperatures around 1800–2200°F (1000–1200°C) and densities of about 180lb/ft³ (2.8g/cm³), are characteristic of low-lying regions of crust, particularly the ocean basins. The least dense and least refractory rocks (melting temperatures 900–1450°F (500–800°C); density

A dolerite dike intruded into Carboniferous sediments on the island of Arran, off the west coast of Scotland. On Arran, 525 dikes totalling 5410ft (1665m) in thickness occur within a 15mi (24km) stretch: this represents a local increase of 7% in the width of the crust. The dikes on Arran are part of the most studied dike swarm, that of the Tertiary volcanic region of northwest Scotland.

160lb/ft³ (2.5g/cm³)) are granites and they are characteristically found in areas of continental crust.

Thus, as the broadest of generalizations, it is possible to view the Earth as a body firmly stratified with regard to density, and (excluding the non-silicate core) with a similar stratification in melting temperatures. All this has probably largely come about by igneous activity.

Granite

Probably the one rock name that is familiar to almost everyone is granite: it is a symbol of all that is hard and durable, it resists erosion and forms age-old hills and rugged cliffs.

Granite is one of a large class of rocks that solidify below ground as an *igneous intrusion, subsequently being exposed to view by the *erosion of the overlying strata. This general group, the plutonic igneous rocks, is of widespread abundance, particularly in deeply eroded terrains where ancient rocks are exposed, and granite, using the term in its broadest sense, is the most abundant type. Granites, in this sense, are coarse-grained rocks (crystals larger than 0.2in (5mm) in diameter) consisting predominantly of *feldspar and *quartz with subordinate amounts of dark minerals such as *biotite, *hornblende and, occasionally, *pyroxene.

In the narrow sense, granite is defined as a rock with more than 20% quartz and with an alkali feldspar (orthoclase, microcline or

Thin section of tourmaline granite under crossed polars at a magnification of about × 50. The large gray crystals are quartz and feldspars, the red-brown crystals biotite. The smaller, blue, crystals are of tourmaline.

perthite) as the dominant remaining constituent. Granitic rocks containing less quartz and a higher proportion of calcium-bearing plagioclase feldspar are termed granodiorites, and these in turn grade into diorites, which are rocks poor in quartz and alkali feldspar, but rich in *plagioclase.

Granites, diorites, and related rock types make up huge intrusive masses termed batholiths in the cores of eroded mountain ranges such as the Sierra Nevada. In the world's most ancient shield areas, granites make up the majority of the exposed rock. It is in these areas – for example, in northern Canada, Zimbabwe, and parts of Greenland, India and Australia – that we see deep into the structure of the continental crust and perceive its dominantly granitic character. In contrast, granites are virtually absent from the ocean basins, in which areas *basalt is the almost exclusive rock type.

Granite seen in close-up. In this sample the groundmass is of potash feldspar.

Rhyolite

Rhyolite is the name given to lavas having the same general chemical composition as granite. Like the granites, they are often rich in visible quartz and alkali feldspars, and may contain these as larger crystals (phenocrysts) sparsely set in a much finer-grained matrix.

They form from granitic melts which are erupted onto the surface of the Earth and hence cool very quickly, as a mass of mainly very small, even submicroscopic, crystals: the lack of willingness of rhyolitic liquids to crystallize is a consequence of the very high viscosity of such melts when they reach the surface of the Earth and lose their dissolved water. Granites, in contrast, crystallize underground, retaining their water, and this, coupled with slow cooling, allows them to solidify as coarse-grained rocks.

A further consequence of the high viscosity of the de-watered rhyolitic melts is the tendency for eruptions to be explosive. Some rhyolites are erupted in the form of gas-charged clouds of molten droplets known as *nuées ardentes*. Such clouds travel down the slopes of volcanoes with immense speed and are highly destructive. The collapsed and solidified products of similar eruptions may reach 1000ft (300m) in thickness and cover tens of square miles. When deposited hot enough for the individual fragments of glass to weld together, such deposits (termed ignimbrites) become massive and difficult to distinguish from lava flows.

Rhyolite eruptions are characteristic of areas of active mountain-building such as island arcs (e.g., Sumatra, Japan, West Indies), and *mountain chains such as the Andes.

Granodiorite

Granodiorite is the name given to one of the most abundant members of the granite family of plutonic igneous rocks. Strictly defined, a granodiorite contains more than 20% quartz, and of the feldspar present more than two thirds is a calcium-bearing *plagioclase. A granite, in contrast, contains a higher proportion of alkali feldspar and less plagioclase. Granodiorites are widespread and abundant rocks occurring in the same sorts of geological environments as granites.

Rhyodacites

Rhyodacites are volcanic rocks found as lava flows and ignimbrites, and have a slightly more basic composition (i.e., they are somewhat richer in calcium, magnesium and iron, and are slightly poorer in silica) than true rhyolites. In chemical composition they are broadly equivalent to the granodiorites. Most provinces of rhyolitic volcanics contain substantial amounts of rhyodacite as well as true *rhyolite.

Syenite

Syenite is a coarse-grained plutonic igneous rock type similar to granite but devoid of essential *quartz. It is very much rarer than granite and is usually found in the eroded roots of volcanoes which have erupted lavas much richer in alkalis than usual (such associated volcanic rocks include phonolites, trachytes, and alkali basalts). Since a richness in alkalis and a poorness in silica relative to granite is the characteristic feature of such provinces, many syenites contain not only abundant alkali *feldspar but also minerals of the *feldspathoid group such as nepheline or sodalite. The dark minerals of syenite are also often different from the *biotite and *hornblende so characteristic of granitic rocks. In syenites we see the comparatively rare sodium-bearing *amphibole arfvedsonite and the sodium-rich *pyroxene aegirine. Apart from the alkali metals, syenites are often relatively rich in rare elements such as rubidium, the rare earth elements, fluorine and chlorine. As a result many rare and unusual accessory minerals may be found in them.

The typical environment of the alkali-rich igneous activity which gives rise to syenites is that of the continental area subjected to intense *faulting and rift formation. One of the best known such areas is the Gardar province of West Greenland, where numerous syenite intrusions of *Precambrian age are found. The volcanism associated with the East African *rift valley also includes syenite, but here it is a rare type, probably because the activity is too young for many of the intrusive rocks yet to have been exposed by erosion.

Dacites

Dacites are volcanic rocks which correspond broadly in chemical composition to the plutonic rock type, quartz *diorite. They are similar to rhyodacites and rhyolites in general character, though less rich in silica. Like these other types, they are usually very fine-grained, though they may contain larger crystals of *plagioclase, *hornblende and *biotite.

Dacites are among the most abundant eruptive products of island-arc volcanoes. They are characteristically accompanied by andesites and more rhyolitic types. As with the latter, their eruptions are frequently explosive.

Phonolite

The name of this lava type is an adapted Greek version of the old name "clinkstone", given because these rocks supposedly emit a bell-like note when struck by the hammer. Nowadays, however, phonolite is defined as a fine-grained extrusive igneous rock characterized by the presence of abundant alkali *feldspar accompanied by the feldspathoid *nepheline. Thus phonolites are the volcanic equivalent of the plutonic rocks known as nepheline syenites. Phonolites are comparatively rare rocks but form extensive *plateaux of lava in parts of the East African *rift valley.

Trachyte

Trachytes are volcanic rocks rich in alkali *feldspar and carrying additionally either *nepheline or small amounts of *quartz. They thus grade with an increase of silica into rhyolites and with a decrease into phonolites. Like these other types, trachytes form flows of generally pale-colored lava because of their richness in feldspar, and this contrasts markedly with the darkness of their common associate, basalt.

It was Charles *Darwin who first speculated that trachytic lavas might be derived from basaltic liquids by a process of fractional crystallization in which minerals that crystallized early, forming while the melt was still underground, became separated from the remaining liquid. The separate eruption of the crystal-rich accumulation and the remaining liquid was supposed to give rise to the two lava types.

Darwin was wrong in detail but right in principle. The modern science of igneous petrology has followed this general idea in many detailed investigations of the origin of igneous rock types.

Carbonatite

For many years carbonatite was one of the most problematic of all igneous rock types.

Carbonatites are mostly found as small intrusions in association with alkali-rich igneous rocks – for example in East Africa – but they are unique in being composed dominantly or exclusively of carbonate material rather than the silicates characteristic of all other igneous rocks. Ancient carbonatite intrusions are composed of calcium, magnesium or iron carbonates; though at least one volcano, Oldonyo Lengai in Tanzania, has in recent times emitted ashes and flows of sodium carbonate: since this material is readily soluble in water it is not surprising that none is preserved among the products of older volcanic activity.

The origin of carbonatites was formerly obscure because carbonate rocks normally occur as sedimentary *limestones, and some time elapsed before it was conclusively shown that carbonatites were not simply large fragments of sedimentary strata accidentally incorporated in intrusive complexes but are themselves intrusive rocks. The discovery of the first carbonatite lava flows near Ruwenzori in Uganda and the subsequent eruptions of Oldonyo Lengai clinched the argument about the existence of molten carbonate liquids as genuine products of igneous activity.

Carbonatites have considerable economic as well as theoretical interest. They tend to be rich in rare elements such as cerium, niobium, thorium and phosphorus, and are extensively mined. One unique carbonatite intrusion, Phalaborwa in South Africa, is the site of a rich copper mine.

Diorite

Diorite is a fairly abundant type of plutonic rock: together with quartz diorites, granodiorites, and granites, it is characteristic of the intrusive igneous activity of mountain-building environments. The cores of eroded mountain chains such as the Sierra Nevada, western USA, contain large masses of all these rock types, commonly nested as separate intrusive bodies but collectively making up the huge plutonic complexes known as batholiths. Diorites themselves are coarse-grained rocks, consisting ideally of about 60% of the *plagioclase feldspar andesine, with *hornblende, *biotite,

*magnetite and minor amounts of quartz and alkali feldspar. Compositionally speaking, they are thus halfway between granites and gabbros.

Andesite

Many of the loftiest peaks of the Andes are towering, steep conical volcanoes in which the lava-type andesite is a prominent constituent. Our everyday image of what a volcano ought to look like is based on such as these, for they are characteristic not only of active areas of mountain-building in continental areas such as the Andes and Central America, but also of the large island arcs like Japan, volcanic peninsulas such as Kamchatka, and the numerous arcs of smaller islands like the Aleutians and the West and East Indies (see *volcanic landscapes).

Steep andesite volcanoes are, of course, rather readily eroded once they have become extinct, and so most of our knowledge of them is derived from modern examples. In the past geological record, andesite is not prominent as such, but great volumes of sedimentary rock are composed of andesitic and rhyolitic debris eroded from former volcanoes and deposited in nearby areas of subsidence.

Andesites are frequently associated with lesser quantities of basalt (a more silica-poor lava-type), and of dacites, rhyodacites and rhyolites. The origin of andesitic melts is still a matter of considerable debate.

Most andesite volcanoes are situated above areas where the sea floor is being subducted into the underlying mantle: indeed, most of them border the Pacific Ocean, and this great collection of volcanoes has been dubbed the "Ring of Fire". The remelting of this material as it is taken down into hotter regions of the mantle is clearly one of the possible sources of andesite melts.

Gabbro is described as a basic rock, implying that it is free from quartz. This is in strong contrast with granite, one of whose primary constituents is quartz.

Gabbro

Gabbros are the plutonic equivalent of *basalt, the most abundant of all lava types. They characteristically have about 50–60% of the calcium-rich plagioclase feldspar labradorite, accompanied by *pyroxene and *magnetite with or without *olivine. Gabbros are considerably poorer in silica than are granites (about 50% by weight as opposed to about 70%) and considerably richer in calcium, magnesium and iron.

Although basaltic lavas are extremely common, gabbro is not itself particularly so; and among intrusive rocks it is much

Gabbro in thin section. The main constituents are plagioclase feldspars (calcium-aluminium-silicate), seen here as elongate gray crystals showing twinning (the alternating black, gray and white stripes represent parts of crystals in which the atoms are differently orientated). The other main constituents are olivine (blue) and pyroxene (here seen as one large purplish crystal enclosing many individual plagioclase crystals). The texture shows that the plagioclase crystallized relatively early, the pyroxene relatively late.

less common than granite. Probably the main reason for this lies in the low viscosity and consequent high mobility of basaltic melts, meaning that they tend to reach the surface before they solidify, and so appear as lava flows rather than as plutonic intrusions.

Nevertheless, gabbroic intrusions have played a highly important part in the study of igneous rocks and the processes by which they are formed. Among others, studies of the Skaergaard intrusion of East Greenland and the Stillwater intrusion in the USA have made it possible to determine the way in which magmas crystallize; that is, the way different minerals appear in sequence with falling temperature and the way in which the remaining liquid progressively changes in composition. If the crystals and liquids are separated from each other, usually under the influence of gravity, the progressive tapping off of the liquid fraction can give rise to a great variety of different rock types. This process, fractional crystallization, is the cause of much of the variation in composition seen in igneous rocks.

Basalt

Basalt is the most abundant of all lava types. Apart from wide occurrence in continental areas, it is the principal rock type of the *ocean floor. Basalts are fine-grained rocks consisting predominantly of small crystals of calcium-rich *plagioclase, *pyroxene and *magnetite and frequently carrying embedded crystals of *plagioclase, *pyroxene or *olivine. Dense and black, basalts frequently show small vesicles

A xenolith of andesite in adamellite from Cumberland, UK. Xenoliths may be fragments that have crystallized from the magma earlier than the surrounding rock, and hence having a slightly different composition; fragments derived from the country rock; or, in the case of those found in kimberlite, fragments brought up from considerable depths within the Earth. The term "xenolith" means, literally, "foreign rock".

Curtain of basalt at Skaftafell, Iceland. Some of the basalt columns have been dislodged by the stream, and their tumbled fragments are visible in the foreground: note their generally polygonal cross-section. Basalt is an extremely common igneous rock, comprising over 90% of all extrusive rocks. Beneath a sediment and lava veneer, basalt dike swarms form 90% or more of the Earth's ocean crust.

where bubbles of gas were trapped.

Basaltic magma is highly mobile, and individual lava flows are capable of covering hundreds of square miles: in some continental areas, lava *plateaux made mainly of basalt have in the past covered millions of square miles. Because of their fluidity, basaltic lavas are often erupted without significant explosive activity, and basaltic volcanoes are normally wide and of low angle compared with those formed from more viscous melts (see *volcanic landscapes; *vulcanicity).

One of the best studied basaltic volcanoes is the currently active island of Hawaii. Much of the volcanism of Iceland in the early 1970s was also basaltic in nature – as befits an area which is, geologically at least, little more than an elevated part of the sea floor.

The study of basalts has led to much information about the interior of the Earth, for basaltic melts are among those least modified by other processes on their way to the surface. It is evident from the wide occurrence of basalt that it must be one of the commonest melting-products of the Earth's mantle. This observation places significant constraints on hypotheses concerning the nature of mantle materials.

Peridotite

A comparatively rare rock type at the surface of the Earth, peridotite is, at depth, probably the most abundant of all the Earth's materials, being a major constituent of the mantle. Peridotites are variable rocks but are essentially characterized by a richness in *olivine and *pyroxene, the latter usually a magnesian rather than a calcitic variety. Peridotites are thus comparatively poor in silica (40–45% by weight) and very rich in magnesium oxide (up to 40% or more). Iron oxide is the remaining major constituent, accompanied by varying minor amounts of calcium, aluminum, sodium and other elements.

Peridotites are found in two important and contrasted environments. Firstly, they occur within fold *mountain chains, particularly where old oceans have closed up and disappeared between two advancing continental blocks. In these situations, parts of the old sea floor together with adjacent parts of the upper mantle are occasionally caught up and incorporated in the fold belts. The whole assemblage of sea-floor basalts and associated upper-mantle peridotites is known as the *ophiolite association*; and its study forms one of the most fascinating recent developments in the Earth sciences, for it is only in such areas that we can determine the nature of oceanic crust and observe the upper mantle directly.

Secondly, fragments of mantle peridotites are brought to the surface as blocks included in the volcanic vents known as *kimberlite pipes. The individual blocks are relatively small (up to about 3.25ft (1m) in diameter) and do not give as much structural information about the mantle as do the ophiolites. Nevertheless, it is possible to show that they come from considerable depths (at least 125mi (200km)) within the mantle, being thus the only samples obtainable from such relatively deep levels within the Earth. All peridotites are more or less susceptible to hydration, with the formation of rocks known as *serpentinites.

Kimberlite

Named after the town of Kimberley in South Africa, kimberlite is one of the world's rarest yet most fascinating igneous rock types, for the narrow pipe intrusions (see *igneous intrusion) of kimberlite bring *diamonds to the surface.

Kimberlite itself is not easy to define as a rock type for it is very variable and subject to much accidental contamination by other rocks torn off the sides of the pipe. Kimberlite intrusion seems to be associated with the emission of large quantities of water and carbon dioxide, so that when an intrusion comes near the surface the eruption becomes violently explosive; and the vents

Xenoliths are fragments of rock included within another rock. Here, xenoliths that are believed to be fragments from the earth's mantle are seen in kimberlite. They are important, not only because they indicate the possible constitution of the mantle, but because they sometimes contain diamonds.

therefore usually widen near the surface, evidently having acted as huge ball-mills as material caved in from the side and was ground to pieces and mixed with kimberlite coming from below by the action of escaping gases: the eruption must involve very rapid transport of material to the surface from great depth because large fragments of dense upper-mantle *peridotites are frequently brought to the surface.

However, when relatively uncontaminated kimberlite is found, it proves to be a fine-grained rock rich in *olivine and phlogopite *mica, usually with a matrix of *calcite and *serpentine. The diamonds are usually rather sparsely distributed within the matrix and it is necessary to process many tons of ore to extract even small quantities.

Kimberlites are common only in South Africa and adjacent areas, and in the Yakutia area of Siberia, though few are sufficiently rich in diamonds to be economically important.

Eclogite

An extremely rare though interesting rock type, eclogite is like *basalt in composition but has a completely different, high-pressure, mineralogy. Whereas a basalt crystallizing near the surface of the Earth usually consists essentially of normal *pyroxene and *plagioclase feldspar, the same chemical composition in eclogite is represented by *garnet plus a rare pyroxene called omphacite. Experiment shows that this mineralogy can be achieved by allowing basalt to recrystallize under a much higher pressure than that under which it originally crystallized. Thus some eclogites represent basalts transformed by intense pressure during, for example, episodes of mountain-building. However, eclogite is also a rare member of those rocks brought to the surface from deep within the mantle by *kimberlite pipes: it is thus a constituent of the mantle – albeit a rare one. Such eclogites may have originated by the trapping and crystallization of basaltic melts deep within the Earth, or may represent fragments of former *ocean-floor basalts which have been subducted and mixed into the upper mantle.

Whatever their origin, eclogites are handsome rocks, consisting as they do of green pyroxene and orange-red garnet. They are also probably the source of most of the diamonds in diamond pipes.

Obsidian

Obsidian is a naturally occurring volcanic glass of rhyolitic composition. Obsidians are usually black, with an intense glassy luster and a marked conchoidal (shell-shaped) fracture. They form by the rapid chilling of viscous, relatively dry rhyolitic magmas, and are mainly known from modern volcanoes since they devitrify rather rapidly. Famous examples of obsidian lava flows come from the Aeolian Islands north of Sicily. Obsidians were much used by primitive Man for the fashioning of arrow-heads and axes.   KGC

Sedimentary Rocks

Although sedimentary rocks form a very small proportion by volume of the rocks of the Earth's crust, the chances of encountering them on the Earth's surface are high: about three quarters of the Earth's surface rocks are of sedimentary origin.

Sedimentary rocks are formed by *diagenesis from sediments, accumulations of solid material formed on the Earth's surface as a result of the various processes that shape the surface of the Earth. Thus sedimentary rocks form a thin surface veneer to the Earth's crust, averaging about 1.5mi (2.5km) in thickness. The oldest sedimentary rocks known are some 3500 million years old.

As the processes which lead to the formation of sedimentary rocks are going on around us, the best way to begin to discover the clues as to how they form is to examine a present-day environment. In a typical coastal environment a variety of sediments are being deposited, and these may later be buried and converted into rocks. Very fine-grained sediments – muds – are accumulating in the salt marshes, whereas coarser grained sediments – sands – are being deposited on the dunes and beach.

What features of these sediments would the geologist expect to be preserved as fossil clues to the interpretation of ancient environments? The size of the sedimentary particles obviously has something to do with the environment of *deposition, for the marsh muds accumulate in relatively calm-water conditions, the dunes are deposited by wind, and the beach sand is being laid down in the area where the waves are breaking – in other words, in turbulent high-energy environments. The distributions of grain-sizes in the beach and dune sands are different, the dune sands showing better sorting (that is, one particular grain size predominates). The shape of the grains in each environment is also distinct, the dune sand grains being very well rounded. All the features just described (grain-size, sorting and shape) are collectively known as the *texture* of the sediment.

Thus sediments transported for long periods in "high-energy" environments and deposited in similar conditions are well-sorted and rounded, whereas lower-energy conditions are indicated by less rounding and sorting. Experiments passing water currents at various velocities over a variety of grain-sizes show (not surprisingly) that faster currents carry larger grains; and reveal that grains are not only carried in suspension in the moving fluid, but also by bouncing (saltation) and rolling along the sediment surface. Thus the muds of the salt-marsh environment were deposited from suspension, but the sands were largely transported by rolling and bouncing.

Sediments and sedimentary rocks may contain other clues to their origins. Ripple marks are a common sight on beaches and can indicate the direction of flow of the current that produced them. But, as well as surface features, there are structures *within* sediments that record the direction of current flow, as can often be seen when a sand dune is cut open. Cross-bedding is a common structure within sandstones, and is produced by deposition of sediment on the steeper sides of ripples or larger structures. Experiments in which the velocity of water flowing over sediment is increased reveal a succession of structures, both laminated sediments and small- and large-scale cross-bedding being present.

Organisms living within, or on, coastal sediments or in other environments are also potential fossil environmental indicators (see *paleoecology).

Examination of the different types of

Eroded chalk in Kansas. Chalks are made up of millions of plates of calcium carbonate ($CaCO_3$) called coccoliths. These plates were secreted by certain unicellular golden-brown algae (called coccolithophores). Strictly speaking, all rocks termed chalks date from the Cretaceous, though the name is sometimes applied to similar rocks of Tertiary age.

During compaction, the constituent mineral flakes (*clay minerals, and often *micas) become oriented parallel to the original bedding, with the result that the shale fractures easily along one plane; this property, which characterizes shales, is known as *fissility*.

Black shales contain small amounts of iron *pyrites (iron sulfide), which renders the whole rock black in color. The iron sulfide is precipitated during *deposition in conditions lacking in oxygen, usually in deep-water areas, or regions without any oceanic circulation.

Oil shales are a variety of shale containing over 30% of organic material, derived either from planktonic remains or from the decomposition of vegetable debris washed in from nearby land.

Marls
These are *argillaceous rocks which contain a mixture of quartz, clay minerals and calcium carbonate, the latter being present in amounts between 35 and 65%.

Argillite
Argillite is a little used term to describe rocks that have characteristics mid-way between *shale (a sedimentary rock) and *slate (a metamorphic rock).

Siltstone
The term siltstone describes *argillaceous rocks that contain grains of diameter 1/16–1/256mm. These rocks, bordering as they do on being *arenaceous rocks, contain more *quartz than other argillaceous rocks.

Siltstones are commonly laminated, the laminations (thin sheets) being due to variations in grain-size, organic content, or amounts of calcium carbonate. When the laminations are due to seasonal changes (such as meltwater during spring, which deposits silts that contrast with clay sedimentation during the rest of the year), they are termed *varves*.

Arenaceous Rocks
Together with *rudaceous rocks, the arenaceous rocks, often collectively known as sandstones, comprise about one quarter of all *sedimentary rocks. Their grain-size is 0.0625–2.00mm, and they include *quartz with smaller amounts of *clay minerals.

Arenaceous rocks are divided into three groups according to the composition of their clasts, the fragments of which are made up. The *quartz sandstones contain only small amounts of *feldspars and other minerals, the *arkoses contain appreciable amounts of feldspar, and the *graywackes show rock fragments set in a muddy matrix.

Quartz Sandstones
Quartz sandstones are the result of a considerable amount of fractionation of rock debris released by *weathering processes, as shown by their being deficient in minerals unable to withstand chemical weathering. They are usually moderate to well sorted, and the clasts are similarly rounded. These textural features result in quartz sandstones often exhibiting high porosity and permeability, at least immediately after deposition: later the spaces between the grains may be filled by mineral cement, and such diagenetic modification destroys the porosity of the rock (the same process affects *conglomerates). Mineral cements are most commonly composed of *quartz or *calcite, but iron minerals such as limonite may also form cementing media. Sediment porosity may also be reduced by compaction, due both to the reshuffling of the grains and to the minerals being dissolved at grain contacts. The porosity and permeability of sandstones has great economic significance, as reservoirs of oil, gas and water may form within rocks in which the pore spaces have not been lost.

Two varieties of colored sandstones deserve special mention. *Greensands* are quartz sandstones which contain a few per cent of the green mineral *glauconite, which forms only in marine conditions. Another iron mineral, *hematite, characterizes the sandstones and shales that make up an association of sedimentary rocks termed *red beds*. The red coloration is due to the presence of coatings over the sand grains of hematite derived by the oxidation of iron-rich minerals swept in from the source area; and indicates a degree of

Oil-bearing shale. This fine-grained sedimentary rock is formed by cementation of particles of silt, usually containing also tiny fragments of other materials. Rich in fossils, shales can be readily split into separate layers, or laminae. Oil shales contain kerogen, a solid material that must be treated before yielding hydrocarbons.

Sandstone with a cement of ferric oxide. About one third of all the sedimentary rocks exposed on the Earth's land surfaces are sandstones; and it is probably owing to this frequency of occurrence rather than to any inherent favorable qualities that sandstone has been so much used as a building stone.

Carboniferous sandstone showing cross-bedding. Much can be learned about a sedimentary rock's environment of deposition by examining its internal structures. Cross-bedding arises when sediment has been deposited on the steeper side of ripples (or larger structures): the scale and nature of the cross-bedding depends upon the velocity of the current.

aridity of the depositional environment, where the water table has remained low, so permitting iron minerals originally in the sediment to be oxidized immediately after burial. Most *arkoses exhibit a red color for the same reason.

Quartz-rich sandstones are common in shallow marine and coastal plain environments

Arkose

Arkoses are *arenaceous rocks that contain not only *quartz but also notable amounts (of the order of 25%) of *feldspar. Feldspar will withstand almost as much mechanical degradation as quartz during transport, but is much more susceptible to chemical breakdown. Thus the occurrence of the mineral in proportions greater than a few per cent is indicative of fairly arid conditions in which transport of detritus from its source area has been relatively rapid after the essentially granitic source rocks have been mechanically weathered. And so most arkose sandstones were laid down not only in fairly arid conditions but also in proximity to source lands experiencing rapid erosion. Arkoses often characterize periods of deposition immediately following mountain-building episodes, and are almost exclusively confined to continental environments. The high content of orthoclase feldspar gives arkoses their characteristic pink color, which may be enhanced by staining by iron oxides.

A graywacke of Silurian age. Graywackes are made up of rock fragments that vary from fine to coarse in quality, sometimes being even pebbly. The fragments are generally poorly sorted. Graywackes are formed in regions of rapid erosion and varied rock, and are commonly found in geosynclinal areas.

Graywacke

The term graywacke is derived from the German *grauwacke*, meaning "gray and hard", a word used to describe the color and texture of a rock commonly found in the Harz Mountains, and containing a mixture of the *weathering products of *igneous and *metamorphic rocks. These products include both particulate material resulting from the mechanical break-up of the source rocks and *clay minerals resulting from chemical weathering. Thus graywackes result from incomplete fractionation of weathering products, reflected in the characteristic poor sorting and rounding of the clasts. Indeed the sand-sized particles often "float" within a matrix of clay minerals (see *conglomerates).

Graywackes are usually dark and extremely hard, and the finer-grained varieties can easily be confused with *basalts. They commonly occur in association with black *shales, forming an alternating sequence of shales and sandstones, the latter often showing evidence of having been deposited by turbidity or density currents. A turbidity current (see *deposition) is a slurry of sediment and water which, being denser than water, will flow downhill within a body of water and, as it does so, deposit a sand that has a mud matrix with sand-sized particles becoming progressively finer upwards; hence the term graded bed is applied to such sandstone units. In addition, graded beds show an upward change in sedimentary structures reflecting the decrease in current velocity as the turbidity current passes by. The base of graded beds may also show erosional features (sole marks), either as flute casts caused by the erosional effect of the turbulent base of the current, or groove casts produced by pebbles or organisms being dragged along and cutting linear marks in the underlying sediment.

Rudaceous Rocks

Being coarse-grained (grain-size greater than 2mm), rudaceous rocks are generally deposited in high-energy environments, and the large rock fragments of which they are formed (pebbles, boulders, etc.) give good indications of the composition of their source rocks. On the basis of grain shape, this rock group is divided into *breccias and *conglomerates.

Breccias

Breccia is Italian for rubble, and, as the word suggests, breccias consist of angular fragments of rock. Such angularity indicates a minimal amount of transport (since otherwise the corners would be knocked off), so we usually find breccias relatively close to their source. They are generally associated with modern and fossil coral reefs. The parts of the reef exposed to wave action are broken up, and the resultant debris accumulates as a submarine scree slope on the open-sea side of the reef.

Pulpit conglomerate near Coalville, Utah, from the top of the Cretaceous. Conglomerates are made up of rounded fragments whose size may vary from small pebbles to large boulders. They have generally been deposited fairly close to their place of origin, with the exception of tillites.

Breccia deposits may form when mechanical *weathering breaks off rock fragments from cliff faces, beneath which talus or scree deposits form. In this case, the breccias will be banked up against their source rocks. They may also be deposited by sporadically flowing rivers in arid regions. Rock debris loosened by prolonged mechanical weathering is washed away during rainstorms, and carried relatively short distances by flash floods. Such deposits are common on alluvial fans and may contain imbricate structures, in which flat pebbles are stacked together and inclined in the direction of current flow.

Diagenetic processes can result in the formation of solution breccias. For example, *evaporite deposits may be dissolved away or partially replaced by limestones, leaving behind a breccia.

Conglomerates

Conglomerates are distinguished from *breccias on the basis of the rounded nature of their clasts.

The clasts may be packed together in two ways. If they all touch each other the conglomerate is said to show *grain support*, and has been deposited in very high-energy conditions which persisted long enough for the sediment to become well sorted. Conglomerates with grain support are likely to have formed in a beach environment, or possibly on the floodplain of a large river not subject to periods of drying up. In contrast, some conglomerates show *matrix support*, in which the larger clasts are held apart by a finer matrix of sand and clay: this indicates that the sedimentary material was transported and/or deposited relatively rapidly, so that little grain-sorting could occur. Conglomerates with matrix support were commonly deposited on alluvial fans as a result of flash floods; in this case the matrix is composed of sand-sized particles.

Conglomerates may be divided further on the basis of the origin of their clasts. *Extraformational conglomerates* are composed of clasts from outside the area of deposition, whereas *intraformational conglomerates* are derived through the erosion of local and recently deposited sediments – for example, from an adjoining river bank. The variety of different rock types making up the clasts again provides clues to the origin of the conglomerate. Pebbles and boulders composed of only one rock type either derive from a source area exposing only one rock type or have resulted from the elimination of all but the most stable components during prolonged weathering, erosion and transport.

Tills and Tillites

Till, or boulder clay, is the sediment deposited directly from the melting ice of a glacier. Tillite is till converted to rock.

The formation of glacial ice involves the incorporation of rock debris, often as scree material. Armored with this rock material, the ice flows over rock surfaces and grinds them away, producing a rock flour which also becomes impregnated in the ice. When the ice melts, all the rock material is released and may be deposited: it is characterized by a huge range of grain-sizes, from clay grains up to boulders. Tills and tillites are therefore distinguished by being extremely poorly sorted, and by matrix support (see *conglomerates) of the larger clasts.

Similar deposits may be produced by mud flows on alluvial fans and submarine slopes. These deposits are termed tilloids when their non-glacial origin can be proved, but this is often hard; clues may be provided by the pebbles in a tillite being striated by glacial erosion and the deposit itself resting on a striated rock surface.

Calcareous Rocks

Calcareous rocks, *limestones and *dolomites, contain at least 50% of either *calcite ($CaCO_3$) or *dolomite ($CaMg(CO_3)_2$). Both minerals may be formed as direct precipitates from seawater, but by far the most important way the calcium and magnesium (originally liberated by chemical weathering) become "fixed" is through secretion of carbonate minerals by animals and plants. At the present time, calcareous sediments (apart from deep-sea oozes) are commonly found only in tropical and subtropical environments where carbonate-secreting organisms flourish. Thus the occurrence of ancient calcareous rocks can be used as a paleoclimatic indicator.

Limestone

The majority of limestones formed in water only a few yards deep. If conditions were turbulent, then the grains within the limestone show grain support (see *conglomerates), with the pore spaces filled with a *calcite cement. However, if conditions were calmer, the pore spaces are filled with a carbonate mud; that is, clay-sized particles composed of calcium carbonate. The mud may even form the bulk of the limestone. There are four main types of grain:

Erosion of thin-bedded limestone at Osmington, Dorset, UK. The two most important constituents of limestones are calcite (calcium carbonate, $CaCO_3$) and dolomite (calcium magnesium carbonate, $CaMg(CO_3)_2$): on occasion, they may include small quantities of iron-bearing carbonates.

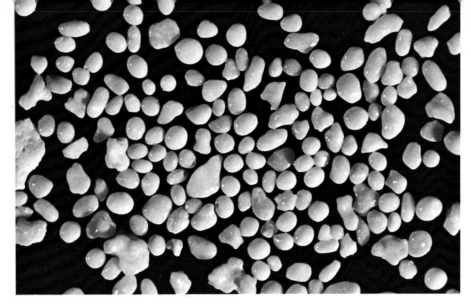

Oolites. These are spherical grains formed by the addition of successive envelopes of carbonate material as they roll around in turbulent environments. The oolitic material is coated around a nucleus, which may be a quartz grain or a fragment of a shell, and the particles reach a maximum size of 0.04in (1mm).

Pellets. These elongate grains are of carbonate mud excreted by sediment-feeding organisms.

Fragments of recently deposited limestone. Such grains, produced by local erosion, look rather lumpy. Examples forming today are termed grapestone.

Shell material. This is a common constituent of many limestones, ranging from undamaged fossils to an accumulation of sand-sized particles produced by the breakup of shells in turbulent conditions.

As the components of limestones form entirely within the area of deposition, rather than having been transported from elsewhere, they provide excellent clues to the nature of the depositional environment. Thus a well-sorted oolitic limestone was probably deposited in a warm, shallow, turbulent tide-influenced sea, for that is where oolites are forming today. In contrast, a carbonate mud containing pellets indicates calm-water conditions.

Reef limestones consist of a framework of organisms, usually corals and algae, filled with broken coral and shell material eroded by wave action in the surf zone of the original reef.

Algal limestones are laminated rocks in which the laminae (sheets) were produced by the growth of algal colonies, the organisms both secreting and, on their sticky surfaces, trapping carbonate material. The laminations exhibit a variety of patterns which may aid environmental interpretation. Today, such algal sediments are forming as "mats" around very flat coastal areas. *Pisolites* are a variety of algal colony in which the algae grow around a nucleus of shell material: they may grow to become several centimetres in diameter.

Deep-sea calcareous oozes are formed in areas of ocean where there is very little deposition of land-derived sedimentary material. Sedimentation is very slow and dominated by the accumulation of the calcareous remains of plankton raining from the surface waters. Such deposits are uncommon in the geological record; but the northwest European Cretaceous, though not a deep-sea deposit, is an accumulation of plankton (see *coccolithophores).

Nearly all limestones forming at the present time are of calcium carbonate in the form *aragonite, which is unstable and so during *diagenesis changes to *calcite. Thus nearly all ancient limestones are of the latter mineral.

Dolomite

Dolomite is a term used to describe both a mineral which is a mixed calcium-magnesium carbonate $(CaMg(CO_3)_2)$ and the *calcareous rock composed of it. Dolomite rocks have two origins, both involving the replacement of *limestone.

One type occurs within the basin of deposition, only a foot or so below the surface and very soon after the deposition of the limestone; this process is associated with the formation of *evaporites.

The second type takes place at depth some considerable time after deposition, and produces a coarse-grained dolomite rock. The replacement is caused by magnesium-rich solutions percolating through the limestone, the magnesium itself being derived from other limestones which generally contain a few per cent of magnesium carbonate – particularly in fossil algae and some animal shells. The dolomitization process occurs by magnesium atoms substituting for calcium "one for one", resulting in a volume reduction of up to 13% which increases the pore spaces in the rock. Thus dolomites are often porous, and can form reservoir rocks for oil and gas.

Certain limestones are relatively more susceptible to dolomitization, especially those, such as reef limestones, with an initially high magnesium content.

Ironstone

There are three principal types of sedimentary ironstones: banded ironstones, oolitic ironstones and clay ironstones. The banded ironstone formations date from the early *Precambrian 3200 to 2000 million years ago, when the Earth's atmosphere contained no oxygen. The other types formed in the geologically recent past when the atmosphere *did* contain oxygen.

Banded ironstone formations consist of alternating laminae (sheets) of iron oxide, iron carbonate or iron sulfide, and silica (*chert), and contain various sedimentary structures, including ripple marks and mud cracks, suggesting that they were deposited

Ironstones are sedimentary rocks containing a high proportion of iron minerals. This sandstone is rich in limonite, once thought to be a single mineral with a fixed chemical composition but now known to be a mixture of minerals, notably goethite, in amorphous, colloidal or cryptocrystalline form.

in shallow water. It is suggested that the Earth's atmosphere at this time contained considerable amounts of carbon dioxide, the presence of which would produce rainwater and river water much more acid than that of today, thus enabling significant quantities of iron compounds to be transported in solution.

Oolitic sedimentary iron ores have formed during the last 600 million years or so (i.e., the Phanerozoic) and possess all the features of *limestones: oolites, shell fragments and mud matrices. But they are composed not of calcium carbonate but of iron minerals, including iron carbonate (*siderite), and iron-alumino-silicates (*chamosite) that can form only in conditions lacking oxygen. Probably these minerals were precipitated just beneath the sediment surface, to be reworked for only short periods into oolites and other particles. Chamosite is known to be forming today in sediments deposited in deeper waters in front of equatorial deltas. This type of iron ore is the only common sedimentary iron ore of northwest Europe.

Clay ironstones, the third type of sedimentary *iron ore, are quantitatively insignificant today but were the origin of the steel industry associated with a number of coalfields. They consist of rounded accumulations of iron carbonate that have replaced the *shales of many coal-bearing strata, especially overlying *coal seams.

Evaporites
Evaporites are sedimentary rocks produced by the evaporation of seawater, and so their presence in the geological record indicates an arid, hot climate.

In an experimental situation, evaporation of seawater results in the formation of *calcium carbonate, then *gypsum (calcium sulfate), and finally the most soluble salts, including *halite (common salt). However, evaporites cannot be accounted for by invoking simple evaporation, for 4.9ft (1.5m) of halite requires the drying up of a sea 325ft (100m) deep – and there are many salt deposits that are many hundreds of feet thick. Moreover, the proportion of different minerals in evaporites is not the same as that produced by the simple evaporation of seawater. So, clearly, evaporites must be formed by some kind of recycling process, whereby water evaporated is constantly replaced.

Before modern examples of evaporite deposition were known, ancient deposits were explained using the barred-basin model, in which a land-locked sea has only one outlet to the open ocean (like the Mediterranean), across which lies a bar of material. However, evaporites are now known to form today in coastal plain areas, sabkhas, in which the *limestone sediments are replaced by evaporite minerals formed by evaporation of water from within the pore spaces of the sediment. The result of this process is that the original limestone is replaced by fine-grained *dolomite, and that calcium sulfate (*anhydrite) grows within the sediment and deforms it.

Phosphorites
The average phosphorus content of *igneous rocks is about 0.1%, but workable deposits (phosphorites) of *apatite – the ore of phosphorus – contain around 30% of this mineral.

The bulk of the world's *phosphorus reserves are in the form of marine phosphorites, found particularly in Morocco, the Spanish Sahara and the western USA. These deposits are of large area, and appear to have been formed by the replacement of *limestones in regions where cold currents welled up from deeper parts of oceans. These phosphorus-rich currents resulted in sea-bottom reactions whereby *calcium carbonate was replaced by apatite and related minerals. The phosphatization produced nodules and pellets up to 0.8in (2cm) in diameter: such nodules are known on present-day ocean floors. Apatite may be formed also by direct precipitation. Another type of phosphate deposit is *pebble-phosphate*, produced as a residual deposit of weathered phosphatic limestone, the best known deposit being in Florida.

The only type of phosphate deposit whose origin is beyond doubt is *guano*, produced by accumulation of bird excreta.

Cherts
Chert is composed of almost pure silica, either extremely finely crystalline (crystals visible only using high-powered microscopes) or crypto-crystalline, showing no evidence of a regular crystal structure. A number of other rock names familiar to the layman are in fact varieties of chert: *jasper is red chert, the coloration being due to iron oxide; flint, which is black, is commonly found in the Chalk of Northwest Europe; and *opal too can be found in chert deposits.

There are two distinct types of chert: cherts replacing *limestones (as chert nodules or chert bands) and truly bedded cherts associated with either *shales or banded *ironstone formations.

The replacement origin of cherts in limestones can easily be proved by direct observation, for often it can be clearly seen that fossils and limestone particles have been replaced by silica. The source of the silica is likely to be within the limestones themselves, in the form of siliceous microfossils such as *sponge spicules, or plankton such as *radiolarians. These remains are distributed throughout the limestone and after burial are dissolved, if the pore waters become slightly alkaline, and concentrated by replacing certain parts of the rock.

Bedded cherts are known from deep-sea sediments of a variety of ages: they have been sampled by deep-sea drilling of both the Atlantic and Pacific oceans. The latter examples appear to be organic in origin, for they contain remains of siliceous planktonic organisms. Cherts are also associated with volcanic rocks, such as submarine lavas, and it is probable that volcanic ash falling into ocean water stimulates "blooms" of siliceous plankton.

However, some cherts may be inorganic in origin, for precipitates of opaline silica have been observed in some Australian lakes which have very alkaline waters. Again, an organic origin for chert in the *Precambrian banded ironstone formations seems unlikely for there are no known siliceous organisms of this age. Perhaps the absence of living organisms resulted in higher concentrations of silica dissolved in seawater.

At present, there is no infallible method to determine whether cherts that do not contain siliceous fossils are organic or inorganic in origin. Indeed, cherts older than 100 million years have recrystallized, so that any fossils that they might once have contained would now have disappeared.

Bauxites and Laterites
Laterites and bauxites are the residual products of chemical *weathering, the material that has not been dissolved after even the most intense attack by acidic groundwater. As well as such chemical attack (largely induced by percolating water becoming acid due to decaying vegetation), conditions in which mechanical *erosion and removal of material is virtually zero are necessary for laterites and particularly for bauxites to form.

Such deposits are therefore found in tropical climates in lowland or flat-lying areas with little surface drainage. The residual cap of this weathering profile, composed of hydroxides of iron and aluminum, is termed a laterite. When most of the iron compounds are leached from a laterite, it becomes bauxite – the ore of *aluminum. Both types of deposit are usually colored in deep hues of red, brown and orange.   RCLW

Bauxite, the major ore of aluminum. Bauxite consists of hydrated aluminum oxide, usually with iron oxide as impurity. It is a claylike, amorphous material formed by the weathering of silicate rocks, especially under tropical conditions. High-grade bauxite, being extremely refractory, is used as a lining for furnaces. Synthetic corundum is prepared from bauxite; and the ore is also an ingredient in some quick-setting cements. Leading bauxite-producing countries include Jamaica, Australia, the USSR, Surinam, Guyana, France, Guinea and the USA (especially Arkansas, Alabama and Georgia).

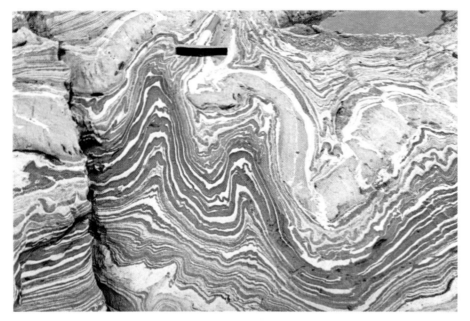

Marble, one of the best known metamorphic rocks, is much used for building and decorative stonework. Marble results from the thermal metamorphism of limestone: if the limestone was pure the marble consists of recrystallized calcite, but original impurities give rise to the rock's characteristic "marbled" appearance. (The term marble is often applied in building to stones that are not, in fact, marble.)

Metamorphic Rocks

Metamorphism is a term that implies change of form. We use it for a set of processes that change the form of preexisting rocks, either without altering their chemical composition or, much more commonly, producing rocks whose compositions are slightly or even wholly new. In general the changes occur in the solid state, although a vapor or liquid phase may also be involved.

Metamorphism. The most common environment in which metamorphic rocks are available to us is the *mountain chain, where erosion of a temporarily thickened part of the continental crust exposes once deeply buried sedimentary and igneous rocks that have been deformed and have undergone mineralogical changes in response to increased pressures and temperatures. Why then do they not change back, on returning towards the surface, into their premetamorphic forms?

As far as metamorphosed *sedimentary rocks are concerned, that is precisely the change effected by *weathering, which alters the chemical composition of rocks by addition of water to produce hydrous silicates, and by addition of carbon dioxide to produce carbonates. The metamorphism of sedimentary rocks, on the other hand, involves the production of water vapor, carbon dioxide and other gaseous substances, which are much less dense than the volatile-depleted silicate minerals and therefore move upward and away during the metamorphic episode, so altering the composition: this is irreversible until the rocks once more reach contact with the airs and waters of the Earth. This type of metamorphism is called *prograde* metamorphism, and takes place principally in response to increasing temperature. However, since the Earth is hotter inside than outside, there tends to be a correlation between pressure and temperature within a particular mountain chain.

*Igneous rocks start off as rather dry mineral assemblages, because they form at very high temperatures from silicate melts. Their metamorphism commonly involves the *retrograde* absorption of volatiles (water, carbon dioxide, etc.), which are borrowed from adjacent metamorphosing sedimentary rock masses. Older metamorphic rocks, whether ultimately of sedimentary or igneous derivation, may be involved for a second time in metamorphic episodes within mountain belts, and their behavior then is more like that of igneous rocks than that of wet sediments.

Temperatures at very great depths within the crust may be so high that the rocks begin to melt. This process starts at about $1100°F$ ($600°C$) in rocks of favorable composition and becomes important at $1300–1650°F$ ($700–900°C$). Because rocks are complex chemical compositions they melt incongruently, the liquid coexisting with solid crystals – in the same way that salty water and ice can coexist – over a range of temperatures. In some cases, the liquid separates from the solid crystals, and two types of rock, one igneous and the other metamorphic, are generated. Clearly neither is likely to retain the chemical composition of the initial rock.

A further environment in which the studies of igneous and of metamorphic rocks come very close to one another is in the mantle, where temperatures are high enough for recrystallization to occur entirely within the solid state, without the participation of volatiles, and where temperature perturbations may result in the production of liquids (magmas) together with a solid residuum. As the mantle is not easily accessible, most of the information about metamorphic changes within it comes from laboratory experiment, coupled with seismic studies and direct inspection of those rare mantle fragments emplaced in the crust by unusual processes.

Classification. Classification is essentially a three-part exercise, involving: a description of the rock in terms of its 1cm–1m texture and chemistry, which may be a guide to the premetamorphic nature of the rock; a description of its mineralogy, which reflects the temperature and pressure of metamorphism; and a description of its fabric, which reflects the type of deformation of the rock. All three tend to be applied genetically though often insufficient information is recorded in the rock for unique classification.

It is sometimes possible to decide whether a metamorphic rock is of sedimentary or igneous parentage by use of exactly the criterion which a sedimentary or igneous petrologist would use: texture. In many weakly deformed sequences of metasediments, sedimentary structures such as grading, bedding, cross-bedding, ripple marks and even fossils are preserved – even though the minerals comprising the original rock have reacted to give new minerals. Similarly, in meta-igneous rocks, the coarse grain-size of plutonic intrusions (see *igneous intrusion) may be inferred, even though the grains themselves are now aggregates of other minerals, as may the former presence of insets in meta-volcanics (see *igneous rocks).

More usefully, the chemical characteristics of sedimentary rocks are frequently apparent, despite the fabric of the rock bearing no relation to the sedimentary environment. The extreme products of physical weathering, *quartz sandstones and quartzites, may be identified in their metamorphosed state by the abundance in them of *quartz, which is stable throughout the crustal pressure-temperature range. (Metasandstones are sometimes called psammites.) The extreme products of chemical weathering are aluminous *clays, in which the ratio Al:(Na+K) – that is, aluminum:sodium-plus-potassium – is much greater than $1:1$, a feature which distinguishes them from acid igneous rocks whose mineralogy is dominated by alkali feldspar ($NaAlSi_3O_8$ or $KAlSi_3O_8$). The aluminous character of metaclays, often called pelites, is revealed by their high content of the aluminous mica *muscovite at low and medium grades of metamorphism and by the presence of *aluminum silicate minerals (Al_2SiO_5) at medium and high grade. Limestones and dolomites retain *calcite and *dolomite to high grade as marbles; and metamorphosed sandy or muddy carbonates may often be distinguished as calcsilicates from metamorphosed intermediate igneous rocks (which they resemble, chemically) by their having a pale colored magnesium-rich *amphibole or *pyroxene, rather than the darker, iron-richer silicates of the meta-igneous group.

Basic and intermediate igneous rocks form metabasites (epidiorites or prasinites to European workers; greenstones to North Americans) on metamorphism, characterized by amphibole with *plagioclase at medium grade and *pyroxene(s) with plagioclase at high grade: at very high pressure such rocks lose plagioclase, and *garnet becomes as abundant as pyroxene.

Ultrabasic rocks appear dark and silky with *serpentine as low-medium grade *serpentinites* and, at high grade, contain abundant *olivine and are termed *peridotites*.

Classification: Mineral Facies of Metamorphic Rocks.

Information about the conditions of temperature and pressure under which metamorphism has taken place comes from considering the relative stabilities of minerals or assemblages of minerals. By way of comparison, the existence of pure water in the form of ice implies temperatures below 32°F (0°C); in the liquid form, temperatures between 32° and 212°F (0–100°C); and as steam, above 212°F (100°C). In the terminology of metamorphism ice, water and steam are three *mineral facies* (sometimes termed metamorphic facies). In the example of water, the temperatures quoted above are correct only at a pressure of 1 atmosphere: at 10 atmospheres, ice is in equilibrium with water at 31.82°F (−0.1°C) and water with steam at 356°F (180°C); so that mineral facies are pressure- as well as temperature-sensitive. If any composition such as a rock can exist as two distinct mineral assemblages (though some minerals may be common to both assemblages) then for a given temperature the pressure is fixed at some definite value. Most rock compositions can exist as numerous different mineral assemblages over the whole range of pressure and temperature encountered within the Earth, so for a given composition a pressure-temperature graph can be divided up into a series of spaces, representing the stability of particular mineral assemblages, separated by lines representing reactions to other assemblages. As most rocks within a broad chemical grouping – such as pelites or metabasites – have a number of minerals in common, reactions between the common set of minerals can be identified in many different individual rocks. By choosing the common mineral set large or small, the number of mineral facies may be increased or decreased to suit particular problems.

Some mineralogies are much less informative about conditions of metamorphism than others. For example, the mineralogy of quartzite (quartz) is practically without information content, while hornblende-plagioclase-metabasite restricts the temperature to less than about 572°F (300°C) without placing a useful limit on the depth of formation. The occurrence of a sillimanite-pelite close by the metabasite would limit the depth of formation to within roughly 9–16mi (15–25km) while further limiting the temperature.

It is common to designate the mineral facies of a metamorphic rock by prefixing the rock-composition name with as much mineralogical detail as desired. However, metabasites are often called by a range of facies-specific names of which the commonest are *blueschist* (glaucophane-lawsonite-metabasite), *greenschist* (actinolite-chlorite-epidote-metabasite), *amphibolite* (hornblende-plagioclase-metabasite), *granulite* (clinopyroxene-orthopyroxene-garnet-plagioclase-metabasite) and *eclogite* (clinopyroxene-garnet-metabasite).

Classification: Metamorphic Fabrics.

The texture of metamorphic rocks provides a valuable range of techniques for finding not merely the conditions of metamorphism but also parts of the path (in terms of temperature-pressure and time) by which the rock arrived at these conditions. The basis for these techniques is the principle that a volume, plane or line must be later than any feature which it cuts.

On the microscopic scale, many minerals or metamorphic rocks characteristically grow as large crystals or *porphyroblasts*, often to as much as 10 times the dimensions of *groundmass* crystals. On the mesoscopic scale, sedimentary or volcanic bedding may be folded and crystals of flaky or tabular minerals such as micas, amphiboles and pyroxenes may be produced in reactions, may rotate, or may recrystallize so as to be aligned with their shortest dimensions perpendicular to the axial planes of the folds in a *cleavage*. Where the oriented crystals are visible to the naked eye (bigger than about

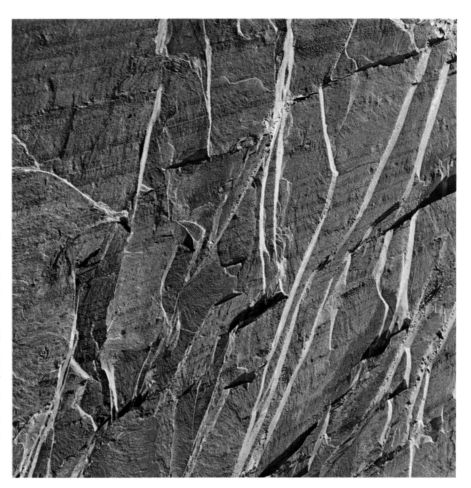

A slightly metamorphosed shale, the clearly defined planes along which the rock has split marking the original bedding planes. The product of the regional metamorphism of shale is slate or schist.

0.1mm) the cleavage is called a *schistosity* (see *schist), and in rocks where schistosity is the most prominent planar feature the texture is often appended to the rock composition name, as in "peliticschist" or "hornblende-schist". Deformation and the development of schistosity may result in the complete obliteration of primary planar features such as sedimentary bedding.

In strongly deformed rocks bands of minerals with different physical properties are often segregated. Thus, in many strongly deformed peliticschists, a compositional banding develops, parallel to the schistosity, defined by alternations of mica-rich and quartz/feldspar-rich sheets (*foliae*). Such a banding may or may not be parallel to earlier compositional bandings – mostly it is quite impossible to tell. It is called *gneissose* banding (sometimes foliation in European literature) and the rocks *gneisses. A rock can be schistose and gneissose at the same time, although the one term does not necessarily imply the other.

Linear fabrics which occur in metamorphic rocks include densely-packed small (0.04–0.20in (1–5mm)) folds affecting bedding, cleavage or schistosity, called microfolds; as well as the alignment of tabular or needlelike crystals so that their long axes lie parallel.

Environments of Metamorphism. The main occurrence of metamorphic rocks is in mountain chains, but there are great differences between the types of metamorphic rocks found in different types and ages of mountain chains.

One of the most restricted types of metamorphic rock association is found in, for example, the Californian Coast Ranges, the Sanbagawa of Honshu (the main island of Japan) and in some parts of the Western Alps of Switzerland. Here the occurrence of glaucophane-metabasites, low-grade pelites and serpentinites implies a depth of around 12.5–18.5mi (20–30km) and a temperature of about 572°F (300°C). Almost all occurrences of such associations are younger than 500 million years, and it is likely that such rocks were rapidly and deeply buried in subduction zones (see *plate tectonics), from which they emerged by erosion before they had a chance to heat up to the temperatures characteristic of such depths.

At the other extreme are mountain chains such as the Sierra Nevada of California, the Ryoke-Abakuma of Japan and parts of the fragmental Hercynian chain of Europe (Western Spain and Portugal, the Central Pyrenees, the Massif Central of France, the Black Forest and the Bohemian Massif), where heating to temperatures around 1100°F (600°C) at depths of less than 6.2mi (10km) is inferred from the occurrence of cordierite-andalusite pelites. Fabric studies show this heating to have taken place after much of the deformation history; and the occurrence of voluminous intrusive and extrusive calc-alkaline *igneous rocks suggests that such regions may be eroded analogues of modern island arcs or Andean mountain chains.

Intermediate between these extremes – low temperature at great depth and high temperature at shallow depth – is possibly the most abundant type of metamorphic mountain chain, exemplified by much of the Alpine chain, the Caledonian-Appalachian mountain belt and perhaps many of the older metamorphic regions comprising the big continental landmasses. Such regions are characterized by mineral facies representing largely post-deformational recrystallization along geothermal gradients of around 58–87F°/mi (20–30C°/km). A search for modern analogues has proved controversial.

Slate
A low-grade metamorphic rock, slate is derived from sand-free *clay with or without a component of volcanic ash. The grain-size is too fine (less than 0.1mm) for individual crystals to be distinguished with the unaided eye; but, under the microscope, slates can be seen to contain abundancies of minerals such as *muscovite and *chlorite and frequently albite ($NaAlSi_3O_8$) and *quartz. There are numerous other minerals (many present in only minor quantities), of which graphite (a form of *carbon) in black slates and *hematite in red slates are notable.

Frost shattering of slates of Precambrian age from Finnmark, Norway. Slate results from the regional metamorphism of argillaceous sedimentary rocks, especially shale: little recrystallization has taken place. Slate's primary importance has been as a roofing material, though it is less used for this today.

All the major minerals in slates – except quartz, albite and hematite – have sheet-like structures and sheet-like form, and are aligned to give one direction of almost perfect "splitability". This is known as slaty cleavage or flow cleavage.

Slates form by water loss (which helps to rotate the flaky minerals into the cleavage plane), compaction and recrystallization at temperatures up to about 850°F (about 450°C) in situations where the principal stress is acting in a direction perpendicular to the cleavage plane. Slates are used in many parts of the world as a roofing material and for decorative stonework.

Phyllite
The low-grade metamorphosed sediments called phyllites are comparable with *slates but are not restricted in premetamorphic composition to very pure *clays. Thus the sheet silicates such as *muscovite and *chlorite are usually less abundant, and quartz and albite usually more abundant, than in slates: for this reason the almost perfect cleavage of slates is only to a lesser extent present in phyllites.

Although it is sometimes said that there is a steady progression in properties from slates to phyllites to *schists with increasing metamorphic grade or temperature, slates and phyllites form alongside each other in the same metamorphic situations, and it seems that compositional controls are more important than temperature. Because of its imprecision, the term phyllite has, outside Europe, fallen somewhat into disfavor.

Schist
Metamorphic rocks characterized by the presence of visible (as opposed to microscopic) flaky or tabular minerals aligned in a cleavage are called schists.

Metamorphosed clayey rocks known as pelites contain the sheet-like micas *muscovite and *biotite in the middle grades of metamorphism, and the crystallization of micas in a cleavage in such rocks gives them the name mica-schists. Metamorphosed intermediate and basic *igneous rocks and some muddy dolomitic *limestones contain green amphibole (*hornblende) at moderate metamorphic grade, and alignment of amphibole in these rocks gives them the name hornblende-schists.

Thus schistosity is a term applying to texture and is not specifically restricted to any one compositional group of rocks. The texture is thought to develop in several different ways, including: concentration of the aligned mineral phases in distinct shear planes through the rock; crystallization or recrystallization of the aligned minerals

Schists split easily along well-defined cleavage planes due to the presence in them of flaky or platy minerals such as the micas and amphiboles. They have undergone metamorphism at comparatively low temperatures and pressures.

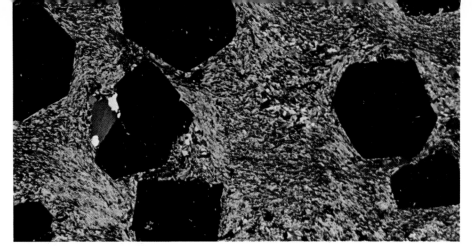

Garnet-muscovite-quartz-schist viewed under crossed polars. Garnet porphyroblasts have grown in a matrix of muscovite (colored), quartz (gray and white) and iron oxide. Note the schistose texture and the quartz segregations. In general, schists contain rather less quartz and feldspars than do gneisses: similarly, though mica schists usually contain muscovite rather than biotite, the latter mineral is also common.

with their smallest dimension parallel to the direction of principal stress; and rotation of the aligned minerals toward the plane of the cleavage by compressive shear deformation. The degree of alignment tends to be less perfect than in fine-grained *slates.

Gneiss

A metamorphic rock characterized by compositional banding of metamorphic origin is known as a gneiss. Many moderate- to high-grade metamorphic rocks, thought to comprise much of the lower continental crust, are gneisses consisting of layers richer in *quartz and *feldspar and layers richer in *amphibole or *pyroxene. Gneisses may be either meta-sediments or meta-igneous rocks. Gneissose banding also occurs, though less commonly, in low- and moderate-grade metamorphism, where mica- or amphibole-rich layers segregate from quartz-feldspar-rich layers.

Many different modes of formation of gneissose banding have been suggested, and it probably can originate by diverse means: differences in the properties of individual minerals can lead to the recrystallization of some away from sites of high stress; at high temperatures silicate liquid may form and separate from refractory crystals (this is one way in which the gneisses called migmatites have been shown to form); and original compositional differences may be preserved through intense deformation which has totally destroyed the original geometry (kneading neapolitan ice-cream has the same effect!). *Augengneisses* are metamorphosed rocks of granitic composition containing large lens-shaped crystals (eyes or augen) of *feldspar in a banded matrix of quartz, feldspar and micas.

Gneisses are hard, massive and decorative rocks and are used in many parts of the world as *building stones.

Hornfels

Hard, fine-grained and often dark *metamorphic rocks, hornfelses lack planar or linear structure and so splinter rather than cleave under the hammer. They originate by rapid metamorphism – leading to

The term gneiss is applied to a broad class of coarse-grained rocks with a banded, foliated structure and poor cleavage that have been subjected to, usually, high-grade metamorphism. The thickness of the bands varies from about 0.04in (1mm) to several centimetres. This picture shows the boundary between two bands, the one to the right being quartz.

A gneiss from the Lugard Falls, Athi River, Kenya, showing characteristic gneissose banding. The rounded shapes are a result of erosion by the waters of the river.

fine grain-size – in the absence of a stress field, so that platy or elongate minerals grow in a criss-cross texture. Such conditions are found close to bodies of *igneous rock intruded at shallow depth (usually not more than about 3mi (5km)); *aureoles* of metamorphism surround such intrusions.

As sediments tend to be the commonest rocks at shallow levels, hornfelses are often meta-sediments, but the term hornfels really describes texture rather than composition. It is easy to crush hornfels into pieces, and so this material is much used for road metal and concrete aggregate.

Mylonite

The grain-size of metamorphic rocks whose constituent minerals have reached chemical equilibrium results from competition between two processes: deformation, which tends to reduce grain-size, and crystal growth, which increases grain-size. Rarely in prograde metamorphic situations, but not unusually in rigid dry bodies of igneous or previously metamorphosed rock, deformation becomes concentrated into thin planar shear zones where its effect is particularly marked. The grain-size of rocks in such zones becomes microscopic or even submicroscopic, and such rocks are described as mylonites.

Because of their fine grain-size, most mylonites are dark gray or black, but usually some banding parallel to the plane of shearing can be picked out through subtle color or reflectivity differences.

Considerable heat is dissipated from mylonitic shear zones and the temperature may rise so that the growth of, for example, *feldspars and *quartz outlasts grinding during deformation. Porphyroblastic mylonites thus produced are called *blastomylonites*. Very rarely temperature may rise enough for melting, and such frictionally-produced melts are called *pseudotachylites*.

Mylonites probably form over only a restricted depth range (possibly about 6–19mi (10–30km)): at greater depths temperatures are high enough for rock masses to deform much more generally; and at lesser depths the stress is insufficient to cause intense grinding and instead a clear fault-plane results (see *faulting).

Amphibolite

These are of moderate grade, of chemical composition similar to basic or intermediate *igneous rocks, and consist mainly of the blue-green or green-brown amphibole *hornblende: thus amphibolite is both a term implying metabasite composition and also a mineral facies term applicable to rocks formed within a restricted range of temperature and pressure conditions.

Hornblende and *plagioclase are stable together during metamorphism in the temperature range 840–1300°F (450–700°C). The association is limited to depths of occurrence probably shallower than about 30mi (50km). Accessory minerals in amphibolite include: *quartz, *epidote and *garnet, confined to amphibolites formed at depths greater than about 6mi (10km); *pyroxene, which appears at lower pressures and higher temperatures; and *sphene and *apatite.

The lower part of the basaltic oceanic crust is probably converted to amphibolite shortly after its formation, and remains thus until taken back into the mantle in a subduction zone. Amphibolite is also an important constituent of *gneisses.   SWR

Soils

For the most obvious of reasons, soil is to Man one of the most important features of the Earth: it supports the plants whose existence we depend on. Only slightly less obviously, soil has determined the course of the evolution of our civilization; for had it not been for the early emergence of the great agricultural civilizations our modern society would indeed be very different.

There are many definitions of soil, but the simplest is that it is the medium in which land plants grow. Plants need an aqueous solution carrying certain minerals, from which the roots absorb their food, and air so that the roots can respire. Soil is, therefore, a complex of air, water, organic matter, plants and burrowing animals, in addition to weathered rock residues. The smallest volume that can be called a soil is the pedon (Greek pedon, ground), and so soil science is known as pedology. (See also pp. 801–10.)

The science goes back to earliest times, but Vasily Dokuchaiev (1846–1903) laid the foundations of pedology in the late 1900s. He concluded that soil formation was the result of the following factors: the climate, the nature of the parent rock, the mass and character of the vegetation, the age of the soil, and the relief of the locality.

Though modern research has modified his work, two main generalizations have resulted from the Russian school: first, that a soil is characterized by a distinct series of layers (horizons) forming a soil profile; and second that, in areas of fairly uniform climate, there exist soil belts corresponding to the *climatic zones.

The soil profile is divided into A, B, C and D horizons, of which D is the bedrock.

In wet climates, leaching of minerals is important in the A horizon, which is then known as the eluvial layer, and the minerals accumulate in the B horizon, the illuvial layer: this is what takes place in a podzol. In a climate with a strong dry season, accumulation of salts may take place in the A horizon, so that eluvial and illuvial layers are reversed, as occurs in a tropical laterite.

The texture and structure of a soil refer respectively to the size and shape of its particles and to whether the soil is blocky, platy, crumbly, etc. These properties are partly determined by the nature of the parent rock but more often by the vegetation. Texture and structure are also affected by the amount of humus, the end-product of organic activity of plants and

Sections through different soils showing how they are composed of layers having distinctive characteristics. *Below left*, a podzol in a sandy regolith. Here the uppermost horizon (A₁) is a thin dark layer rich in humus. This overlies the gray leached horizon (A₂) for which the podzols are named. Immediately below this is the dark horizon (B₂ₕ) charged with humus illuviated from the A₂ horizon. Deeper down (B₂₂ and B₃), the proportion of humus decreases until the zone of unaltered regolith (C) is reached. *Below right*, waterlogged soil showing gleying and reflecting the influence of Man in pedogenesis. Here the parent material is a 5000-year-old marine

animals in the soil. Soil fertility is determined by the amount of organic activity, and humus, particularly alkaline humus, greatly improves the structure of the soil. The amount present varies greatly: peaty soils may contain 100% organic matter, whereas in desert or Arctic climates soils contain very few species of plants or animals, and hence less than 1% organic matter.

A soil developed over a long period *in situ* usually has a well developed profile with conspicuous horizons, and is described as a mature soil. In areas of recent alluviation or glacial deposition, young soils, with poorly developed profiles, occur; these may also be called residual and transported soils, depending on their origin.

Because of their close association with vegetation, and hence climate, soils were classified by Dokuchaiev into zonal belts paralleling the climatic belts – for instance, podzols are associated with cold humid climates and *chernozems* with sub-humid to semi-arid steppe. Thus soils may be zonal, in equilibrium with the climatic (weathering) regime; intrazonal, modified and with anomalous constituents; or azonal, not yet in equilibrium.

These ideas were accepted in the USA, and the concepts of pedalfers and pedocals added: *pedalfers* are leached soils in humid areas where aluminum and iron accumulate in the B horizon, and *pedocals* occur in more arid regions where calcium and other minerals accumulate in the A horizon. Tropical soils are characterized by the leaching out and elimination of silica and alkaline earths, and the concentration of hydrated iron and aluminum oxides. Such soils are often lateritic, but tropical soils can also be marly and black, then being known as margalitic. The most important factor in the distribution of margalitic soils, it has been suggested, is not overhead climate but actual soil climate.

Climate-oriented classifications are useful under conditions of uniform climate, but certain rock types exert a profound influence on soil type. This is seen particularly in limestone soils which contain much more lime than do normal zonal soils. Relief also affects soil development: soils on the hilltops are, for instance, better drained than those in the valleys, where *gley* soils occur. A topography of alternating hills and valleys produces alternating belts of soils, a feature known as a *catena* (Latin, chain). In western Europe the brown forest soils have been subjected to long-continued cultivation by Man and are now essentially manmade soils.

Soils develop over a long period, and may reach a steady state or equilibrium. However, if slopes are being actively eroded, the material removed is deposited on lower slopes or in the valleys. Such activity produces an erosion/deposition phase or cycle in the process of soil formation. Soils may also become buried, in which case they are known as fossil soils – examples of such soils are rare.

Both the classification and the mapping of soils are a subject of some controversy because there is no sharp borderline between one soil-type and another. Detailed work shows that there is probably no single factor predominant in soil formation, and this is reflected in the different systems of classification. The US, European and UK systems all use as a basis for classification different criteria which reflect national landuse policies (or lack of policy, as in the UK). In the USA soils are classified according to their visible characteristics in the field, and not on a genetic basis: since 1960 the official classification has been known as the Seventh Approximation. In the UK the classification and mapping of Soil Series and Soil Types reflect local conditions of humus, drainage and texture. MMS

clay deposit. Under changed conditions a layer of peat many metres thick was built up on the surface of the clay. With the exception of a thin band, this was all dug away by Man, the peat workings being subsequently flooded. A silty ooze was deposited on the bed of the resulting mere; this forms the A horizon of the present soil. When the mere was drained, the upper surface of the clay cracked, allowing air to penetrate and oxidize the iron salts present, giving rise to the yellow coloration along the cracks (C_{1g1}). Further down (CG and G), the iron remains in a lower oxidation state, the waterlogged clay retaining its blue-green "gleyed" appearance.

The Geological History of the Earth

The Age of the Earth

If there is a single quantity that appears to us limitless, unplumbable, infinite, then that quantity is time. Yet modern scientific investigations assure us that, although there is a great deal of it, time is of strictly finite extent. In a more restricted sense we talk of "geological time", meaning the timespan encompassing all matters connected with the origin, evolution and structure of the *Earth. It is now known with some certainty that the Earth formed about 4600 million years ago.

The incredible trial-by-error process of *evolution has produced Man from microbe, and microbe from primeval aggregation of complex organic molecules, over a period of some 3500 million years. Early geologists obtained a historical perspective of the Earth from the succession of sedimentary strata and from the progressive evolutionary sequence shown by the fossils which they contain. Fossils may be used for stratigraphic correlation of sedimentary rocks in different parts of the Earth. A *relative* time-scale based on stratigraphical and paleontological evidence was first produced early in the last century and has been used, with improvements and refinements, ever since. However, until quite recently, there was no adequate way of deciding the true ages (sometimes called *absolute* ages) to be attached to the relative time-scale. Nor was it possible to correlate from one region to another the vast thickness of largely unfossiliferous Precambrian rocks.

A momentous scientific discovery, made in 1896 by Henri Becquerel, was the radioactivity of the element *uranium. Much later, it was found by other workers that *thorium and certain varieties (isotopes) of *potassium and *rubidium are also radioactive, and that they all decay by atomic transmutations into decay (or daughter) products at characteristic rates totally unaffected by any known physical or chemical conditions. By the early years of this century, Rutherford and co-workers were attempting to determine the absolute ages of certain uranium minerals by measuring their contents of radioactive uranium and radiogenic lead: given the approximately known rate of radioactive decay of uranium to lead, the ages could be calculated. For various reasons, these early attempts were rather inaccurate, but they sufficed to show that the history of the Earth could be measured in terms of thousands of millions of years.

Only within the last few decades has it become possible to measure the absolute age of rocks (and their constituent minerals) of almost any geological age with a high degree of precision and accuracy. The basic geological events which can be dated are the crystallization of an *igneous rock from a molten magma, and the recrystallization of an igneous or *sedimentary rock to form a *metamorphic rock. Other geological events sometimes amenable to dating are the deposition of a sedimentary rock and the uplift and cooling of a mountain belt.

Absolute age measurements based on radioactive decay are usually termed "isotopic", "radiometric", "radioactive" or "radioisotope" ages. That branch of the Earth sciences concerned with the interpretation of the ages of rocks is geochronology, while the more specialized technical and methodological aspects related to the measurement of absolute ages are termed geochronometry.

Principles of Radioactive Decay and Isotopic Dating. A specific kind of atom characterized by a particular atomic number and mass number is termed a nuclide: the atomic number is the number of protons in the nucleus, while the mass number is the sum of the number of protons and neutrons in the nucleus. Isotopes of a given element have the same atomic number, but different mass numbers.

Three types of radioactive decay are of direct interest to the geochronologist. In *alpha-decay* the nucleus of the parent atom emits two protons and two neutrons, that is to say a helium nucleus, so that the mass number decreases by four and the atomic number by two. In *beta-decay* the nucleus emits an electron so that one of its neutrons turns into a proton, and the atomic number increases by one. In *electron-capture*, a proton picks up an orbital electron and changes into a neutron, so that the atomic number decreases by one. The last two processes leave the mass number unchanged.

The radioactivity of a given radionuclide decreases by an exponential process. The fundamental law states that the number of atoms disintegrating in unit time is proportional to the total number of radioactive atoms present, with a proportionality factor λ (lambda, the decay constant) which has a characteristic value for each radionuclide: it represents the probability that an atom will disintegrate in a particular unit of time, which is mostly in years for longlived radionuclides.

An alternative constant is more commonly used to characterize a radionuclide. This is the *half-life* and represents the time required for the number of radioactive atoms in any given initial amount of radionuclide to decrease by half. It can be shown that the half-life equals $0.693/\lambda$.

Once λ has been evaluated for a particular radioactive element, we have a basis for calculating absolute geological ages from laboratory data.

To be of any real use to the geochronologist, a radionuclide must have a half-life within one or two orders of magnitude of the age of the Earth. If the half-life were much longer than this, the accumulated amount of decay nuclide would be too small to measure, while if the half-life were very much shorter the radionuclide would have decayed completely.

Several assumptions are necessary for calculating the age of a rock from the measured parent-to-daughter ratio and the appropriate half-life. The calculated age will be the time since crystallization of the rock or mineral only if there has been no loss or gain of either parent or daughter nuclide by processes other than the radioactive decay of the parent, if the half-life of the parent nuclide is accurately known, and if accurate correction can be made to allow for any of the daughter nuclide having been incorporated into the rock or mineral from the environment or from the source region of the rock at the time of crystallization.

In very many cases, the validity of the above assumptions can be demonstrated beyond any doubt. In other cases there may be various complicating factors – which can nonetheless yield highly useful geological information. For example, some minerals only begin to retain atoms of the daughter nuclide within their crystal lattice at a temperature much below that of crystallization. In this case, the calculated age may be significantly lower than the true age of crystallization, but may yield the age of uplift and cooling of a mountain belt.

Direct measurements of half-lives are, of course, basic to geochronology. Much patient effort has gone into the exact measurement of the radioactivity of such nuclides as uranium-238, uranium-235, thorium-232, potassium-40 and rubidium-87.

Precise measurement of the radioactivity of a rock can be extremely difficult because of the low disintegration rate and/or the low energy of the radiation of some long-lived radionuclides, and because they generally make up only a tiny proportion of the rock

A rock sample is taken prior to its being dated using the principle of radioactive decay.

in which they occur.

In practice, the amounts of both parent and daughter nuclides in a rock are precisely measured by means of a mass-spectrometer; and, by isotopic analysis with the same instrument, both parent and daughter nuclides can be distinguished from respectively non-radioactive and non-radiogenic nuclides.

The uranium-to-lead (U-Pb) method is historically the most important of the radioactive rock-dating methods. However, the potassium-argon (K-Ar) and rubidium-strontium (Rb-Sr) methods are nowadays used far more widely because they are applicable to such a very wide range of commonly occurring igneous, metamorphic and sedimentary rocks and minerals. In contrast, uranium and thorium minerals are relatively scarce although when they do occur they can yield very valuable data.

Whenever possible, more than one of these methods is applied to a given rock. All common potassium minerals also contain small traces of rubidium, because these two elements are chemically very closely related: consequently, both the potassium-argon and rubidium-strontium methods may frequently be carried out on the same sample. Furthermore, a given rock body may contain a sufficiently wide range of minerals for *all* the major dating methods to be used. A typical case would be a ★granite or a ★gneiss.

Many cases are known where two or more of the dating methods yield the same age (within analytical error) for different minerals separated from a single rock sample. In such cases the age of a particular geological event is obviously well established; and the rock is said to possess a "concordant age pattern". However, many cases are also known where different minerals from the same rock sample, or rock unit, yield different apparent ages – where either the same dating method or different dating methods have been used: in such cases the rock is said to possess a "discordant age pattern". Such patterns may give much fundamental information on the history of a rock, particularly should it come from a terrain that has been subjected to several igneous and/or metamorphic events at widely separated times.

The Carbon-14 Method. The dating methods we have discussed are applicable to rocks mostly in the age range of millions of years, although the potassium-argon method can sometimes be used for dating rocks significantly younger than one million years. Another important method, and perhaps the most familiar, is the carbon-14 method used for dating archaeological material. This method works on somewhat different principles to those described above, although radioactivity is still the fundamental process.

Natural carbon consists of the stable isotopes carbon-12 and carbon-13 in the

ratio 89:1. In addition, minute amounts (of the order of one part in one million million) of radioactive carbon-14 are continuously generated in the upper atmosphere by the action of cosmic-ray-produced neutrons on the stable isotope nitrogen-14. After combining with oxygen to form carbon dioxide and mixing with the lower atmosphere, the rate of decay of carbon-14 (it has a half-life of 5570 years) reaches equilibrium with the rate of production of new carbon-14.

The carbon-14 dating method depends on the following assumptions: the rate of carbon-14 production in the upper atmosphere over the period of usefulness of the method has been constant; the rate of mixing of carbon-14 in the atmosphere-biosphere-surface ocean reservoir is rapid relative to the rate of decay; when carbonaceous material is completely removed from the reservoir by, say, the death of an organism, no further carbon-14 is added, while that which is present decays with a half-life of 5570 years; the concentration of carbon-14 incorporated into living or-

ganisms over the period of usefulness of the carbon-14 method has remained constant.

It follows that if the carbon-14 concentration in the carbon from a piece of fossil wood of unknown age were measured and found to be one-half that in a living piece of wood, the age of the fossil wood would be 5570 years. To generalize, the period since the time of isolation from the active reservoir can be measured by determining the amount of remaining carbon-14 and comparing it with the original (i.e., equivalent to present) amount of carbon-14. Materials which can be dated include wood, charcoal, peat, leaves, flesh, hair, horn, bone, hide, rope, parchment and carbonate shells.

Although the overall concentration of carbon-14 is very small, it can be quantitatively measured by its radioactivity. The low disintegration rate of carbon-14 (about 16 atomic disintegrations per minute per gram of modern carbon), as well as the low energy of carbon-14 beta-particles, necessitates the use of high-sensitivity, low-

The Age of the Earth

Cenozoic

Life on the land in the Cenozoic has been characterized by the radiations of the mammals and the insects in the animal kingdom and of the angiosperms (flowering plants) in the plant kingdom. There has been a continuation of sea-floor spreading, perhaps the major results of which have been the separation of Australasia from Antarctica and the convergence of Africa–Arabia on Eurasia. Climate has deteriorated progressively throughout the era, the climax of the deterioration being the ice age, still continuing, of Quaternary times.

Mesozoic

On land, life in the Mesozoic was dominated by the dinosaurs and the gymnosperms (naked seed plants); dominant in the sea were the marine reptiles among the vertebrates and the ammonites among the invertebrates. The Mesozoic saw the progressive breakup of Pangaea, and late in the era, the creation of most of our modern continents. The climate was warm and equable throughout.

Paleozoic

Most invertebrate groups evolved early in this era, the faunas being characterized by, for example, the trilobites, graptolites, primitive mollusks, arthropods and brachiopods. With respect to the floras, the first vascular plants emerged early in the era, and plants first colonized the land during the Silurian. The first vertebrates (the jawless fish) evolved in the Ordovician, and primitive amphibians took to the land during the late Silurian/early Devonian. Towards the end of the era the amphibians were replaced by the reptiles as the dominant land animals. Climate alternated between warm equable periods and rather shorter ice ages. The seas were comparatively widespread, especially in the early part of the era. Successive closures of ancient oceans resulted in the welding together of continental masses to form Pangaea.

Precambrian

This is a long, complex and comparatively poorly understood phase of Earth history. There were a number of important mountain-building episodes and at least one major ice age, late in the Proterozoic. In the early Archaean occurred the differentiation of the lithosphere, hydrosphere and atmosphere, and that of the crust, mantle and core. Later, possibly in the late Archaean, free oxygen became available in the atmosphere for the first time, almost certainly as a result of photosynthesis on the part of primitive plants (algae). The first multicellular organisms appeared close to the end of the Precambrian.

Period		Epoch	
Quaternary	2	Holocene	0.01
		Pleistocene	2
Tertiary		Pliocene	7
		Miocene	26
		Oligocene	38
		Eocene	54
	65	Paleocene	65
Cretaceous	135		
Jurassic	195		
Triassic	225		
Permian	280		
Carboniferous		Pennsylvanian	325
	350	Mississippian	350
Devonian	400		
Silurian	440		
Ordovician	500		
Cambrian	600		
Proterozoic	2600		
Archaean	4600		

- Early civilizations
- Emergence of Man
- Start of main Himalayan folding
- Extinction of dinosaurs
- Main fragmentation of Pangaea; transgression of sea over land
- Start of fragmentation of Pangaea
- Worldwide regression of sea from land
- Formation of Pangaea
- Animal life takes to the land
- First land plants
- Major transgression of sea over continents
- First multicellular organisms
- ? 3000: Free oxygen in atmosphere
- ? 3500: First unicellular organisms
- 3780: Age of oldest known terrestrial rocks
- 4600: Formation of Earth
- ? 10,000: "Big Bang"

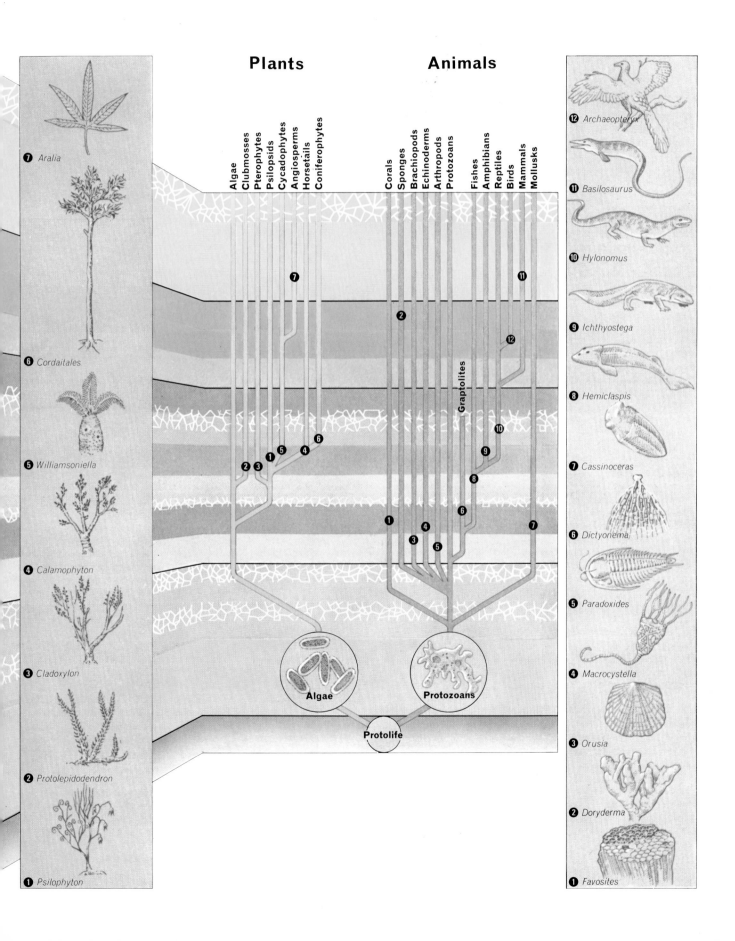

The geological timescale. In the left-hand column of this diagram are the **eras** of Earth history. In the next column of this diagram are the **periods** into which the eras are subdivided: the Archaean and Proterozoic are frequently considered as eras in their own right; the Carboniferous period is often considered to comprise two periods, the Mississippian and the Pennsylvanian; and the Tertiary and Quaternary are further subdivided into **epochs**. In the third column are shown the more notable events in Earth history: ice ages are shown by a white ice symbol (the ice age early in the Proterozoic is uncertain). On the opposite page are shown the evolution of and possible relationships between the major plant (green) and animal (brown) groups: each is illustrated by an early member. (All dates are in millions of years before the present.)

Plants

Algae
Clubmosses
Pterophytes
Psilopsids
Cycadophytes
Angiosperms
Horsetails
Coniferophytes

Animals

Corals
Sponges
Brachiopods
Echinoderms
Arthropods
Protozoans
Fishes
Amphibians
Reptiles
Birds
Mammals
Mollusks

Graptolites

Algae

Protozoans

Protolife

7 *Aralia*

6 *Cordaitales*

5 *Williamsoniella*

4 *Calamophyton*

3 *Cladoxylon*

2 *Protolepidodendron*

1 *Psilophyton*

12 *Archaeopteryx*

11 *Basilosaurus*

10 *Hylonomus*

9 *Ichthyostega*

8 *Hemiclaspis*

7 *Cassinoceras*

6 *Dictyonema*

5 *Paradoxides*

4 *Macrocystella*

3 *Orusia*

2 *Doryderma*

1 *Favosites*

The carbon-14 method of dating is accurate for samples that are up to 40,000 years old. To avoid error, extremely precise measurements are required that can only be obtained from complex apparatus such as is seen here in the British Museum, London.

background-radioactivity counters. (In contrast to the other dating methods we have discussed, carbon-14 cannot be measured by mass-spectrometry.)

The maximum practical age limit of the most sensitive counting methods now in use is about 50,000–60,000 years. Above about 40,000 years only about one per cent of the original amount of carbon-14 remains and measurement becomes correspondingly difficult. Five to ten grams of a fairly young carbon sample can be measured routinely to about 0.5 per cent, corresponding to an error of as little as ±30 years on the date. In practice, however, a single carbon-14 date in the range of about 0–5000 years may have an actual error of about ±150 to 200 years because of uncertainties arising from various factors associated with variations in atmospheric carbon-14 concentrations.

The reliability of the carbon-14 method has been tested by dating materials of independently known age. Back to about 5000 years ago this is possible by using known archaeological, historical and tree-ring dates. In fact, evidence from tree rings has shown that the rate of carbon-14 production in the upper atmosphere has *not* been constant in the past, and our techniques of calculation have been adjusted accordingly.

Application of the carbon-14 method has shed light on numerous aspects of late Pleistocene geology and paleontology, the study of vegetation development (in combination with pollen analysis) and, above all, the dating of archaeological specimens, which so dramatically illustrate the rise of mankind.

Age of the Oldest Terrestrial Rocks.
On every continent there are large Precambrian "shield" areas composed of igneous and sedimentary rocks, ranging from weakly metamorphosed to strongly metamorphosed, with isotopic ages of about 2600–2800 million years. Areas yielding this age make up about 5% of the Earth's land surface. Younger shield areas can sometimes be shown from the study of discordant age patterns to be reheated and reworked 2600–2800 million-year-old rocks. It is now thought that about 50% of the area and volume of the Earth's continents may already have been in existence about 2600 million years ago.

Recently there have been discovered a few areas on Earth which have isotopic ages greater than 3000 million years. The oldest reliably dated rocks come from West Greenland. They comprise a surprising variety of metamorphosed igneous and sedimentary rocks, including granitic gneisses, volcanic lavas, banded ironstones, schists, quartzites, etc., mostly characteristic of the well-known early Precambrian assemblage termed the "granite-greenstone" associ-

ation. Rubidium-strontium and uranium-lead measurements conclusively show that all these rocks were formed between about 3700 and 3800 million years ago. Rocks of similar age and character are currently beginning to be found on the North American and African continents.

Contrary to many earlier ideas, it is now evident that by about 3800 million years ago, and possibly well before this, surface cooling and geochemical differentiation of the Earth had progressed sufficiently to produce continental crust not too greatly different from that in evidence today, although it was probably much smaller in area and considerably thinner. From the sedimentary rock types present it can be concluded that free water already existed on the Earth's surface.

The Age of the Earth. As we have already said, the Earth is considered to be about 4600 million years old, although no terrestrial rocks approaching this age have yet been found – indeed, it is rather unlikely that they ever will be. The evidence from recent studies for this estimate of the Earth's age is circumstantial and is based upon the following indications:

Isotopic age measurements by the uranium-lead and rubidium-strontium methods on most *meteorites have yielded a solidification age close to 4600 million years. Meteorites are of interest in that they solidified very early in the history of the Solar System.

The oldest rocks and soils from the *Moon yield isotopic ages close to 4600 million years. This has therefore been interpreted as the age of solidification and chemical differentiation of the Moon.

The growth on the Earth of the two radiogenic lead isotopes, lead-206 and lead-

207, approximates closely to a very simple pattern that would show that 4600 million years ago the isotopic abundance ratios of lead were identical in the parent material of the meteorites and of the Earth. The overall growth curve is based on several major lead ore deposits of different geological ages, independently dated by other isotopic age methods. If the growth curve is extrapolated back through time from the oldest lead ore deposit, using the simple radioactive decay equation described earlier, it passes through the measured lead isotope ratio of 4600-million-year-old iron meteorites. The latter contain no uranium, so that no radiogenic lead has had a chance to form within them since they solidified. Lead-204 is a non-radiogenic isotope which has always been constant in amount, and forms a reference against which the quantitatively varying radiogenic isotopes can be compared.

Thus, although it is highly probable that the Earth attained something like its present form and overall consistency 4600 million years ago the term "age of the Earth" is used in the current scientific literature to signify that point of time, 4600 million years ago, when the isotopic composition of lead was the same in the Earth and in the parent material of the meteorites. It seems very likely, nonetheless, that the entire Solar System condensed within a relatively short period of time from disaggregated primeval matter about 4600 million years ago.   SM

Principles of Stratigraphy

Stratigraphy is essentially the study of the history of the Earth as preserved for us in the stratified rocks. That history includes great episodes of mountain building, the intrusion and extrusion of vast quantities of molten rock, and the alteration of huge areas of older rocks by heat and pressure.

The early history of stratigraphy centers around two great battles between wealthy intellectuals, the "neptunists" versus the "plutonists" and the "catastrophists" versus the "uniformitarians", plus the sound common sense of one simple working man – William *Smith, who is well named the "Father of Stratigraphy".

The "neptunists" were those, mainly German, thinkers who back in the 18th century maintained that all the rocks had been laid down as chemical precipitates in water. The great Goethe, himself an amateur geologist, adhered to this school. The "plutonists", on the other hand, recognized (symbolically at least) the hand of the fiery king of the underworld in rocks which were so like the lavas seen erupting from modern volcanoes that they must have formed in a hot molten state. Both schools were right, of course, each in their own way. The battle is long over, though geologists still find details to argue about.

And most geologists would probably say that the second battle, that between the "catastrophists" and the "uniformitarians", has also ended – in favor of the latter. The great catastrophe of Noah's flood was long seen as the explanation for

An early view of the origin of the rocks of the Earth, that held by the "catastrophists", illustrated in a painting by John Martin.

most of the phenomena of the rocks, especially the fossils they contain. But as knowledge of the stratigraphical record grew, more and more catastrophes and new creations had to be dreamed up to explain the long succession of faunas and floras in the stratified rocks.

The uniformitarians, on the other hand, maintained that everything in the rocks could be explained by the processes seen going on in the world at the present day. Given enough time (and geologists were provided with more and more of it as the 19th and 20th centuries rolled by!), the ordinary processes of *erosion, transport and *deposition were sufficient to interpret everything that we see in the sedimentary and the activity of modern volcanoes explained the volcanic rocks.

The great battle-cry of the uniformitarians was the dictum "The present is the key to the past!", and the man who shouted this battle-cry most loudly was *Lyell, whose book *Principles of Geology* was the foundation stone of all modern geology, and of stratigraphy in particular. The frontispiece of that book and the clearest demonstration of the principle of uniformitarianism was a picture of the Roman pillars in the Temple of Serapis near Naples. These bear, in the boring made in them by marine organisms, an obvious record of the rise and fall of the sea since Roman times.

While the educated men fought about theories, more practical men were recognizing the principles of stratigraphy without really realizing what they were doing. As far

back as 1719, John Strachey recognized the meaning of the succession of strata in the Forest of Dean coalfield of western England. And at the end of the 18th century William Smith, son of a Cotswold blacksmith, was seeing the realities of stratigraphy as he surveyed coal mines and the routes of canals in the brief heyday of that form of transport. He was not an educated or wealthy man, he did not succeed as a businessman (in fact he went to prison for debt), and he was not an intellectual giant, but he recognized two simple principles of stratigraphy – practically the only two principles the science has, even today.

He recognized firstly the Law of Superposition, which states simply that in normal circumstances the younger deposits will rest on the older, that the succession will follow bed upon bed in chronological order. This may seem so obvious that it hardly needs spelling out – and indeed the principle had been recognized back in the 17th century by *Steno – yet it had been overlooked by most of the learned armchair geologists of the day.

Of course, it is not always as simple as this. With lateral movements of the Earth's crust, the strata may be tilted; and greater dislocations can even lead to older strata being pushed over younger – in major mountain belts, where compressive movements have reached their greatest intensity, the strata may be completely inverted. But all these complications can be recognized for what they are, and the simple truth remains that, when comparatively undisturbed, younger rocks must always rest

on older.

William Smith's second great principle was that layers of sediment can be recognized by means of the fossils they contain. In other words, rocks in different places can be recognized as having been formed at the same time because they contain the same sorts of fossils. They can be *correlated*. Thus fossils embedded in a block of sandstone on the north coast of France are very similar to those found in the Portland Stone of southern England: they can therefore be recognized as of approximately the same age (in fact, both were formed towards the end of the *Jurassic).

As the work of unravelling the geological history of the Earth went on, it was soon realized that, at any one place, the record was far from complete. Thus, on the south coast of England near Seaton, Cretaceous rocks rest directly on Triassic rocks, with no Jurassic sediments preserved in between. This is a very simple example of an *unconformity*. Such breaks in the record had, in fact, been recognized long before by *Hutton, the first protagonist of uniformitarianism.

The older rocks may have been folded and altered considerably before the younger

An unconformity between Ordovician and Cambrian rocks in Wales. The older Cambrian rocks were first deposited and tilted then, after a period of erosion, Ordovician rocks were deposited on the Cambrian surface. The unconformity represents a period of many millions of years during which there was no deposition.

The catastrophic theory of the origin of rocks was replaced by the views of the "uniformitarians" who maintained that different layers of rock represent different periods in a long history of deposition, younger rocks therefore appearing above older rocks. This principle is demonstrated here in an illustration from Sir Charles Lyell's *Elements of Geology* (1838).

rocks were laid down across their eroded surface. Thus in the Grand Canyon of the Colorado River, where Cambrian marine sediments rest on the dark, much altered rocks of the early Precambrian near the bottom of the gorge, we find that much of the later part of the Precambrian record is missing, the unconformity being a very obvious one. Far less obvious is the break *above* the Cambrian, where the next, similarly horizontal, sediments are of Carboniferous age (in some places, Devonian) – there are no sediments from the Ordovician or Silurian. Then follow Permian sediments, with here and there along the rim of

the canyon some patches of Triassic strata. But there's nothing from the last 200 million years or so of the Earth's history.

The stratigraphical record is therefore full of gaps, even in the best of sections, and nowhere on Earth do we appear to have anything like a *complete* pile of sediment.

Just as the rocks may be present in one place and absent in another, obviously they may change in character from place to place. The sum total of the characteristics of a rock is what we call its *facies*. We say that one set of strata are in a "sandy facies", another of approximately the same age in a "limestone facies". Or we may go further

and interpret the actual environments that the rocks represent. We talk of a "shallow marine facies", or a "sand-dune facies", and so on.

The next stage in working out the stratigraphy of an area is therefore to interpret the successive environments recorded in the sediments. In this way we build up paleogeographical maps which show the supposed geography of a particular region at some specific time in the past.

Obviously the fact that strata vary laterally in their facies makes correlation all the more difficult (and all the more fun). What is more, it is not only the rocks that vary but also the fossils they contain, since clearly one can't expect to find the remains of a marine creature in a desert sand or the inhabitants of deep muddy seas in limestones that were laid down in shallow water. Therefore some fossils are much more useful to us than others. A free-swimming, rapidly-evolving creature is more useful for correlation than a slowly-evolving form that only lived on a particular type of sea floor. Microscopic organisms are often more useful than larger forms because there are far more of them and one can find large numbers in a very small sample of rock (such as is recovered from a borehole). In recent years, for example, the fossilized remains of plant spores and pollen have proved extremely valuable, not only because they are abundant and easily preserved, but also because they tend to be scattered everywhere, both in the sea and on land, and can be said to be relatively independent of facies.

Since rocks of a specific age vary in facies from place to place, it also follows that rocks of the same facies may differ in age from place to place. This is known as *diachronism*, where the rocks, as it were, cut across the time planes.

Apart from fossils there are several other ways of correlating rocks. These may be listed as follows:

(*i*) *Radiometric methods:* In these the known rates of breakdown of the radioactive isotopes of particular elements (such as rubidium, potassium and carbon) are used to provide an estimate in years of the age of the rock concerned (see *age of the Earth).

(*ii*) *Tectonic methods:* The use of major events, particularly mountain-building episodes, to elucidate the history of the Earth is full of difficulties. There is no real evidence that such major events were synchronous over the whole of the Earth's surface or even parts of it (and this method is anyway reminiscent of old-fashioned catastrophism). Nevertheless, within particular areas, the effects of major Earth movements must have been widespread.

(*iii*) *Paleomagnetic methods:* The periodic reversals of the Earth's magnetic field, as recorded in certain rocks, particularly those of the *ocean floor, have provided a very useful tool for dating the later part of the stratigraphical record, and especially for unravelling the story of the relative movements of the continents.

(*iv*) *Paleoclimatic methods:* Marked changes in climate, often accompanied by marked changes in the relative height of land and sea, provide another obvious means of correlation (though used mainly for the *Quaternary).

(*v*) *Volcanic methods:* Volcanic events are often sudden, short-lived and widespread in their effects. Lavas and ashes which are erupted at the surface (or on the bottom of the sea) will obviously take their place in the regular succession of strata, and they can therefore be used as marker horizons.

However, we have to recognize that intrusive rocks, often emplaced far below the Earth's surface and only exposed as a result of deep erosion, do not follow the rules: they commonly cut across strata of different ages. This does not mean that they, and rocks altered out of recognition by heat and pressure (see *metamorphic rocks), are not part of stratigraphy. They are just a more difficult part of the story.

It has been suggested that the catastrophist school of thought was demolished by the uniformitarian school. It must be said, however, that in recent years there has been something of a swing back, if not to catastrophism, then to what may be called "neocatastrophism". This involves the recognition that Man's experience has not been long enough to recognize all the processes that are going on at the present day, and that the stratigraphical record (and equally the *fossil record) reveals a certain periodicity that involves both sudden violent happenings as well as long periods of "nothing much in particular". In these terms, it can be argued that the theory of *plate tectonics itself is somewhat catastrophic in theme, since long periods of "quiet" subduction of ocean floor are followed by short periods of "violent" continental collision. The argument is hardly over; perhaps it has barely begun. (For the geological record see also pp. 739–51.) DVA

Precambrian

Most of the Earth's history belongs to that period of time known as the Precambrian. Problems such as where the Earth originated, how it evolved, how the continents and oceans took shape, and what conditions were like on the proto-Earth are a constant source of speculation – and hypotheses relating to the early development of the Earth abound. A prime difficulty with a more objective geological approach is to construct some sort of meaningful timescale. Just how difficult this is can be judged from the way that the Earth's "age" has increased a million-fold (from 4004BC to 4,600,000,000BC) over the last few centuries as we have gradually begun to appreciate the enormity of geological time. Progress in understanding the Precambrian has gone hand-in-hand with the construction of reliable timescales.

The development of stratigraphic principles during the 19th century led to great advances in our knowledge of the fossiliferous sediments deposited on the Earth's surface since the beginning of the *Cambrian some 600 million years ago. Fossils allowed sedimentary rocks from widely different geographical areas to be arranged in a definite time sequence. But the lack of easily recognizable fossils in rocks that were clearly older than the Cambrian sediments posed great problems to the early stratigraphers. They were content, therefore, to group these rocks into one great geological period, the "Pre-Cambrian", and to concentrate their efforts on the fossiliferous strata of the Phanerozoic (post-Precambrian). Nevertheless, as the science of geology has advanced, so new techniques have been developed for dealing with unfossiliferous Precambrian rocks in order to place them in some sort of time sequence and thus relate them to the events that were taking place on Earth. This has been made possible through detailed studies of:

(*i*) the igneous history of the Precambrian: periods when magmas were formed, volcanoes erupted and dike swarms injected;

(*ii*) the metamorphic history: periods when rocks were heated as a result of igneous activity or deep burial, and as a consequence changed their mineralogy;

(*iii*) the structural history: when the rocks were severely strained, folded and faulted through Earth movements;

(*iv*) the sedimentary history: periods when erosion took place, basins were formed and the eroded debris dumped in them.

By examining the ways these processes interrelate it has been possible to build up a *relative* time-scale of events in the Precambrian in many parts of the world. Moreover, with the development and application of methods for dating rocks using radioactive isotopes and their decay products, it is now possible to set these events against an *absolute* time-scale (see *age of the Earth). Of course, much more work needs to be done before a detailed picture emerges.

What, then, do we know about the earliest stages of the Earth's history? The answer is: very little. The *Earth is known to be about 4600 million years old. Rocks formed more than 4000 million years ago have been recovered from the *Moon – indeed there are few lunar rocks younger than 3200 million years – yet on Earth the oldest crustal rocks so far recognized are no more than 3780 million years old, and there are only a few areas of Precambrian rocks where ages greater than 3200 million years have been recorded. Does this mean that during the first third of its history the Earth was so hot and mobile that the rocks then formed have only rarely been preserved? or does it mean that the continental crust as we know it did not exist in any great volume prior to 3800 million years ago? The solution of this problem is fundamental to an understanding of early Precambrian geology.

Whatever the explanation for the absent record of the first 700 million years or more of the Earth's history, it is clear that our planet's surface must have been very different 4000 million years ago. Some reflection of this difference is found in Precambrian terminology: terms such as "greenstone belt", "komatiite", "anorthosite" and "granulite" rarely appear in the literature of Phanerozoic rocks, but are part of the basic vocabulary of the Precambrian geologist.

The Precambrian, though several times longer than all the other geological periods combined, has not suffered repeated subdivision into smaller and smaller time intervals. This is partly because such detailed evidence is usually lacking. Nevertheless, due recognition of the changing character of crustal processes during the Precambrian is provided by division into the (earlier) Archaean and the (later) Proterozoic, the dividing line lying approximately 2600 million years ago. The Archaean seems to have been primarily a period of crustal formation, while the Proterozoic is characterized by extensive "reworking" of this older crust in several periods of deformation, metamorphism and associated magmatic activity. However, this reworking was not entirely pervasive, since many areas of essentially unmodified Archaean crust still survive on all continents, being commonly known as Archaean kratons. Areas of the Earth's crust which have remained relatively stable since the end of the Proterozoic are known as shield areas, the best example being the Canadian Shield.

It is worth reiterating that Phanerozoic principles of stratigraphy are difficult to apply to the Precambrian, especially the Archaean. Although, locally, vast thicknesses of Precambrian sedimentary rocks do occur, episodes of sedimentation are in fact subsidiary to periods of magmatism and crustal generation, metamorphism and deformation. Hence it is necessary to treat Precambrian history in terms of such events. Most geological events, whether episodes of magmatism, metamorphism, deformation or erosion and sedimentation, are related in one way or another to convection in the Earth's mantle, and ultimately to the operating thermal regime. Since sedimentation is directly linked with *erosion, and erosion is dependent on relief above sea level, the thinner sedimentary record in the Archaean might just be a reflection of a thinner continental crust.

Archaean. Most geologists recognize two different types of Archaean terrain – low-grade and high-grade respectively – which tend to be separated geographically. Low-grade terrains include the greenstone belts, which have generally been deformed, but have suffered metamorphism at relatively low temperatures. The high-grade terrains, on the other hand, are composed largely of granitic *gneisses which have suffered strong deformation and recrystallization at moderate to very high temperatures. The relationship between the low- and high-grade terrains in terms of Precambrian crustal processes is not known.

Greenstone Belts. A typical greenstone belt consists of a thick (several kilometres) sequence of basalt lavas and overlying sediments which have been folded into an upright syncline and invaded by granite. Individual greenstone belts may be separated by intervening regions of granite *gneiss.

Many of the lavas are pillowed flows, the pillows having formed as the hot lavas were extruded under water. Similar pillow structures characterize basaltic lavas erupted on the present *ocean floors at mid-ocean ridges and in marginal-basin spreading centers behind island arcs. Indeed some geologists regard the greenstone belt lavas as preserved relics of the basaltic crust of Archaean oceans or marginal basins.

The lavas are rather unusual, however, in that many are much richer in magnesium than modern ocean-floor lavas (their special name, komatiite, taking account of this and other chemical differences). The differences imply much more extensive melting of the Earth's magnesium-rich mantle than is possible at present spreading centers, and some geologists have speculated that meteoritic impacts (as on the Moon) may have triggered off this extensive melting. However, at higher levels in many greenstone-belt sequences, lavas such as *basalt, *andesite and *dacite, with close compositional similarities to lavas of present-day volcanic island arcs, are found: this would suggest a marginal basin model.

Above the lava sequence there is normally a succession of immature sediments (*graywackes), probably derived by rapid erosion of the adjacent pile of volcanic lavas and granite gneiss and dumped into the basins with very little chemical *weathering. Other types of sediment, such as silica-rich *chert and banded *ironstones, may be present but are subordinate to the graywackes.

The greenstone-belt cycle seems to have been terminated in most cases by folding and deformation of the lavas and sediments. At the same time, the lavas were altered and metamorphosed so that the original igneous minerals were replaced by green-colored secondary products such as chlorite and hornblende (hence the name "greenstone"). At the same time the belts were invaded by granitic magmas, which were themselves often highly deformed.

Greenstone belts appear to have been formed over a period of almost 1000 million years. Those in southern Africa are older

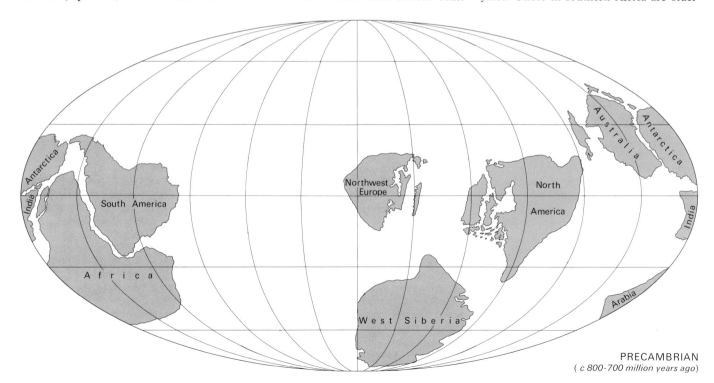

PRECAMBRIAN
(c 800-700 million years ago)

(3400–3000 million years) than those in Canada and western Australia (2900–2500 million years), although belts of different ages may occur in adjacent areas. The younger greenstones tend to occur in a series of roughly parallel belts, while the older ones are more irregular and cuspate in form. Nevertheless, the general characteristics of individual greenstone belts are essentially similar through this period. Why they apparently ceased to form after the close of the Archaean is not known.

Many major economic *ore deposits (nickel, chromium, copper, gold, silver) are closely associated with greenstone belts.

High-grade Gneiss Terrains. The best example of a high-grade gneiss terrain is the North Atlantic kraton, extending from Labrador through Greenland to northwestern Scotland, though equivalent rocks are found on other continents. The dominant rock type in the high-grade terrains is a "gray gneiss" composed essentially of the minerals quartz, plagioclase, hornblende and biotite. Chemically these gneisses are equivalent to the huge batholiths of granite, granodiorite and tonalite which dominate the Andean cordillera and western North America; and it is probable that most gray gneisses are just plutonic igneous rocks of this type but strongly deformed.

Sediments do occur in these high-grade terrains, but are shelf-type sediments such as sandstones, shales and limestones – obviously of different character from the ill-sorted graywacke sediments of the greenstone belts. Moreover, they form smaller, thinner units and have, like the gneisses, almost everywhere suffered high-grade metamorphism so that they are now represented by quartzites, kyanite schists and marbles (see *metamorphic rocks). Interbedded or associated with these sediments are considerable proportions of basic and ultrabasic *igneous rocks, but like the sediments these are so strongly deformed and metamorphosed that it is impossible to guess at their original nature. They could represent lava flows or sills of basic magma intruded into the sediments. It is usual to refer to this assemblage of rocks as supracrustal, the supposition being that they were deposited on a gneissic continental crust.

Two other rock types are commonly found in the high-grade terrains: granulites and anorthosites, and there is still considerable uncertainty as to their origin. Granulites are often very dry, having clearly been metamorphosed at such high temperatures that the water normally present in minerals such as biotite and hornblende has been expelled, so that anhydrous minerals such as pyroxene have crystallized in their place. Moreover, most granulite terrains have a higher proportion of basic rocks than the normal gray gneisses. This would concur with the suggestion that granulites may be sections of the deeper continental crust that have been uplifted during Earth movements.

Anorthosites appear to be restricted to the Precambrian, but they occur in both

Precambrian phyllites showing the tight folds typical of ancient rocks.

Archaean and Proterozoic. They are usually found in the same areas as granulites, suggesting that they may be a rock type characteristic of the deeper parts of the Earth's crust.

They are coarse-grained *igneous rocks similar to gabbros, but much richer in calcium-rich plagioclase (anorthite). A point of great interest is that similar anorthosites are abundant on the Moon, and make up a large proportion of the primitive lunar crust.

Just as greenstone belts seem to have formed over almost 1000 million years of Archaean time, so the high-grade gneiss terrains give a range of ages, and these are interpreted as times of crustal generation. During this period the gneisses were often strongly deformed and complexly folded. There is evidence in many areas of high-temperature metamorphism producing granulites about 2800–2600 million years ago. This seems to have coincided with attainment of some degree of crustal stability and the change from Archaean to Proterozoic types of crustal evolution.

Proterozoic. The Proterozoic was, compared with the Archaean, dominantly a period of crustal reworking rather than of crustal generation. Some idea of what this means can be seen by comparing the Andean and the Alpine mountain belts of the present day. The (Archaean) Andean belt is characterized by extensive crustal generation, in the form of huge batholiths, with subsidiary deformation; while the (Proterozoic) Alpine belt is characterized by strong deformation producing abundant thrusts and folds, but with very little granite. Obviously there are gradations between these two extremes.

In the northern hemisphere in particular there are two main episodes of Proterozoic activity: the first closely followed the Archaean itself, but peaked about 1800 million years ago; the second peaked about 1000 million years ago. Equivalent Proterozoic activity is known from elsewhere in the world, though not necessarily peaking at the same time.

There are two other ways in which the Proterozoic differs from the Archaean. Firstly, over large parts of the Archaean which were later to become active Proterozoic belts there were extensive swarms of roughly parallel basic dikes. In these areas the crust was fractured and extended and basic magma from the mantle was injected in large volumes, in some cases over a period of more than 100 million years. Curiously, the main trends of the later episodes of deformation run parallel to these dikes.

Secondly, the pattern of sedimentation in the Proterozoic bears more resemblance to that in later (Phanerozoic) mountain belts. Geosynclinal sedimentary basins have been recognized in northwestern and northeastern Canada and equivalent sedimentary

basins are known on other continents, all about 2200–2000 million years old. An interesting feature of these basins is the presence of considerable thicknesses of banded ironstones formed largely of magnetite and quartz: such sediments are not found from the later Proterozoic or Phanerozoic. It has been suggested that they are mainly chemical precipitates associated with a change in the character of the Earth's atmosphere from reducing to oxidizing. This may bear some relation to the rapid evolution of photoautotrophic organisms such as blue-green *algae.

The event some 1800 million years ago was a major period of crustal shortening. This produced major thrusts and folds, particularly near the margins of the mobile belts with the stable Archaean kratons. Some idea of the amount of deformation which took place can be gained by examining the basic dike swarms. These show clear cross-cutting relationships on the kratons but, traced into the Proterozoic mobile belts, are deformed and flattened almost into parallelism with the enclosing gneisses. At the same time, the original igneous minerals in the dikes were replaced by hydrous minerals such as hornblende, so that the whole rock has taken on a new planar fabric. The gneisses and associated sediments were strongly deformed and recrystallized in a similar manner, so that effectively the whole crust developed a new grain parallel to the margins of the mobile belt. It is clear that there was considerable ingress of water – presumably from the Earth's mantle – during the development of these fold belts.

The later Proterozoic Grenville belt of southern Canada, and its probable equivalent in southern Scandinavia, is a linear belt with more similarities to the younger mountain belts of the Phanerozoic. Certainly there are associated sedimentary rocks and considerable deformation. But a characteristic of the Grenville belt is the presence of very large bodies of anorthosites, some over 60mi (100km) across. Anorthosites are also common in southern Scandinavia. The Grenville belt has been interpreted as a continent-continent collision, like some of the Phanerozoic orogenic belts (e.g., the Himalayas), but this was accompanied by very high-temperature metamorphism with extensive melting of the lower crust or mantle to produce the anorthosites and dehydration of the sur-

Some of the earliest fossils occur in Precambrian limestones. These algal mats called stromatolites are up to a metre in diameter.

rounding rocks to produce granulites. Why this particular belt should be characterized by such high-temperature metamorphism is not known.

Conclusion. In summary, it is possible to see a continual change in tectonic processes through the Precambrian. The Archaean was dominantly a period of crustal generation and very mobile tectonic conditions, so that most of the rocks were deformed and folded and generally "gneissified": sediments played a relatively minor role. Toward the end of the Archaean, parallel linear series of greenstone belts began to develop. By the end of the Proterozoic, however, the pattern of tectonic processes was much closer to that seen in the Phanerozoic. Mountain belts were much more linear and sediments were relatively more important.

It is tempting to link these changes to an increasing influence of *plate tectonics as we know it today – perhaps with much smaller lithospheric plates or even a different mechanism of convection. This change would be expected if thermal gradients were higher in the Archaean, gradually falling as short-lived radioisotopes decayed away and other heat-producing elements such as uranium, thorium, potassium and rubidium were gradually trans-ferred to the continental crust through magmatic processes.   JT

Paleozoic

The Paleozoic, the era of ancient life, lasted roughly 375 million years, from about 600 to about 225 million years ago. It encompassed the Cambrian, Ordovician and Silurian in the lower Paleozoic, and the Devonian, Carboniferous (Mississippian and Pennsylvanian) and Permian in the upper Paleozoic.   AI

Cambrian

In 1831 Adam *Sedgwick, professor of Geology at Cambridge University, traveled to north Wales to try to unravel the geological succession of the deformed and poorly fossiliferous rocks of this area (his earliest researches were aided by a young student, Charles *Darwin). His labors culminated in his defining the Cambrian, naming the system for the Latin name for Wales, Cambria.

The scope of the Cambrian has been rather reduced since Sedgwick's original definition. Sir Roderick *Murchison's

work in southeast Wales resulted in his defining the *Silurian system: each worker included as many strata as possible in their respective systems as they worked up and down the geological column. Before long it was realized that there was a major overlap which was only resolved later, after much acrimony, by Charles *Lapworth – who established the *Ordovician.

The importance of the Cambrian lies in the fact that, although the Earth is about 4600 million years old and life at least 3500 million years old, the beginning of the Cambrian heralds the appearance of metazoa (multicellular animals) with mineralized skeletons capable of being preserved as fossils. Furthermore, these fossils occur in relative abundance. In general, Precambrian rocks have only a sparsely preserved flora of microscopic *algae and fungi, as well as more prominent algal mounds called stromatolites. A notable exception is a late Precambrian soft-bodied fauna of coelenterates and worms.

Unfortunately, in only a few areas of the world was deposition of sediments continuous during the Precambrian-Cambrian transition: more usually there is a prominent unconformity. The lowermost Cambrian in many places is characterized by *conglomerates and coarse *sandstones that represent ancient beach deposits formed as the sea transgressed over the Precambrian continents. Local topographic features of these continents can often be recognized where the conglomerates have accumulated in hollows and depressions. The continents as a whole were, however, almost completely worn down to pediplains (see *plateaux). The worldwide transgression of the sea continued, with some halts and reversals, for much of the Cambrian at a modest rate of about 10mi (16km) per million years. By the end of the period the land area had been greatly reduced and there were vast areas of shallow, warm sunlit seas.

Although the base of the Cambrian is recognized by the advent of fossils with hard parts, debate on the exact horizon has been prolonged, and an International Commission is now working toward an acceptable solution. The boundary may be drawn within what is now the lowermost Cambrian, which is zoned, in the absence of *trilobites, by use of *archaeocyathids and small shelly fossils. This procedure will automatically place below the Cambrian some fossils with hard parts, but these are restricted to the uppermost Precambrian.

Radiometric dating determines the base of the Cambrian as being about 600 million years old and the top as being about 500 million years old. Worldwide subdivision of the Cambrian has not proceeded apace with other systems, and only the broad divisions of lower, middle and upper are used. Each division, with the exception of the lowermost Cambrian, is zoned by trilobites. The regional distribution of trilobites, combined with our imperfect knowledge, means that the Cambrian of each major area

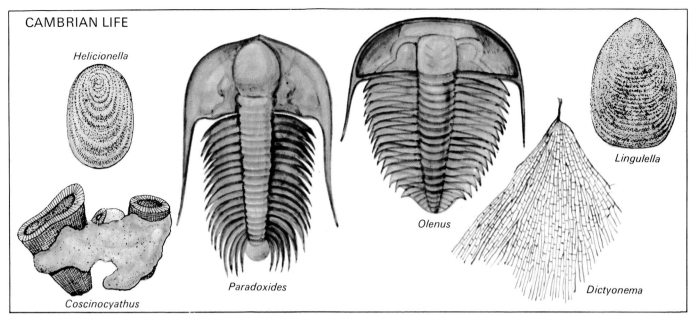

CAMBRIAN LIFE

Helicionella

Coscinocyathus

Paradoxides

Olenus

Dictyonema

Lingulella

has its own subdivisions which are yet to be united in a worldwide system.

The Origin of Hard Parts. The appearance of the Cambrian faunas is often regarded as sudden or abrupt. In terms of the Earth's age this is true, but the development of fossils with hard parts took at least 20 million years. Why did fossils appear in appreciable numbers when underlying Precambrian rocks which have suffered no subsequent metamorphism fail to yield fossils despite careful and widespread searches? The possible reasons for the development of hard parts remain a subject of lively debate, and no single idea has yet won general acceptance. Many representatives of the fauna must have had Precambrian soft-bodied ancestors that failed to fossilize: it is often argued that animals akin to trilobites and *brachiopods could not exist

without fossilizable hard parts, but in fact the exoskeleton need only be chitinous and weakly mineralized to function efficiently. Furthermore, the earliest Cambrian trilobites have noticeably thin exoskeletons.

Factors that have been invoked to explain skeletalization include the amount of free oxygen, the development of new ecological niches and food chains, and the late Precambrian ice age. The primitive atmosphere of the Earth was oxygen-free, the build-up to the present atmospheric level of 21% being due to the photosynthetic activity of plants, in particular marine algae. It has been proposed that, by the beginning of the Cambrian, oxygen had reached about 1% of modern levels. This value would, by allowing the synthesis of skeletal tissues such as collagen, enable the metazoa to diversify rapidly. Increased oxygen may

have also permitted more sophisticated behavioral activities, so promoting further skeletalization. Many of the earliest Cambrian fossils are very small, and the subsequent increase in size could again be connected with greater amounts of oxygen. The addition of oxygen to the atmosphere would shield the Earth from lethal ultraviolet radiation and allow organisms to live in very shallow water and near the surface of the oceans where algae, the primary producer in food chains, flourish.

Another theory suggests that at the end of the Precambrian a supercontinent broke up. The consequent development of mid-ocean ridges (see *ocean floor) would displace sea-water and account for the observed transgression. The increase in the area of shallow marine environments caused by continental fragmentation and this trans-

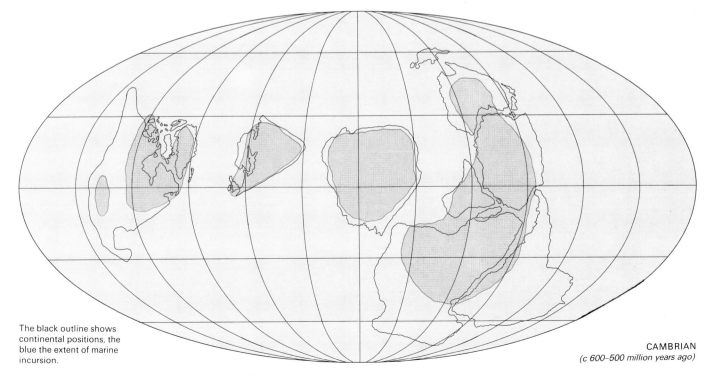

The black outline shows continental positions, the blue the extent of marine incursion.

CAMBRIAN
(c 600–500 million years ago)

gression would have offered many ecological niches that in turn encouraged diversification.

It has also been argued that hard parts evolved as protection against predators. The notion that the Cambrian was largely free from predators is being discredited, but the acquisition of an exoskeleton was probably connected more with the support of walking and feeding organs than with defense.

Cambrian Faunas. Not only is the Cambrian uniquely interesting because of the appearance of fossils, but the faunas, which were all marine, underwent fascinating developments in character and diversity. Many of the earliest Cambrian creatures disappeared after a relatively short time to be replaced by more long-lasting groups. Early Cambrian faunas are notable for their paucity of species, but diversity thereafter rapidly increased. By the end of the period every skeletonized metazoan phylum, with the exception of the *Bryozoa, had arisen, although the individual members are often very different from their modern descendants.

Phosphatic skeletons characterize many of the earliest fossils, which include inarticulate *brachiopods and *mollusks such as gastropods and the "cap shells" or monoplacophora. Several groups of small tubular and cone-shaped shells are of uncertain classification, and some may have been skeletal plates of larger animals. The distinctive hyolithids first occur in the lowermost Cambrian: they had a conical calcareous shell with a plate to fit over its opening, and two curved struts that may have been involved in locomotion. The archaeocyathids also had a calcareous skeleton that formed a single- or double-walled cup perforated by holes for feeding from water currents. They have affinities with the *corals and *sponges, but are regarded as a distinct phylum. It may be significant that archaeocyathids and sponges are rarely found together. Although the former flourished in the lower Cambrian, they were extinct by the end of the period, perhaps due to their inability to compete against the sponges.

Phosphatic skeletons were superseded by the widespread adoption of calcareous ones. The reasons for this change may be attributable to a decrease in the magnesium:calcium ratio of seawater, which would have enabled rigid skeletons to form. The argument that the Cambrian seas were less acidic, so allowing secretion of calcareous skeletons, is negated by the existence of Precambrian limestones and calcareous *algae. The biochemical pathways that led to calcification are still being studied.

Slightly later, the *trilobites arose and rapidly dominated the Cambrian seas. Their main evolutionary trends in the Cambrian were the fusion of the posterior segments into a solid plate (pygidium) and lateral migration of the eyes. Other mollusks include tiny bivalves, but the cephalopods did not appear until the uppermost Cambrian. The *echinoderms are especially interesting. One significant development in the eocrinoids and crinoids was a protrusion of the lower body as a stem to lift it clear of the sediment. Some echinoderms, such as the crinoids and edrioasteroids, continued successfully into post-Cambrian times: a conspicuous number, however, had a brief heyday but died out before the end of the Cambrian. Pentaradial symmetry, so characteristic of later *echinoderms, was by no means prevalent and different groups ranged from asymmetrical to radially symmetrical. These odd echinoderms are best regarded as "experimental" forms that despite their novelty could not compete against their better adapted relatives. Similar features may be seen amongst other Cambrian phyla – indeed, in some cases the entire phylum became extinct.

*Graptolites, which achieved a great diversity in the Ordovician and Silurian, first appeared in the middle Cambrian. Unlike the great majority of later graptolites, which floated, those in the Cambrian seas were sessile.

Conodonts have been recovered in sparse numbers. A few have peculiar shapes that were presumably "experiments", but the great majority are simple cones. The apparatus of the conodont animal must have been much simpler than in the later Paleozoic, when the shapes of conodonts became more diverse and complex.

Some of the varying activities of the fauna are preserved as *trace fossils: these are invaluable because they are often found in rocks, like sandstone, which lack body fossils. Several distinctive varieties are attributed to trilobites ploughing through the sediment; but it is curious that some of these trace fossils occur before the appearance of trilobites, and so may represent the activities of other arthropods. The growing diversity of the faunas is reflected in the increasing number and type of trace fossils above the basal Cambrian. Many trace fossils were produced by soft-bodied animals; and the presence of worms, possibly phoronid-like, and naked mollusks has been identified.

The Burgess Shale. Our knowledge of Cambrian faunas and the early evolution of metazoa without any hard parts would be greatly impoverished were it not for the celebrated middle Cambrian Burgess Shale, discovered accidentally by the American geologist C. D. Walcott in the mountains of southern British Columbia. He collected thousands of superbly preserved specimens from a small quarry which he opened above the town of Field. The fossils include numerous arthropods which are only distantly related to trilobites: it is significant that their exoskeletons are often thin and would not in normal circumstances fossilize. Trilobites with their limbs preserved are also known.

The completely soft-bodied worms show the most remarkable preservation. The gut, sometimes with food inside it, muscles and other organs can be identified. Some of the worms can be placed in groups which exist today, while others seem to be primitive chordates that by the beginning of the Ordovician had evolved to true fish.

A number of worms cannot, however, be placed in any known group. They had unusual or even bizarre morphologies: their approaches to problems like walking on or burrowing in sediment were rather unorthodox and not, in the long run, successful.

The Burgess Shale also contains a large number of sponges and some coelenterates.

Cambrian floras. Little is known about the Cambrian floras. The Burgess Shale has many macroscopic algae (seaweeds), which no doubt reflects their general abundance. Calcareous algae were sometimes sufficiently prolific to form reefs. Microscopic algae were also present but scant information is available. The continents, devoid of vegetation and subject to severe erosion, were deserts.

Paleogeography. The mechanism of *plate tectonics can explain many hitherto unconnected geological facts, although the concept will need some refining in due course. One consequence is that it allows us to work backwards, using present-day plate movements combined with a knowledge of the rates of sea-floor spreading, to reassemble the continents as they were in the past. Following this procedure back as far as the *Permian, we can deduce the presence of a supercontinent (Pangaea). Pre-Permian continental configurations remain rather speculative, as it is not easy to determine the size and shape of the continents that went to form Pangaea.

Several avenues of approach lead to a possible Cambrian paleogeography, but the paucity of data leaves many conclusions rather unfirm. It is argued that mountain-building results from the collision between two continental plates previously separated by an ocean, and so the identification of post-Cambrian/pre-Permian mountain ranges may indicate the sites of Cambrian oceans. The best documented of these is the proto-Atlantic, of approximately the same shape as the modern North Atlantic, whose closure later resulted in the Caledonian orogenesis. Paleomagnetic data gives information on the paleolatitudes of continents, but the scatter of results is often embarrassingly wide (see *geophysics).

Despite the uncertainty of the available information, Cambrian continental or kratonic areas were probably centered on North America, the Siberian shield, China-Korea, and the Baltic shield. In addition, Africa, Australia, South America and Antarctica formed a very large landmass called Gondwanaland. This supercontinent may have been a single whole, but some geologists believe that it was split by a central sea so that Africa-South America and Australia-Antarctica formed separate blocks – the critical evidence may be buried beneath the Antarctic icecap.

The Main Range of the Canadian Rockies. This section of the Rockies was formed by overthrusting of blocks of Cambrian limestone originally deposited in marine environments.

The relative positioning of the Cambrian continents across the globe depends largely on scanty paleomagnetic data, and considerable refinements and rearrangements will probably be necessary in the future.

Faunal Provinces. Only for trilobites have faunal provinces been recognized. Other groups are either insufficiently known or do not appear to show any systematic geographical variation capable of being resolved into provinces.

The distribution of trilobites was only partially controlled by sedimentary facies, and biogeographical factors are more important. The swimming or floating agnostid trilobites, however, ignored most provincial barriers that constrained the other bottom-living trilobites and had a widespread distribution.

It has been shown that some of the Cambrian continents were encircled by broad sedimentary belts that changed systematically from the shallow water of the continental shelf to the deeper water of the open sea. First identified in North America, these consist of an inner detrital belt of sand and mud derived from weathering of the continent, a median carbonate belt of limestone and dolomite, and an outer detrital belt of dark muds, silts, impure limestones and sometimes cherts, that were deposited in deeper and often oxygen-poor water on the continental slope. Occasionally carbonate conglomerates slumped over the shelf edge into this outer belt. The same threefold division of sedimentary belts has been recognized off the Siberian and Chinese-Korean continents, but in the Baltic region the median limestone belt is generally absent and so it is believed that the open ocean came close to the Baltic landmass.

In the lower Cambrian, two main trilobite provinces have been identified. The Olenellid province consists of two subprovinces centered on North America and northwest Europe/maritime North America. The Redlichiid province includes Australia, southeast Asia, Africa and Antarctica. The affinity, for instance, between the trilobites of northwest Europe and maritime North America is taken as evidence of their proximity on one side of the proto-Atlantic. When the Atlantic reopened the province was split into two sections that now lie thousands of miles apart.

Better knowledge of middle and upper Cambrian faunas gives a more complex pattern. The trilobites of the inner detrital belt and most of the carbonate belt are largely endemic. Four endemic trilobite faunas can be recognized in Siberia, North America, China-Australia and central Europe. Endemism arose because access by more cosmopolitan trilobites, including the otherwise ubiquitous agnostids, was restricted, sometimes to the extent of making correlation with other areas difficult. In some places the carbonate belt acted as a faunal barrier. Elsewhere, no obvious barrier is present and factors like temperature and salinity, which left no trace in the sediments, must be invoked. In contrast, the outer detrital belt was an area of open access to migrating trilobites because it lay on the edges of the open sea. The consequent mixing makes separate provinces difficult to identify. The lower Cambrian provinces seem, however, to persist and three provinces centered on western Europe, North America and southeast Asia/Australia have been defined.

Climate. The end of the late Precambrian glaciation must have heralded a distinct amelioration of climate that persisted during the Cambrian. The widespread distribution of carbonates and *evaporites suggests that much of the Earth's surface was warm. Archaeocyathids could form patch reefs, and it has been suggested that, like modern hermatypic corals, they could only live in tropical and subtropical conditions. The continents are generally assumed to have been dry for all or much of the year. The poles may have been in open seas, icecaps being apparently absent. Latitudinal temperature gradients do not appear to have been extreme.

Conclusion. The Cambrian is one of the most exciting geological periods to study, the great length of time that separates us from it making the intellectual challenge all the greater. Future research should reveal exactly why fossils with hard parts appeared relatively quickly, and what steps were involved in this process. Cooperation with other scientists and the development of new analytical techniques will help to clarify our notions on Cambrian faunas and their distribution.   SCM

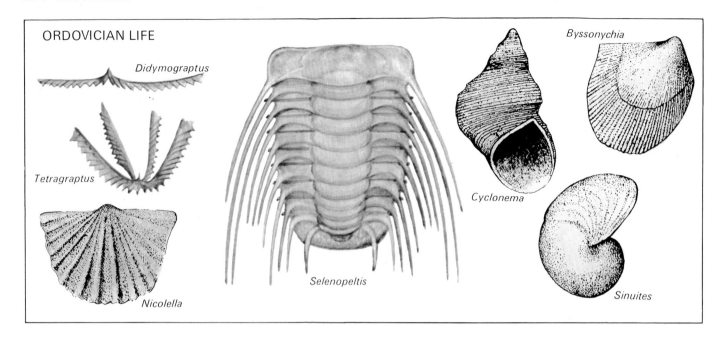

ORDOVICIAN LIFE

Didymograptus

Tetragraptus

Nicolella

Selenopeltis

Cyclonema

Byssonychia

Sinuites

Ordovician

The term "Ordovician" was introduced by Charles *Lapworth in 1879 to include those rocks which had been described as upper Cambrian by Adam *Sedgwick and as lower Silurian by Roderick *Murchison. When the *Cambrian and Silurian systems were first proposed it was believed that the Cambrian included rocks entirely older than the Silurian, but as investigations proceeded it became apparent that the two systems overlapped, and that the upper part of Sedgwick's Cambrian was essentially the same as the lower part of Murchison's Silurian. In an attempt to resolve this conflict of opinion Lapworth introduced the name Ordovician for the disputed beds. The name is for the Ordovices, a tribe of Celts from Wales.

On the radiometric timescale, the Ordovician period is accorded a duration of approximately 60 million years, from around 500 to about 440 million years ago.
Ordovician Fossils. Ordovician strata yield representatives of all the major invertebrate phyla; and it is from this period that abundant fish remains first occur.

The *trilobites, which were the dominant organisms in the Cambrian, are present also in great abundance in Ordovician strata; and many genera, and even families and higher taxonomic categories, appear for the first time in this period. Likewise, trilobites persist in great strength into the Silurian, but with the appearance of many new forms replacing earlier stocks.

In the Ordovician, and for the first time in the geological record, *brachiopods, *bryozoans, *gastropods, *bivalves,

*nautiloid cephalopods, *crinoids, *echinoids, and rugose and tabulate *corals all become locally common. The Ordovician representatives of these groups, together with the trilobites, were primarily, but not exclusively, inhabitants of the sea floor, and collectively they constitute the so-called shelly facies. Their abundant fossil representation is generally indicative of the fact that the sediments containing them accumulated in shallow seas, on or bordering the continental areas.

Ordovician sediments which accumulated in the deeper waters, beyond the epicontinental seas, yield abundant remains of pelagic organisms. Chief among these are the *graptolites; appreciably less common are the remains of inarticulate ("horny") brachiopods and phyllocarid *crustaceans. This association of graptolites with the

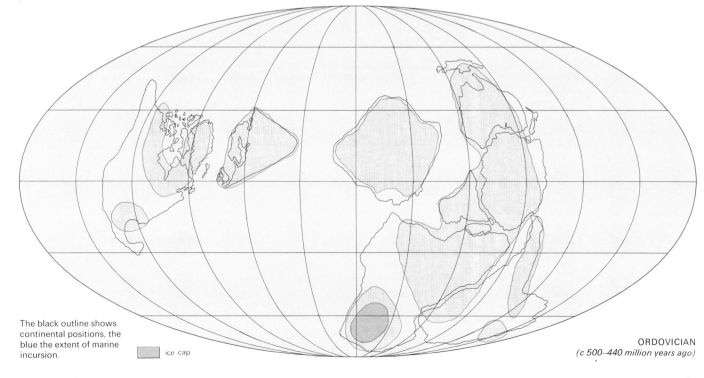

The black outline shows continental positions, the blue the extent of marine incursion.

ice cap

ORDOVICIAN
(c 500–440 million years ago)

Ordovician black shales exposed on a beach at Abereiddy Bay, Wales. These shales contain graptolites and indicate deposition in deep water during early Ordovician times.

remains of other pelagic organisms, and the virtual absence of shelly fossils, characterizes the Ordovician graptolitic facies.

Correlation. Fossils provide the primary evidence enabling the recognition of Ordovician strata throughout the world and their detailed correlation with the standard British Ordovician succession. The problems attending the classification and correlation of Ordovician rocks merely within the confines of the British Isles, arising from the diversity of their contained faunas, are considerable: on a world scale, such problems are increased, and the issue is still further complicated by the increasing appreciation that most, if not all, Ordovician faunas were differentiated into provinces, just as are organisms of the present day.

The outcome of this is that different classifications have had to be erected in different areas, because the fossil faunas, the bases of these classifications, are different. The sea-floor-dwelling shelly faunas appear to have suffered a greater degree of provincialism than the pelagic graptolites. For this reason, the shelly faunas play a restricted role in world-wide correlation, while the graptolites offer the most useful means of establishing contemporaneity. Interchange of faunas between provinces occurred from time to time

and instances of complete merging have been documented: this has enabled the correlation of the several schemes of classification to be made with a fair degree of confidence.

Ordovician Rocks. For descriptive purposes, present-day occurrences of Ordovician rocks can be grouped into two broad categories based on tectonic and lithological criteria: those preserved on the relatively stable *Precambrian shield areas (kratons); and those found in long, linear fold belts bordering the kratons.

The kratons are composed of Precambrian *igneous rocks and *metamorphic rocks covered with a veneer of younger sediments. Several such kratons, of continental proportions and varying relative elevation, existed during the Ordovician.

The European kraton was centered about Finland and western Russia; the presently exposed portion is referred to as the Baltic Shield. The Ordovician North American kraton included the present Canadian Shield, while the Siberian kraton extended over most of what is now northeast Asia. The immense Gondwanaland kraton of the Ordovician Period was subsequently dismembered by continental rifting, and the separated fragments are now widely distributed throughout the southern hemisphere: they include the eastern half of South America (the Brazilian Shield), much of Africa and Antarctica, and the western half of Australia (the Yilgarn and

Pilbara Blocks).

The Ordovician sediments which accumulated on these kratons are principally of shallow-water origin. Variations in thickness reflect differential warping of the kratons, such that the successions may be grouped generally into thinner carbonate platform facies and thicker basinal facies of rocks made up of eroded and weathered particles (clastic rocks). The relative stability of the kratons has ensured little, if any, structural disturbance of the Ordovician rocks there since the time of their formation.

However, Ordovician rocks exposed in the fold belts bordering the kratons have been intensely deformed, and generally exhibit metamorphism – to varying degrees. The successions attain a great thickness, usually of the order of thousands of metres, and the different rock types can be seen to have accumulated in a wide range of depositional environments. Fossiliferous limestones, together with sandstones, siltstones and shales, were laid down in the relatively shallow waters of continental shelf areas. Other sedimentary rocks (e.g., *graywackes) give evidence of their having been transported by turbidity currents and having accumulated in waters deeper than those in which they were initially deposited. Deeper water, abyssal environments are represented by cherty and argillaceous *limestones and black, often pyritic, shales with graptolites.

For descriptive purposes, it is convenient where possible to distinguish between eugeosynclinal and miogeosynclinal Ordovician successions within the fold belts (see *geosynclines): the former are thick sequences of sediments with associated volcanic rocks which formed some distance from the kratons; the latter are adjacent to the kratons and lack volcanic rocks.

Acceptance of the theory of *plate tectonics has necessarily modified earlier interpretations of the origin of linear fold belts. They are now considered to have arisen at ancient destructive, or compressional, plate margins and to define the sites of former oceans. Stages in ocean closure, leading to the ultimate collision of the bordering continents, are reflected in successive episodes of deformation and metamorphism in the rocks of the fold belts. The distinctive characteristics of the miogeosynclinal and eugeosynclinal successions within these belts can readily be interpreted in the context of this dynamic process.

The non-volcanic miogeosynclinal facies incorporates those sediments which were deposited on the submerged margins of the continental portions of adjacent plates: their major structural characteristics were acquired only at a late stage in ocean contraction, when opposed continental margins collided. Sediments of the eugeosynclinal facies, on the other hand, accumulated on the oceanward sides of the continental margins and include ocean-floor (or abyssal) deposits together with continental-slope and -rise turbidites. The abundant volcanic rocks incorporated within the eugeosynclinal successions, the evidence of successive phases of deformation and metamorphism which they portray, and their association with upthrust wedges of very dark rocks, all point to their intimate involvement in the contraction process. The scale and intensity of deformation may have been such as to force slices of the eugeosynclinal facies along shallow-dipping thrust planes into the miogeosynclinal or even the kratonic regions. Hence, whereas the relationship between these three facies was essentially gradational at the time the sediments were deposited, the boundaries of the eugeosynclinal facies are now usually tectonically defined in the ancient fold belts.

The proto-Atlantic. The Paleozoic Caledonian and Appalachian fold belts, or orogens, portray a classic series of ancient plate-tectonic processes. A combination of paleomagnetic, tectonic, petrological and sedimentary evidence points to the existence of what has been termed a proto-Atlantic Ocean occupying approximately, but not precisely, the site of the present Atlantic. The spreading process which initiated the proto-Atlantic commenced as far back in time as the late Precambrian and continued through the succeeding Cambrian, when, paleomagnetic evidence suggests, the opposing continental margins achieved a maximum separation of the

order of 1250mi (2000km). Contraction of the proto-Atlantic commenced at the start of the Ordovician and finally led to the collision of the opposing continents in Silurian and Devonian times. In terms of present-day geography, the resulting mountain belt, the Caledonian-Appalachian orogen, extends from Spitzbergen through Scandinavia and into Britain and Ireland; and it is traceable on the western side of the North Atlantic from Newfoundland southward to Alabama.

The geosynclinal belt in Europe extends from western Ireland, through Wales, the English Lake District and Scotland to Norway. The Ordovician successions within this belt vary considerably in thickness, owing partly to the different environments in which the sediments were deposited and partly to the extent of the development of volcanic rocks. Thicker successions, totaling many thousands of feet, are present in north Wales and the English Lake District; in both areas, volcanic *andesites and *rhyolites are extensively developed. The successions contrast markedly with, for example, the 110ft (34m) of Caradoc and Ashgill black graptolitic shales, with thin volcanic ashes, exposed at Moffat in the Southern Uplands of Scotland.

There is local evidence of plate-tectonic processes. Thus at Ballantrae in southwest Scotland an association of early Ordovician black graptolitic shales with ocean-floor volcanic lavas and wedges of black rocks is interpreted as the site of a subduction zone along which the floor of the contracting proto-Atlantic was consumed.

The separate recognition of eugeosynclinal and miogeosynclinal facies within the geosynclinal belt is most readily achieved in Scandinavia, on the southeast side of the proto-Atlantic Ocean. The contraction is now tectonically defined: slices (nappes) of eugeosynclinal rocks resting on, and partially masking, the miogeosynclinal successions were carried eastward into their present positions along low-lying thrust planes as the margins of the proto-Atlantic converged in mid-Paleozoic time. Limited exposure, coupled with major faulting in post-Ordovician times, obscures facies relationships on the northwest side of the proto-Atlantic Ocean. However, in northwest Scotland, early Ordovician platform carbonates are preserved which compare readily with those of similar age in North America; it is concluded that these carbonates accumulated on the Ordovician North American kraton and that their present location on the eastern side of the North Atlantic is a consequence of continental rifting and sea-floor spreading from the Mesozoic onward.

A complete section through the Appalachian orogen is best seen and documented in Newfoundland. Ordovician strata in east Newfoundland compare with those which accumulated on the margin of the European kraton and thus reflect the conditions in Ordovician time on the southeast side of the proto-Atlantic Ocean. Westward, the Or-

dovician of central Newfoundland is contained within a belt of volcanic-bearing rocks of great thickness, analogous to, and originally continuous with, that extending from Ireland to Norway. The Ordovician of western Newfoundland includes platform carbonates like those in northwest Scotland; moreover, these rocks are over-ridden by thrust sheets composed of rocks originating in the volcanic geosynclinal belt and carried westward during the contraction phases of the proto-Atlantic Ocean.

Ordovician Geography and Climate. To the extent that ancient linear orogenic belts define the sites of former oceans, it is believed that four major continental areas existed during the Ordovician Period. These were: (a) North America and Europe west of the Caledonian-Appalachian orogen (the North American kraton); (b) Europe and North America east of the Caledonian-Appalachian orogen and north of the Hercynian fold belt (the European kraton); (c) Asia east of the Urals (the Siberian kraton); and (d) Gondwanaland, comprising South America, Africa, India, Australia and Antarctica.

The precise outlines of these continents and the widths of the intervening oceans are still matters for speculation. Paleomagnetic data provides evidence for the latitudinal positioning of the continents, but they are of course unable to provide information on their longitudinal separation.

In terms of present-day geography, paleomagnetic evidence suggests that the Ordovician south pole was located in northern Africa, and therefore the Ordovician equator must have extended from California, west of Hudson's Bay, north of Greenland and Scandinavia, across northeast Asia, to western Australia. This configuration of lines of latitude places the bulk of the Ordovician continental areas in the southern hemisphere. Only southeast Asia, the eastern portion of Australia and northwestern North America were located in the Ordovician northern hemisphere, and all of these were within approximately 30° of the Ordovician equator.

Confirmation of this latitudinal positioning of Ordovician continental areas has been provided from other sources. Intensive postwar exploration in the Sahara under the auspices of the oil industry has revealed decisive evidence, including glacial sediments (tillites), glaciated surfaces and glacial striations, pointing to a late Ordovician ice advance, with the ice sheets radiating from a polar region in the continental area of northern Africa. The undoubted presence of late Ordovician tillites in the Saharan region has supported the theory that deposits with similar characteristics exposed elsewhere are likewise of glacial origin.

The composition and distribution of Ordovician marine faunas, coupled with the nature and distribution of sediment types (particularly *evaporites), support the location of the Ordovician equatorial zone in the present Arctic and sub-Arctic regions of

Volcanic rocks are commonly found in the Ordovician succession. These mountains in Borrowdale, England, are formed of Mid Ordovician volcanic rocks extruded subaerially. They were exposed as a result of uplift and erosion some 500 million years later during the Tertiary.

northern Europe and North America. In addition, the faunas and sediments provide some evidence for a progressive strengthening of *climatic zones during the Ordovician, lowest temperatures being achieved late in the period.

We have already mentioned the marked provincialism displayed by Ordovician marine faunas, and available evidence strongly supports the view that the overriding influence in the development and distribution of the provinces was climatic – more specifically, latitudinal variation in water temperature. In the North Atlantic region, where Ordovician faunas have been studied in greatest detail, two major provinces – named American and European – can be deduced from brachiopod, conodont, graptolite and trilobite fossil remains. If the geographic distributions of the two provinces are plotted on the Ordovician map, the American province can be seen to straddle the paleoequator, extending from about 30°N to about 30°S, while the European province occupies middle and high southern latitudes.

The two provinces became increasingly differentiated during the early Ordovician, reached a maximum disparity in the middle of the period, and then merged in the late Ordovician, giving virtually cosmopolitan faunas in the North Atlantic region. This breakdown of provincialism is generally attributed to the contraction of the proto-Atlantic Ocean, which opened up new migration routes and led to a merging of hitherto distinct faunas.

In the case of the graptolites, however, it seems at least equally likely that climatic deterioration in higher latitudes, as evidenced by the late Ordovician glacial advance, played a primary role. All late Ordovician graptolite faunas are confined to within a few tens of degrees either side of the Ordovician equator – that is, within the limits of the early and middle Ordovician American province. It would appear that the European province no longer existed in the late Ordovician, presumably because water temperatures in middle and high latitudes fell below the tolerance limits of the graptolites.

Conclusion. We have seen that the Caledonian-Appalachian orogen and the bordering North American and European kratons preserve contrasting facies of Ordovician rocks. From their nature and their present-day distribution it is concluded that an ancient ocean – the proto-Atlantic – occupied the site of the orogen in late Precambrian and early Paleozoic times.

Loss of ocean crust along subduction zones on the margins of this ocean was accompanied by the convergence of the North American and European kratons; and their ultimate collision and joining later in the Paleozoic resulted in the disappearance of the proto-Atlantic.

At the opening of the Ordovician, the ocean had reached its maximum width, which may have been as great as 1250mi (2000km). The period was to witness the first stages in the contraction of this ocean. Viewed in this context, the lithological characteristics of Ordovician strata become meaningful, and the present distribution on either side of the modern Atlantic is readily explained. DS

Silurian

The Silurian system was named by *Murchison in 1835 after an ancient British tribe which inhabited South Wales and parts of the Welsh Borderland, where Murchison did much of his early fieldwork. In these areas, Murchison described sequences of Silurian sediments which were rich in marine fossils, mostly *brachiopods, *trilobites and *corals.

*Sedgwick, who named the Cambrian system, did not describe his faunas in the same detail as Murchison, leaving most of the paleontology to others, and by 1852

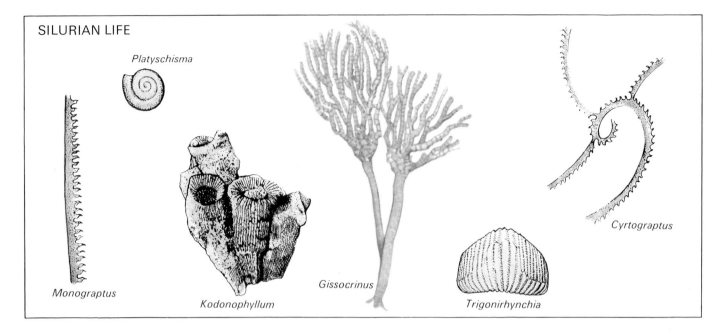

SILURIAN LIFE

Platyschisma

Monograptus

Kodonophyllum

Gissocrinus

Trigonirhynchia

Cyrtograptus

Murchison was claiming most pre-Devonian rocks for his own Silurian system. It was not until after Murchison's death in 1871 that Charles *Lapworth redefined the Silurian.

The four series in the Silurian are, from youngest to oldest: the Pridoli (named after a town in Czechoslovakia); the Ludlow (a town in Shropshire); the Wenlock (Wenlock Edge is a scarp formed by the Wenlock Limestone in Shropshire); and the Llandovery (a town in South Wales).

At the moment, it is not possible to be precise about the relative lengths of time represented by each series, but both graptolites and brachiopods show more evolutionary changes during the Llandovery than during any of the other series, so it may be that it represents about a quarter of the 40 million years or so of the Silurian, whose

approximate span is from 440 to 400 million years ago.

Life in the Silurian. The later parts of the Silurian probably saw the first colonization of the land by primitive plants, though life's real conquest of the land had to wait until the Devonian. Some freshwater fish were present in rivers and lakes, but the vast majority of Silurian life was marine.

The marine faunas in the Silurian have two main components: those animals, such as the brachiopods, that lived on the sea floor (benthos) and those, like the graptolites, that inhabited the water above. Although trilobites occur, they are far less important than in the preceding Ordovician. Mollusks, corals, bryozoans, ostracods, crinoids and fish are also present, but are only common in a few out of the many marine environments.

The proto-Atlantic, which in the Ordovician separated the Canadian Shield (including Scotland) from the Baltic Shield (to which England was attached), became progressively narrower during the Silurian. As a result the free-swimming (pelagic) larval stages of brachiopods and trilobites were able to cross the ocean freely, so that these faunas were the same on both sides of the ocean. In the early Silurian most brachiopods and trilobites were worldwide in their distribution – no ocean was wide enough to act as a permanent barrier to their pelagic larvae. Many *ostracods, however, do not have a pelagic larval state – their eggs hatch out on the sea floor – and as a result even the narrow Silurian proto-Atlantic was a barrier to their migration. The freshwater fish were also restricted until the late Silurian (when Norway may have collided with

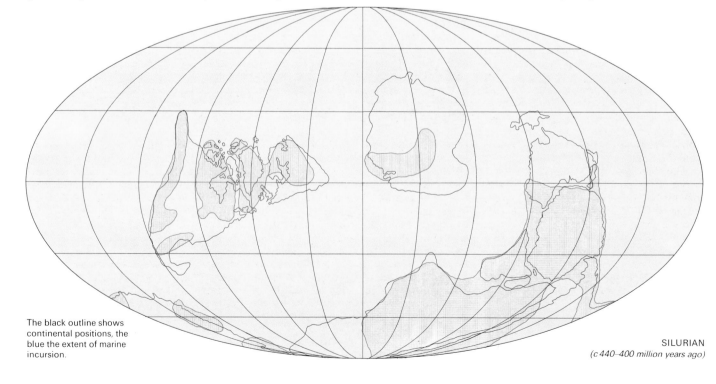

The black outline shows continental positions, the blue the extent of marine incursion.

SILURIAN
(c 440–400 million years ago)

Scottish black shales, similar to those of Ordovician age, are also found in the Silurian. They contain graptolites, and were deposited at the same time as shallow-water facies found further south in the British Isles.

Greenland).

The early Silurian brachiopods of Britain were among the first group of fossils in which communities have been described. These communities appear to be more closely related to varying depths of water than to varying types of sediment. Three lines of evidence for this are: firstly, that maps of community distribution at any one time show a consistent community sequence from the shore to deep water; secondly, in the transgressive lower Silurian of the Welsh Borderland different local successions show the same vertical sequence of communities (from shallow to deep); and, finally, in modern marine-bottom communities there is a progressive increase in the diversity of animal species with depth, and similar increases in diversity with depth are seen in the Silurian brachiopod communities.

Brachiopods make up as much as 80% of the preserved Silurian benthos. They are all suspension feeders; and, apart from competition for food, there was probably no interaction between one brachiopod and its neighbors on the sea floor. Each brachiopod community, therefore, did not form a discrete unit; there is little correlation between the ecological distribution of any two species, and there is a continuous gradation of changes in the brachiopod distribution from the shore to deep water, with no natural breaks.

Stratigraphical classification. Murchison defined the Wenlock and Ludlow as formations (that is, as mappable sedimentary units) which he could trace across the Welsh Borderland and South Wales. But as stratigraphy developed it became necessary to have a term which referred to rocks of the same age as these formations but in distant areas. Hence the concept of "series" developed: this is a time-stratigraphic unit, which embraces all rocks formed during a defined interval of time. At present, series can be correlated only by means of fossils; in time, radioisotope methods may become sufficiently accurate, but errors of 10 million years (perhaps up to 10 graptolite zones) are still present in the lower Paleozoic timescale.

The Llandovery, Wenlock and Ludlow series were established on the basis of brachiopods, trilobites and corals, which occur in the shelf sediments of the type areas. Subsequently, Lapworth and others recognized graptolite zones in deeper-water sediments of Wales, northern England and southern Scotland. These deep-water sediments include very few brachiopods and trilobites, and those that are present are usually of different species than are the shallow-water shelly faunas, so it was not easy to correlate the graptolite zones with the established series. It is only in recent years that this correlation between the

deep-water graptolites and the shallow-water shelly faunas has been achieved.

There are two main snags in correlating the graptolite zones with the shelly faunas: one is that graptolites are not very common in shallow-water deposits, and the other is that it is not very easy to use many shallow-water fossils as accurate time indicators. In contrast with the graptolites, most brachiopod lineages do not show progressive evolutionary changes through time: most alterations in brachiopod assemblages are the direct result of environmental changes, and so cannot be used for correlation with any degree of certainty, as the environmental changes are unlikely to occur simultaneously over wide areas. Most

Silurian brachiopod species appear suddenly over much of the world, survive for 10 or 20 million years without much change, and then become extinct. However, a few lineages – such as *Eocoelia* and *Stricklandia* – show progressive evolutionary changes with time, and it is these that are most useful in correlation.

Both *Eocoelia* and *Stricklandia* occur in the lower Silurian beds near Llandovery in South Wales, so that the presence of members of either lineage in other places enables a correlation to be made with the sequence at Llandovery. A few graptolites are also known from the Llandovery area, but many more are known from other areas where *Eocoelia* and *Stricklandia* occur. It is thus possible to correlate most fossiliferous lower Silurian beds with the type sequence at Llandovery.

In 1925, O. T. Jones mapped the Llandovery area, and instead of giving formal names to the formations there, he gave them letters and numbers. In correlating shelly facies it has now become common usage to equate the brachiopod faunas to these formations at Llandovery; for example, some sandstones in Scotland can be referred to "C_1" if they contain an *Eocoelia* with strong ribs (*E. hemisphaerica*) similar to that occurring in the C_1 mudstones at Llandovery. It has been accepted by many stratigraphers that stratigraphic zones should be based on a type section, but it is only in the Llandovery that this concept is carried through to its logical conclusion: shelly faunas all over the world can be dated by direct reference to the type area.

Sufficient links are now known between these key Llandovery brachiopod lineages and zonal graptolites for the two systems to be fairly well integrated. This integration has allowed stages to be erected for the Llandovery (a stage is a time-stratigraphic term intermediate between a zone and a series and it, too, should be based on a type section). The four Llandovery stages have been defined most specifically by the level of their *base*. As the basal Llandovery formation (A_1) at Llandovery rests unconformably on the Ordovician, and as it is very sparsely fossiliferous, the basal stage (Rhuddanian) has its type section in the south of Scotland where deposition was continuous from the upper Ordovician into the Silurian. The other three Llandovery stages all have their type sections near Llandovery.

In the Wenlock and Ludlow, there are no described lineages in shallow-water brachiopods, so graptolites present the only reliable means of correlation over large distances. Fortunately, in the type areas (Wenlock Edge and Ludlow are both in Shropshire), recent work has provided many new graptolitic horizons, and the Wenlock and lower Ludlow graptolitic beds over most of the world can be correlated with the type sections.

The graptolites and brachiopods are the main groups of fossils which have so far proved most useful in correlation, but other groups are also likely to be valuable. *Conodonts can be used to distinguish most of the Llandovery and Wenlock stages (but not the finer divisions recognized by graptolites and brachiopods). Ostracods, acritarchs (see * dinoflagellates) and also spore assemblages are beginning to prove useful in the upper Silurian, but again no very fine stratigraphic intervals have so far been shown to be correlatable over large distances. Conodonts and acritarchs can occur in most types of marine facies, while spores and ostracods are more abundant in shallow-water environments. All these groups have great potential for stratigraphic zonation of the upper Silurian, but before they can be of much use many more detailed studies will be necessary.

Geography, Sediments and Climate. During the Silurian, the continents were distributed very differently from the way that they are today. Their positions can be deduced (with varying degrees of certainty) partly from paleomagnetic data, partly from faunal distributions (especially Ordovician faunas, which were much more provincial than those in the Silurian), and partly from distributions of igneous rocks (which indicate ocean floor or continental margins above areas where ocean floor was being subducted). (See *plate tectonics.)

The continents were never too far apart for the pelagic larval stages of brachiopods and trilobites to cross the relatively narrow oceans, and few continents acted as barriers to migration because, for much of the time, they were covered by sea. Thus most of the Silurian marine faunas have a worldwide distribution. The principal exception was with Gondwanaland, the large southern-hemisphere continent which split up in the Mesozoic to later form South America, Africa, Antarctica, India and Australia. Gondwanaland was covered by sea only around its margins and in a few other localized areas. Argentina was probably close to the south pole in the Silurian and the regions near this pole show a peculiar cold-water marine fauna containing a limited number of brachiopod and trilobite species (the *Clarkeia* fauna).

At the end of the Ordovician the south pole was situated in what is now the Sahara Desert (it was not until later that Gondwanaland had moved such that the pole had migrated to Argentina). Glacial deposits and erosive features are now exposed clearly in the Sahara, and glacially derived sediments may have extended as far east as Arabia, as far north as Normandy, and as far west as Argentina. When large masses of ice are present on continents (as they are today), there is a corresponding drop in sea-level. In the very late Ordovician the seas were restricted in area, and a non-sequence is present in most shallow marine sedimentary deposits at the base of the Silurian, probably as a result of the late Ordovician ice cap. During the Llandovery, sea levels rose, and most Llandovery marine sequences show a progressive deepening (and spread) of the sea, which may be linked to melting of the ice.

Shropshire, Wales, Western Ireland, New England and New York State all lay on one or other margin of the proto-Atlantic, and all these areas show the effects of this rise in sea-level. In North America the gradients were much less than in Britain, and the sea spread rapidly over a much greater area of the continent, but by the end of Llandovery time, even in Britain, there were very few land areas left outstanding. As a result, the supply of land-derived sand was often reduced, and limestones and muds are the characteristic deposits in shelf areas. In those parts of North America and Europe (notably England and Sweden) where limestones and dolomites occur, corals, bryozoans and algae often flourished, as these areas were not far from the equator, and the shallow seas were warm enough to support a rich abundance of life.

In the late Wenlock, many seas in North America and western Europe became shallower, and it may yet be shown that some of the changes in sea-level are eustatic (that is, world-wide), perhaps once again connected with the development of ice sheets, though the eustatic changes could equally well have been caused by uplift (or subsidence) of an oceanic ridge. *Tillites of Silurian age occur in Argentina and Bolivia: they appear to be early Silurian, but tillites do not contain fossils, and it is quite possible that some parts of Gondwanaland were covered by ice throughout the Silurian.

Limestones or dolomites covered parts of Australia and a strip of Asia extending from Malaysia to Afghanistan as well as the central parts of northern Europe and North America. Over other parts of the continents there was extensive deposition of mud, especially to the east of the carbonate belt in Asia and across central Europe.

On the margins of many continents, sites of former subduction zones can be detected by the presence of *andesites and other calc-alkaline *igneous rocks. In these belts, where oceanic crust was descending beneath the continents, the sites of ocean trenches may be marked by great thicknesses of slumped deposits; or, in other areas, large quantities of graywackes originally deposited on the ocean floor may have been scraped off above the descending ocean plate and plastered onto the margins of the continents. Belts of deep-water sediments occur along both margins of the proto-Atlantic (notably in southern Scotland, Ireland and Newfoundland) and also in Nevada and California (on the western margin of North America), and in eastern Australia. In each of these examples, considerable amounts of material were added onto the margins of the continents. The presence of calc-alkaline igneous rocks in these areas confirms their association with subduction zones active during the Silurian.

In the Ludlow of many areas (including North America, Britain and North Africa) there was a gradual retreat of the sea. In Michigan, Ontario and New York, rock salt and other *evaporite deposits indicate high temperatures with evaporation of the shallow seas during the latest Silurian time. But in other areas there was a gradual change in the environment from marine sediments to river sediments, as in the Old Red Sandstone deposits of northwest Europe and northeast North America. This Old Red Sandstone continent developed after the closure of the proto-Atlantic. It is likely that collision took place between Norway and Greenland in the late Silurian, but the ocean did not finally close, in the northern Appalachians, until late in the early Devonian.

At one time all Old Red Sandstone deposits were thought to be of Devonian age, but we now know that river floodplain environments appeared in many areas well before the end of the Silurian. The red color is not diagnostic of desert environments: all the Old Red Sandstone sediments were laid down in water, either on floodplains or in lakes, the red coloring being due to the ferric oxide *hematite, which coats the sand and mud particles. Many Silurian marine sequences also contain red beds associated with local transgressions of the sea over nearby land. As the land surface was oxidized at this time, more hematite was transported and deposited without reduction at these times of transgression than would otherwise have been the case. Though red sequences can occur in marine sediments which were deposited in a variety of water depths, they are more common in thicker sequences that have been deposited more rapidly.

Conclusion. Plate-tectonic theory shows us that, compared with today, the continents and oceans were arranged very differently in the Silurian. But looking at the Silurian world in more detail we find that the nature of an ocean would not have been very different from that of a modern ocean; the only obvious distinctions would be in the marine organisms – for example, graptolites would be there instead of modern *coccoliths and *diatoms (though the *radiolaria would be much the same). By contrast, apart from the ice caps, the Silurian continents were very different from those of today: the areas where rocks were exposed above sea-level were bright red and lacked soils. These land areas were much smaller than are the extensive land areas of today, most of the continents being covered by shallow seas. The bottom faunas of these seas were dominated by brachiopods, with the occasional patch of coral or calcareous algae in some of the warm shallow areas. In the rivers and lakes, there were a few primitive fish, but most of the land areas were almost barren of life, except for some rare rootless plants that were just starting to colonize the soil-less landscapes. During the Silurian, living was undoubtedly much easier in the sea than on the land.   WSM

Devonian

The Devonian lasted for approximately 50 million years, from about 400 to 350 million years ago. It is the first period from which fossil remains of animals are common, with extensive preservation of continental sediments. The highlights of the period were the establishment of land plants, the appearance of abundant freshwater life, fish and arthropods, and, with the first tetrapods around the end of the period, the initial stages of the vertebrates' conquest of the land. The period also probably witnessed the evolution of insect flight, a development associated with the evolution of larger plants, though the first fossil winged insect is not known until the upper

Carboniferous. In the marine facies, the period witnessed a most remarkable surge of reef growth, largely due to an enigmatic group of fossils, the *stromatoporoids.

Devonian sediments are exciting in their diversity. The shorelines of the continents advanced and retreated during the period; and, in areas of subsidence, the sedimentary record shows evidence of extensive deltas, coastal plains and beaches.

On the other hand, the economic potential of Devonian rocks is limited. No substantial *coals were formed and there are only minor amounts of *iron ore. Devonian fossil reefs (in the form of limestones) are extensively used in the marble industry. The best-known oil-bearing rocks of Devonian age are the Alberta reefs and sandstones of the Moscow area on the Russian Platform.

The name Devonian was proposed by Adam *Sedgwick and Sir Roderick *Murchison in 1839 when it was realized that the fossils that could be found in south Devon, UK, were the marine equivalents of the Old Red Sandstone continental sediments, farther north in the UK, which were unquestionably stratigraphically below the *Carboniferous yet above the *Silurian. The relationships were confirmed in Germany, Belgium and Russia, where marine and continental facies are interbedded. In North America the same type of alternation between marine and nonmarine sediments is superbly displayed in the Catskill Mountains of New York and in gorges and creeks westwards.

The Devonian system is now divided into seven stages, and during the last few years it has become possible to begin to define these stages in an internationally acceptable scheme. But there are still difficulties over the precise interpretation and limits of some of the stages. *Graptolites, which prove so useful for the correlation of strata in the Ordovician and Silurian, became extinct quite early in the Devonian, but the *ammonoids, which replaced the graptolites in terms of stratigraphic usefulness, are not sufficiently abundant until the middle and upper Devonian to form a satisfactory basis for correlation. Thus any scheme of zones and correlations is particularly uncertain for the lower Devonian. A series of *conodont zones is used for the correlation of marine strata.

Paleogeography. In a reconstruction of Devonian world geography the large land mass comprising what are now northern North America, Greenland and northern Europe, was situated astride the equator. Australia was also in the tropics and formed the northern part of the southern continent of Gondwanaland.

For the most part Devonian sedimentation follows sequentially that of the Silurian. There are breaks, particularly where continental Old Red Sandstone facies rests on older rocks of the Caledonian fold belt and, for instance, where sediments of mixed facies transgress the *Precambrian rocks of the Russian Platform. From an inspection

of the paleogeographic map, and from all other available evidence, we find that the Euro-American Old Red Sandstone continent and the sea surrounding it enjoyed a tropical climate. Evidence for glaciation is more limited than in the Silurian or Carboniferous. The south pole was situated in the area of Buenos Aires, and glacial sediments of Devonian age are known from adjacent areas of South America and from South Africa.

The global structure during the Devonian and the distribution of plates and continents are still very uncertain. For instance, the geosynclinal belt across Europe, with its associated zones of spilitic volcanics and serpentines, has been interpreted as site of an old ocean; and the thin oceanic-type deposits of the central European Devonian may also be associated with this ocean.

But detailed examination does not justify such assertions. There is no doubt that the Devonian was a time of global mobility, but the major tectonic events in Europe and North America appear to be those already initiated in the early Paleozoic and represent merely the continuation of Caledonian plate movements and the welding of the Old Red Sandstone continent. The lower to upper Devonian Acadian orogeny which affected the Appalachian region, with extensive metamorphism and granitic intrusion, probably represents a further episode in continental growth.

Life. The Devonian is often referred to as the "Age of Ferns" or the "Age of Fishes". Although nonvascular plants must earlier have been present on the land, probably since Precambrian times, it was only in the late Silurian that there evolved vascular plants with a waxy cuticle and stomata so that they could live out of water; and the first well-preserved vascular plant fossils are known from the lower Devonian, those petrified in silica in the Rhynie Chert of Scotland being especially famous. Starting from small leafless and rootless *psilopsids vascular plants evolved to *ferns, seed ferns, calamites and lycopods by the middle Devonian, many reaching considerable size and growing in forests such as that described from the upper Devonian of New York. In contrast with later Paleozoic floras, those of the Devonian are remarkably cosmopolitan.

The lower Devonian fish faunas are dominated by pteraspid and cephalaspid ostracoderms (see *jawless fishes), and mostly bottom-dwelling forms with a flattened body and extensive armor: the only survivors beyond the Devonian of such jawless fish are the lampreys and hagfish.

The origin of jaws is still not fully understood, but it is now clear that the small, jawed *acanthodians had evolved towards the end of the Silurian. The *placoderms, which are related to the cartilaginous-skeletoned sharks, evolved jaws independently and appeared in the early Devonian. A group of the placoderms, the arthrodires, often reached large size and

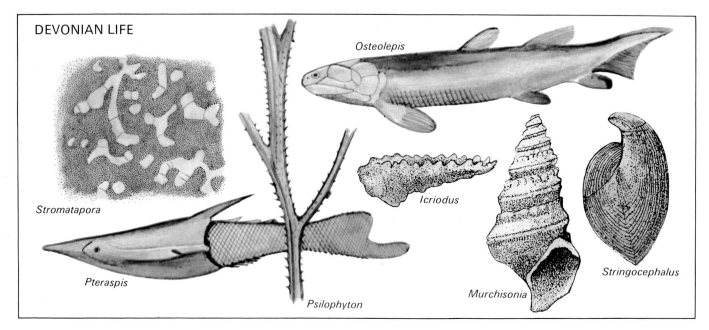

DEVONIAN LIFE

Osteolepis

Stromatapora

Pteraspis

Icriodus

Psilophyton

Murchisonia

Stringocephalus

were the dominant carnivores. (It is likely that complex food webs – plant, invertebrate, vertebrate – evolved about this time.) True sharks are known from the middle Devonian, as are the more advanced lungfish and coelacanths.

In addition, Devonian rocks contain the first well-preserved specimens of *bony fish. There are a few scales preserved from earlier rocks that indicate that this group had its origins in the *Silurian, but upper Devonian sandstones from Australia have recently been discovered containing almost perfectly preserved remains of a bony fish, *Moythomasia*, which is probably the ancestor of the group.

The extensive preservation of fossil fish in the Devonian is probably because of the combination of the relatively good preservation potential for their bony skeletons

in the many estuary and lake environments, and the evolutionary burst of the ostracoderms at the beginning of the period. The evolution of the lungfishes, which can breathe not only with gills but also with an adapted air bladder, is consistent with the periodic drying-out characteristic of tropical areas of low rainfall or periodic rainfall. In some respects, it is surprising that the emergence of the tetrapods from the water was delayed as long as it was, but presumably this event must have had to await the necessary evolutionary combination of extra-aquatic support and air respiration. In respect of support, the ostracoderms, with their bony external skeleton of large plates, were better adapted than the group which, though they had internal bony skeletons, actually made the evolutionary advance.

The marine faunas, in many respects, continue the general scene set during the Silurian, and there are relatively few Devonian innovations. Orthocone *nautiloids were already on the wane, but goniatitic *ammonoids became important. The establishment of the terebratulid brachiopods in the early Devonian completed the evolution of all the orders of the phylum *Brachiopoda.

The rugose and tabulate *corals are represented by essentially the same forms as in the Silurian, but there is an evolutionary burst of diversity and abundance and in size of the *stromatoporoidea: the biological affinities of this group are still somewhat puzzling, but it is possible that they are related to the *sponges. Reefs in which stromatoporoids are the principal skeletal elements are widespread, particularly from

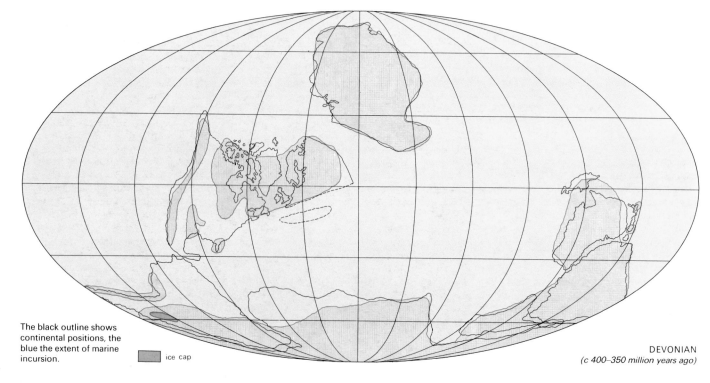

The black outline shows continental positions, the blue the extent of marine incursion.

ice cap

DEVONIAN
(c 400–350 million years ago)

Reef deposits forming high ground in the Atlas Mountains of Morocco. These limestones were deposited near the shoreline of the Devonian continent.

the middle Devonian: those in Alberta are important oil and gas reservoir rocks. (The role of *algae in the Devonian reefs is somewhat uncertain, but certainly it was no greater than it had been in the Silurian.) The reefs frequently exhibit vertical and lateral facies changes, and much prominence has been given to the proposed analogues between this lateral distribution of sediments and modern tropical reefs: reef, forereef and backreef facies have been recognized in the Devonian. However, there is little evidence of any actual reef zone that reached above wave base, and in general the reefs were constructed in quiet-water environments – though subject to storm damage. Many of the stromatoporoids grew in very shallow and extensive lagoonal areas associated with *stromatolites. In the late Devonian the stromatoporoid-dominated reefs suffered drastic reduction, and the communities and facies of the uppermost Devonian and the following Carboniferous are for the most part relatively poor.

The *trilobites of the Devonian, although represented by fewer taxa than in the lower Paleozoic, exhibit much skeletal elaboration. Loss of visual areas and blindness are characteristic of the trilobites found in deeper-water facies. Devonian *bivalves continue stock already present in the lower Paleozoic.

The Devonian in Europe. There are several well known areas of Devonian sediments. ·

In the British Isles, north of the line of the Bristol Channel and Thames estuary, which corresponds with the trend of the Devonian shoreline, the sediments are mainly of continental Old Red Sandstone facies: estuary, river and lake environments. Soil horizons similar to present-day caliches (crusts of calcium carbonate typical of subtropical areas) are frequent and are locally referred to as cornstones. No wind-blown dunes are known, although the climate was likely to have been dry over northern and northwest Europe. The river sediments are frequently in cycles in each of which the finer particles are toward the top: the conglomeratic bottom part of the cycles has been interpreted as river channel deposits, the finer upper part probably representing overbank and floodplain deposits. The conglomerates frequently yield fish and plant debris, though of a fragmentary nature.

Sedimentation in southern Britain and Ireland was interrupted by a major tectonic phase of the Caledonian orogeny during the middle Devonian, so that there is regional uncomformity between the lower and upper Devonian, with the middle Devonian missing.

The shoreline which ran across southern Britain continued eastward through Belgium and northern Germany into Russia. But this shoreline oscillated, with transgressions and regressions of the sea, and at times lay much farther to the south. South of the general line of the shore the thickness of Devonian sediments rapidly increases; this essentially east-west belt of mainly marine sediments across northern Europe is referred to as the Armorican geosyncline. In the south of Belgium, around Couvin, the thickness exceeds 16,000ft (5000m) and south of the Ruhr it exceeds 22,500ft (7000m).

The facies about the shoreline are highly diverse – as is to be expected. Relatively little work has yet been done but beach, estuarine and intertidal facies are well represented. Carbonate sedimentation is well-developed in the Torquay, Brixham and Plymouth areas of southern England, the Eifel area of Germany and the Namur district of Belgium. On the east side of the Rhine the Rhenish Slate Mountains are formed of mainly clastic sediments with apparently greater deltaic influence.

The sea floor did not constantly deepen southward. A number of submarine rises are known, and these have a general trend parallel to the shoreline. Sedimentation on these relatively positive areas is often quite thin. Some of the rises were volcanic, and marine sedimentation was interrupted by lava flows and ashes. Several atolls have been described from northern Germany where corals and stromatoporoids grew on extinct volcanic piles in a manner remarkably like those of the Pacific ocean today. Land-derived sediment scarcely extended to such areas and so the sediments are often almost completely formed of the remains of marine organisms: goniatite and clymenid *cephalopods, styliolinid *mollusks and *conodonts.

The extensive Devonian sediments that outcrop on the Russian Platform between Minsk, Leningrad and the Baltic are much thinner – only a few hundred metres – and because of this the general facies picture differs markedly from that of western Europe. There is great facies diversity but sedimentation is the result of local and irregular subsidence of the basement allowing lenses or wedges of river, evaporitic and shallow marine sediments to be preserved. Shallow marine carbonates are persistent during the early upper Devonian, but there are repeated and widespread discontinuities and no extensive reef formations. In contrast, the Devonian in the Ural Mountains is more complete, geosynclinal and akin to that of western Europe.

The Devonian in North America. In many respects the Devonian sediments of North America are a reflection of those of Europe. In recent years, knowledge of the North American Devonian has been greatly extended beyond the classic areas of the Appalachians and eastern Canada to include the Canadian Arctic Islands, Alaska and western North America.

The Rocky Mountains were the site of a large *geosyncline, with sedimentation continuing from the Silurian. Thinner sequences are present on the kraton, including the famous Alberta reefs and evaporites. In East Greenland, Bear Island and Spitzbergen, sedimentation was continental. The Devonian of the Canadian Arctic Islands has many similarities with that on the opposite side of the Old Red Sandstone continent in northwest Europe, with alternations of thick marine and nonmarine sediments. Similarly, the Devonian of the North West Territories, Alberta and Saskatchewan, are the mirror image of the Devonian of the Russian Platform and the Urals, though evaporites and reefs are more prominent. In British Columbia the stratigraphy is less clear in the tectonized zone of the Rockies, and sedimentation appears to have been oceanic, with volcanics, cherts and shales. The thick clastics and turbidites of the upper Devonian of the Yukon seem to be derived from an oceanic zone of uplift rather than from the Old Red Sandstone continent.

In the Eastern and Central United States of America the Devonian can be traced in great detail from the thick continental facies of the Catskill Mountains westward, as the thickness decreases and marine sediments, at first clastics and then limestones and shales, predominate. Repeated marine transgressions result in an alternating succession of shales and limestones, and this is most prominent in western New York between Buffalo and the Finger Lakes and in the corresponding area to the south in northern Pennsylvania. Relatively little modern work has been done on the shoreline and continental sediments of the Catskills, where around 10,000ft (3000m) of mainly upper Devonian sediments can be inferred to have been deposited.

Elsewhere. The structural relationships of the Devonian of northwest Africa are not properly understood, but the stable African kraton did not supply much clastic sediment. However, the proximity of this area to Europe, and more especially to North America, is clear from repeated faunal similarities. The Devonian of northwestern Australia is somewhat analogous to that of north Africa with prominent carbonates and reefs in the early upper Devonian. The separated Devonian deposits of eastern Australia are geosynclinal in character.

Conclusion. We have already described the Devonian as both the "Age of Ferns" and the "Age of Fishes", but we could well add to these honorific titles a third, the "Age of the Conquest of the Land". By the end of the period both plants and animals were well established on land, in striking contrast to the situation in the preceding Silurian; and in a geologically rather short extent of time, by the end of the succeeding Carboniferous, the world would see the rise of such comparatively advanced forms as the reptiles. Only a little reflection is necessary to realize the immense importance of the revolution that took place in the Devonian.   RG

Carboniferous (Mississippian and Pennsylvanian)

The Carboniferous world was dominated by three major continents: Laurasia, made up of North America, Greenland and Europe west of the Urals; Angaraland, formed of Siberia with China and Korea; and Gondwanaland, extending over India, Africa, South America, Australia and Antarctica. The reconstruction of these continents depends on detailed evidence from common rock sequences, common floras and common faunas.

Since the end of the Carboniferous these continents have moved in relation to each other, and, in the case of Laurasia and Gondwanaland, the continental regions have divided. Detailed comparison of the geology and fossils of the separated continental fragments can give proof of their original contiguity and, in some cases, rough and relative estimates of the time when the fragments separated.

Paleogeography. The positions of the continents during Carboniferous time can be found by determining paleomagnetic properties of their rocks. Certain igneous and sedimentary rocks contain magnetic minerals that may, at the time of the rocks' formation, become aligned to the magnetic lines of force around the world. Delicate experiments on oriented rock samples can determine the direction of the Earth's magnetic field at that time, giving a figure for the latitude of the sample region. In this way the position and orientation of the continents can be deduced (though their positions relative to the lines of longitude cannot be determined).

From paleomagnetic observations an interpretation of world paleogeography during the Carboniferous can be made, the data on the positions of Laurasia and Angaraland being very much more precise than those for Gondwanaland. This is a field of geology where much progress is being made at the present time and revision and improvements in our knowledge of Carboniferous geography are to be expected in the future.

Even during the Carboniferous the three great continents were moving relative to each other: Laurasia was rotating in a clockwise manner, and Angaraland was closing with Laurasia on a line now represented by the Ural Mountains. These two continents collided later, during the Permian, causing orogeny along the Ural line. Gondwanaland was also drifting during the period, but our knowledge of this is less precise.

The paleogeographical maps show that the three continents spread across most of the climatic zones of the Carboniferous world. Angaraland was mainly boreal, stretching almost to the Arctic; Laurasia lay in the equatorial and boreal zones; and Gondwanaland, though partly equatorial and partly austral, was largely centered over the South Pole. Carboniferous rocks were therefore deposited under widely varying climatic conditions, allowing glacial deposits to be laid down over a wide region of Gondwanaland, while tropical coal swamps spread over large areas of Laurasia.

Stratigraphy. No one method of stratigraphical division and correlation can be used throughout the widely different sedimentary environments found in the various climatic zones of the Carboniferous continents: the equatorial zone is the only region where the Carboniferous rocks can be divided and correlated on a truly international basis, though even here three major methods have been established in, respectively, northwestern Europe, the USSR and North America. No comparable series of divisions exists for either the boreal Angaraland region or the austral and glacial Gondwanaland area.

The absolute age of the Carboniferous system has been determined radiometrically. Results suggest that the period began 350 million years ago and ended about 280 million years ago. Absolute dating work is still being perfected and the present results will doubtless be subject to revision in the future. Nevertheless, the Carboniferous dates are well founded and the period is

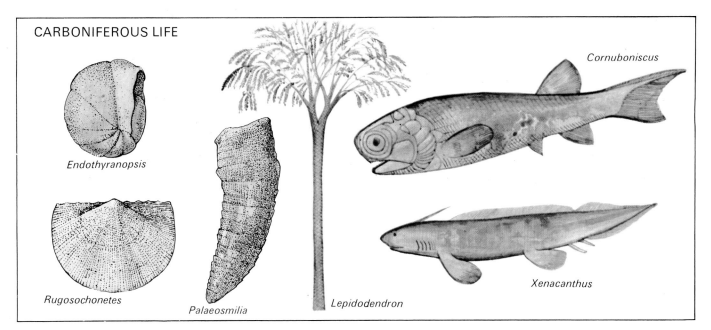

CARBONIFEROUS LIFE

Endothyranopsis

Rugosochonetes

Palaeosmilia

Lepidodendron

Cornuboniscus

Xenacanthus

dated more precisely than most of the others in the stratigraphical column.

The Carboniferous is divided into two parts, lower and upper Carboniferous, that are recognized under various names in many parts of the world. Originally the system was divided in Great Britain during the early part of the 19th century into lower Carboniferous or Carboniferous Limestone, a dominantly marine succession, and upper Carboniferous or Millstone Grit and Coal Measures: the Millstone Grit is a marine deltaic sequence and the Coal Measures a succession formed under dominantly terrestrial delta swamp conditions. No one group of fossils can be used to divide and correlate these rocks, formed as they were under different environmental conditions.

Classically corals and brachiopod shells are used as zonal fossils to divide the marine

sediments of the Carboniferous equatorial belt. To a certain extent these groups have now been augmented by fossil *foraminifera as well as conodonts, which are minute toothlike fossils probably formed by lowly fishes. The marine deltaic sequences are divided into zones using conodonts and goniatites (coiled and chambered mollusk shells) and the delta swamp environment by mussel shells, plants and fossil plant spores. The microfossils foraminifera, conodonts and plant spores are particularly important for division and correlation of the Carboniferous because of their great variety and number and their occurrence in many different types of sedimentary rock. Some of these groups are sufficiently widely distributed to make possible correlations between distantly separated regions.

In the USA the Carboniferous is often divided into the Mississippian, beginning some 350 million years ago, and the Pennsylvanian, beginning around 325 million years ago.

Carboniferous Equatorial Belt. Over much of the equatorial and warmer boreal belts, the *Devonian ended with a rise in sea level and the corresponding flooding of low coastal plains about the continents by transgressive seas. Wide shallow shelf seas were formed, and here marine life found conditions suitable for rapid establishment and development. The change from Devonian red sandstones and siltstones, formed in arid desert conditions, to Carboniferous gray and blue-gray marine limestones and shales is often striking.

This change in sedimentation, however, did not take place at the same moment of

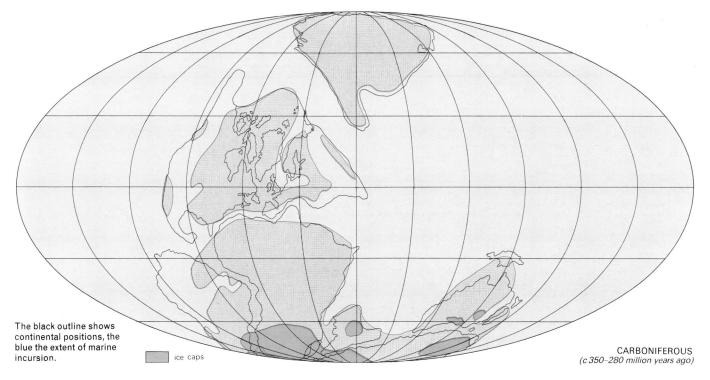

The black outline shows continental positions, the blue the extent of marine incursion.

ice caps

CARBONIFEROUS
(c 350–280 million years ago)

A Carboniferous landscape:
1 *Cordaites* (primitive conifer)
2 *Lepidodendron* (club moss)
3 Tree-ferns
4 Horsetail "creepers"
5 Club moss root stock
6 *Sigillaria* (club moss)
7 *Meganeura* (insect)
8 *Eogyrinus* (amphibian)
9 *Arthropleura* (centipede)
10 *Calamites* (horsetail)
11 *Eryops* (amphibian)

During late Carboniferous times, many coals were formed in swamp environments. Plant remains are common and, in some localities, even large trees have been preserved.

time around the world. The Devonian land surface was irregular in some regions, with uplands and intervening basins: the basins were first flooded by the Carboniferous seas, the uplands standing out to form islands. Elsewhere, in places where coastal lowlands were absent, desert conditions persisted into the Carboniferous. In Devonian marine basins sedimentation continued into the Carboniferous without break.

Along the margins of the seas, quantities of detritus from eroding mountain chains were carried down by rivers to form wide deltas and delta-swamps. The deltas were formed of thick wedges of sand separated by bands of silt and clay: deep burial and cementation have changed the sequences into sandstone, siltstone and shale. The deltas often built up above the sea level and exposed sands and muds to form a land surface. Under tropical conditions this low-lying land was rapidly colonized by terrestrial vegetation to form luxuriant swamp forests only just above the sea. The forests produced quantities of woody plant debris which fell below the water in the swamps to form thick layers of peat, and subsequent burial of the peat beneath later sediments caused the slow transformation of the peat into *coal.

Further out to sea, beyond the swamps and deltas, muds were laid down; and beyond this, in clear-water marine conditions, limestones were formed on the sea bed. Under favorable conditions of sinking sea floor and warm climate, coral and algal reefs and shell banks were formed. Where a restricted embayment of the sea developed in a hot climate, high evaporation resulted in the crystallization of *evaporites on the sea bottom.

All these marine sediments occur in the shallow shelf regions around the Carboniferous continents. In the deeper regions of the ocean, marine trenches gathered thick sequences of sands and muds which can now be recognized by successions, often folded, of dominantly gray and black sandstones and shales.

Life was abundant on land and in the tropical and subtropical seas. After a significant crisis among the marine invertebrates that had taken place toward the end of the Devonian, members of many old lines becoming extinct, a new period of evolution and diversification began with the opening of the Carboniferous. The wide shallow shelf seas around the continents gave abundant secure habitats for creatures with calcareous shells and skeletons. *Corals, *brachiopods (lamp shells) and *mollusks abounded and dense masses of *crinoids (sea lilies) formed groves on the sea floor in clear-water conditions: many limestones, known as crinoidal limestones, are largely composed of the separated fragments of

sea-lily stems, cups and arms. *Crustaceans were also plentiful, as were the rapidly evolving *insects on land. Among the vertebrates, fish were present in both marine and lake environments. The first evolutionary radiation of the tetrapods (four-legged animals) was in progress, with numerous true *amphibians and the first *reptiles appearing before the close of the period.

The flora was equally diverse and luxuriant in the equatorial belt. The seaweeds were widespread, with some marine forms forming thick calcareous crusts that are now algal limestones. On land, plant life had developed to a rich flora of giant tree-ferns, horsetails and seed-bearing ferns that grew in extensive swamps.

Western Laurasia: North America. The western extremity of the Laurasian continent comprised what is now North America. Here, a twofold division of the Carboniferous has been conventional since the last century, the divisions being in 1906 raised to the rank of systems, the Mississippian and Pennsylvanian, because of significant differences in their lithology and their separation, over wide areas, by a major hiatus. This division of the Carboniferous is roughly in agreement with the divisions in Western Europe (but not with the Russian system, where a threefold division is used).

The Carboniferous was a time of crustal unrest in North America, with downwarping of wide basins and uplift of broad

Limestone is the rock type typically found in lower Carboniferous deposits in many parts of the world. This hollow was partly filled with sand during a period of uplift, when shallow seas covered these limestones.

highlands. In Canada to the north lay an ancient landmass, and surrounding it a wide flat-lying shelf that was progressively covered by the Carboniferous sea. This shallow sea spread completely across southern North America and in its clear, warm waters vast spreads of limestones were deposited: these thick, pure limestones characterize the Mississippian succession. Earth movements caused a progressive reduction in the shelf sea towards the end of the Mississippian, and at the same time uplift produced the new highlands of the Oklahoma ranges, the ancestral Rockies and others. Uplift and erosion caused a widespread unconformity at the top of the Mississippian.

The earliest Pennsylvanian seas were restricted to a narrow belt between the ancient landmass to the north and an encroaching landmass, Llanoria, to the south. During the early and middle Pennsylvanian the sea spread widely over the shelf, covering much of what is now the USA, and newly formed uplands stood out of the sea as extensive elevated islands. The Pennsylvanian sea, like its Mississippian predecessor, was not to persist for long and, before the end of the period, the seas were once more receding.

The best section of the Mississippian is along the Mississippi River in Iowa, west Illinois and west Kentucky. Most of the lower half of the succession is richly fossiliferous limestone, including the Burlington Limestone and the oolitic Salem Limestone. The latter is extensively quarried in southern Indiana and is used as *building stone in many public buildings in the eastern USA. The lower Mississippian limestones stretch over the central and western part of the USA and into Canada.

In the Appalachian region to the east a sinking basin received sandy, non-marine sediments, but sediments of more marine aspect were deposited further to the south, where the basin was sinking more rapidly. These sand and clay deposits represent sediments carried in from land areas, including Llanoria, in the region of the eastern seaboard. The upper part of the Mississippian is not so well developed and is missing over most of the states west of the Mississippi River. Where found, it tends to be composed of alternating bands of sandstone and limestone.

The Pennsylvanian started with a new transgression of the sea over the low land of the central North American continent. At this time the eastern and southern seaboard was rimmed with actively rising mountain chains from Nova Scotia through to Texas. Canada was largely a vast emergent land surface and, between it and the marginal mountain chains, a broad basin developed that quickly involved much of the USA. In this basin, marine conditions encroached

from the west and east and great quantities of sediment from rapidly eroding mountains spread in wide deltas over the basin floor. East of Kansas and Oklahoma, both deltaic and marine sediments were laid down in cycles of deposition, each cycle being of the general sequence: limestone, shale, sandstone, fossil soil and coal. In Illinois, where the cycles are well developed, there are about one hundred cycles in the Pennsylvanian succession, each representing a period when the sea spread over the region from the west and allowed limestone to be deposited; followed by deltaic sedimentation from the east, first muds then sands, building up to sea level and allowing terrestrial swamp forests to develop. Peats that formed below such forests were later changed to *coal after burial below further sediments. In general,

subsidence of the basin kept up the sedimentation – when subsidence was greater than deposition, marine conditions from the west advanced over the region; when it was less, the deltas advanced over the area from the east. Some of the coal beds are thin and impersistent, indicating localized and temporary swamps, while others, such as the Pittsburg coal, are continuous over hundreds of square miles and may be more than 5ft (1.5m) thick.

The sea did not reach parts of the east side of the Pennsylvanian basin, and here thick sequences of non-marine strata were laid down. In Nova Scotia some 13,000ft (4000m) of non-marine strata were deposited in mountaingirt basins on the edge of the Canadian Shield. At Joggins on the Bay of Fundy these beds are exposed in sea cliffs that show the stems of trees preserved

A coal seam interbedded with sandstones and shales exposed in a quarry face. Coal deposits make upper Carboniferous rocks the most economically important rocks in North America, Europe and Russia.

vertically in their position of growth, an indication of rapid deposition, since the trees were buried before they had had time to fall and decay.

The deltas spreading from the east dwindled and failed in the mid-continent region west of Kansas and Oklahoma. Here the marine influence is of increased importance, and so limestones form a larger portion of the succession. Clastic sediment derived from various land areas caused breaks in the limestone deposition, and in some regions thick conglomerate and sandstone sequences were laid down. In the western cordillera, complex Carboniferous sequences indicate that fragments of continental crust may have migrated from the south and west to become fused with western North America, possibly during Mesozoic times. Both Mississippian and Pennsylvanian rocks are present, and consist of limestone with wedges of clastic sediment and volcanic lavas, non-marine strata and coal seams being rare.

Central Laurasia: Western Europe. In Carboniferous times, western Europe lay adjacent to maritime Canada, with the central Laurasian uplands of the Canadian shield, Greenland and Scandinavia forming a continuous whole to the north. On the southern margin of the uplands, the Carboniferous shoreline can be traced across the UK on the flanks of the Scottish Highlands, continuing beneath the North Sea, where it is known from subsurface data, under Denmark and beneath the North German plain. Only in Britain is the shoreline exposed at the surface, elsewhere being deeply buried by younger rocks.

A wide continental shelf developed seawards from the shoreline. This can be seen in Britain stretching from southern Scotland across England to the southwest peninsula of Devon and Cornwall, where it terminates against a deep marine trench. The shelf can be traced eastward across Europe, and the seaward trench continues as far as Germany.

The base of the Carboniferous is marked by a change from continental to marine conditions over the shelf region. This was a major marine transgression which started in the south, adjacent to the trench, and progressively moved northwards during early Carboniferous times. The shelf region was a series of uplands and basins, so that the basins were invaded by the sea first with the uplands standing out as islands for much of the early Carboniferous. In many cases it has been shown that the uplands were positioned over Devonian *igneous intrusions of granitic rock (the low-density granite tends to rise and give upland topography). The whole shelf region was unstable and tended to sink, so the local movements of basins and uplands are superimposed on a broad pattern of re-gional subsidence. During the Carboniferous the emergent islands were progressively inundated by the sea, though some may have persisted as islands throughout the period. Because of their tendency to rise, the islands have no, or only a relatively thin, cover of Carboniferous rocks. In contrast the basins sank more rapidly and continuously and so contain thick sequences of Carboniferous strata.

Southern Europe. South of a line through southwest England, Belgium and Germany, Carboniferous geography, structure and history are quite different from those of the shelf-region to the north. Here, after a period of early Carboniferous deposition of limestone, shale and sandstone about emergent islands, strong Earth movements and volcanic activity produced a new series of mountain ranges across Europe. These mountains were formed during the early late Carboniferous, while sediments were being laid down on the floor of the more stable northern shelf. At this time, an arm of the sea is believed to have separated the northern shelf from the new mountains of southern Europe, but throughout the period the floor of this sea was being consumed along lines of subduction on the south side, adjacent to the new mountains. In fact, the new mountain ranges seem to have been caused by uplift, folding and igneous activity associated with the subducting ocean floor. (The present day Andes formed on the margin of the Pacific in the same way.)

During the latter part of the late Carboniferous, deep mountain-girt lake basins developed in southern Europe. Here thick coal seams represent periods when dense vegetation grew on swamps associated with the margins of the lakes, and these are quite distinct from the similar coal seams formed on swamps at the edge of the Carboniferous sea in Britain, Belgium and Germany.

Towards the end of the Carboniferous, the seaway between the northern shelf and southern Europe narrowed and finally closed. This collision caused a folding episode on the margin of the northern shelf, particularly well seen in southwest England. Uplift and folding ended Carboniferous deposition on the shelf; and the emergent land area began to undergo an extended period of erosion. In the landlocked lake basins of southern Europe, sedimentation was continuous from the Carboniferous through into the Permian.

Eastern Laurasia: The Russian Platform. The wide Russian Platform which forms Eastern Europe was a stable shelf area stretching east from the Baltic landmass. In pre-Carboniferous times it had only gentle vertical movements of uplift and subsidence. Shallow-water marine, deltaic and terrestrial deposits were laid down over the region and these conditions persisted throughout the Carboniferous period. After marine late Devonian conditions, the Carboniferous started with a limestone sequence followed by sandstones and shales with productive coal seams. The upper Carboniferous returns to a bedded limestone sequence particularly rich in fossils. This marine succession continues into the Permian without break though, during the early Permian, continental conditions again became established over the shelf.

To the west, the Russian Platform is continuous with the north-Europe/British shelf, with a common shoreline developed round the Baltic landmass. In the southwest of the platform the Ukraine Shield may also have been emergent during the Carboniferous, but between this region and the main Russian Platform a deep sedimentary basin developed.

This is the Donetz Basin, a deep trough in which the full Carboniferous succession was laid down with only minor breaks. There are some 32,800ft (10,000m) of sediments in the basin compared with about 1600ft (500m) on the platform. The initial lower Carboniferous limestones were followed by cyclic marine, deltaic and continental deposits, including thick coal seams. This sequence continues through the upper Carboniferous and into the Permian. During deposition, subsidence kept pace with sedimentation so that a continuous sequence of shallow-water deposits was laid down.

Angaraland. Angaraland comprised what are now the USSR east of the Urals and China: it is a vast area, now divided into several geological regions. Our knowledge of Angaraland is more limited than is the case with Laurasia and only tentative reconstructions of the geography can be made at the present time.

A central landmass appears to have provided sediment to surrounding wide continental and marine shelves to the west, east and south. Central Siberia (west and central Angaraland) was a shallow shelf region over which alternately spread marine and continental conditions. Only thin sedimentary deposits, composed of marine limestones with deltaic and continental strata up to a total of 650ft (200m), are present. Coal-bearing sequences associated with limestone continue to the top of the Carboniferous.

A deep basin, the Angara Trough, developed in the south and southwest, and much of it is filled with continental sandstones and shales, sediments derived from the central landmass. Marine limestones are found only in the center and south of the basin. A thick coal-bearing series is developed in the upper part of the lower Carboniferous.

At the beginning of the early Carboniferous, land was emergent over the Angara Trough as continental deposits of red sandstones spread south from the upland region. A later terrestrial coal-bearing series has wide distribution and is of latest Carboniferous and Permian age. The region was structurally unstable with volcanic activity present from the Devonian right through into Permian times.

The geology of eastern Angara, including the eastern USSR and China, is not known in detail, but the broad picture is generally similar to that for the western region.

Gondwanaland. The vast Gondwanaland continent lay in the southern hemisphere during Carboniferous times, stretching from the austral to the antarctic climatic zones. The southern part of the continent was centered over the South Pole and during the upper Carboniferous suffered a major period of continental glaciation. Ice sheets and subsequent meltwater laid down typical stratigraphical sequences composed of boulder clay, gravels and sands. Over large parts of Gondwanaland the glaciers invaded a previous land surface and initiated a thick succession of mainly unfossiliferous continental deposits that extends from the late Carboniferous through early *Cretaceous times.

Outside the area of continental glaciation, wide shelf seas and sinking basins allowed Carboniferous deposits to accumulate round the margins of Gondwanaland. In eastern Australia, glacial deposits follow marine lower Carboniferous limestones: in the west these fossiliferous marine limestones are again well developed, but the upper Carboniferous is thin. A break in succession occurs widely at the top of the lower Carboniferous, and this was possibly caused by a lowering of the sea level at the beginning of the Gondwana glaciation (a lowering resulting from the extent of the *glaciation).

Other fragments of Gondwanaland – such as India – show the continental margin with glacial deposits and marine shelf sedi-ments. In peninsular India, glacial tillite is developed at the base of a thick sequence of sediments laid down on a land surface. Marine conditions are found in the Salt Range to the north, where fossiliferous late Carboniferous or Permian limestones overlie the tillite beds. Similar deposits are found in South Africa and South America.

In northern Gondwanaland, now North Africa, unstable shelf conditions at the margin of the continent allowed marine and continental deposits to be laid down. In the west, lower Carboniferous marine limestones are followed by continental deposits, but in the east early alternating continental coal-bearing deposits, with marine intervals are followed by a dominantly marine upper Carboniferous.

Conclusion. From the economist's viewpoint, the Carboniferous is the most important period of the Earth's past, for it was during the Carboniferous that much of the world's important coal-bearing deposits were laid down. To the paleontologist it is also a time of importance, since the period saw the spread of the amphibians and of the shark-like fishes, and, most important of all, the beginnings of the rise of the reptiles. The insects too, were evolving rapidly. All these evolutionary trends were to be continued and accentuated in the succeeding Permian. GALJ

Permian

The Phanerozoic phase of Earth's history is beginning to emerge as an era encompassing one full cycle of global activity – commencing with a number of continental masses more or less widely scattered across the face of the globe, their gradual convergence to form a united supercontinent (Pangaea), followed by rebound and drifting apart of differently delineated continents to occupy their present positions. The individuality of the Permian lies in its having occupied the pivotal position during this accordion-like cycle.

The Permian, named for the Perm province of the USSR, was instituted and described by the British geologist Sir Roderick *Murchison in 1841 while carrying out a geological survey of the Russian Empire: he based the system on his studies of portions of a thick pile of strata exposed along the western flanks of the Ural mountains. The stratigraphic confines of the Permian have been intermittently stretched throughout the past century, and even now no precise, internationally accepted definitions of its upper and lower limits have been reached. However, we can consider its start to have been around 280 million years ago, its end around 225 million years ago.

Stratigraphic Definition. Standard reference sequences for the preceding *Carboniferous and succeeding *Triassic systems may be based on more or less uninterrupted *fossil records, but there is no such simple solution for the Permian – small wonder in view of the unsettled

PERMIAN LIFE

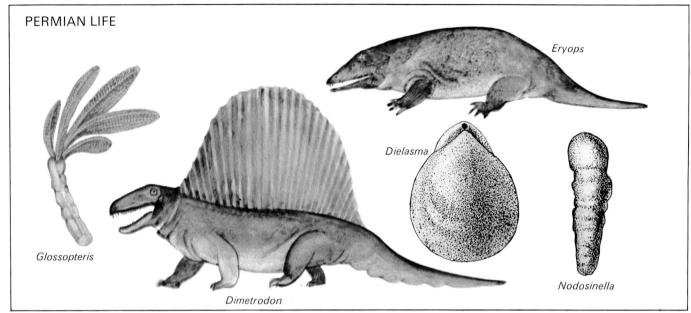

Eryops

Glossopteris

Dielasma

Nodosinella

Dimetrodon

history of the Earth's crust during the period's course. A composite reference sequence has therefore been established, incorporating the most complete, suitably exposed, comprehensively studied marine sections from widely scattered areas. The lower Permian is thus represented by the southern Uralian Geosyncline, the middle Permian by the Texan Sea and the upper Permian by the Iranian Sea.

The lower stratigraphic limit of the Permian is generally taken at the contact between the Orenburgian Stage (uppermost Carboniferous) and the Asselian Stage (lowermost Permian) of the southern Uralian Geosyncline. An apparently uninterrupted marine succession here spans the boundary between the two systems. Marine strata of the uppermost Permian (Ali-Bashian Stage) are known only from the Iranian Sea

and the South China Sea and in each area an apparent interruption (possibly relatively brief) occurs between these strata and the overlying marine beds of the Griesbachian Stage (lowermost Triassic). For this reason, no mutual boundary can be defined between the Permian and Triassic systems.

There are four main phases of the Permian: early lower, late lower, middle and upper; though exact definitions of the boundaries between them are a subject for debate.

Tectonic Events. The major tectonic and physiographic features of the Permian world can be most effectively portrayed in the light of the theory of *plate tectonics. We may consider five major continental plates being actively thrust up against one another through the persistent inward push of a series of encircling oceanic plates.

By the end of the middle Permian the union of these five plates had been well established. The continued subduction of the leading edges of the oceanic plates beneath the continental margin of the supercontinent so formed, Pangaea, now caused widespread uplift and the draining of virtually all major seas. In the late Permian we thus encounter a single sea-less supercontinent, a phenomenon probably unique in the history of the Earth.

Climate. With the virtual closure of the ocean between Laurasia and Gondwanaland toward the end of the Carboniferous, oceanic and atmospheric circulation patterns were radically altered, and this had far-reaching effects on global climatic conditions. Strongly differentiated climatic belts emerged on the continents, which were now strung out to form a broad arc

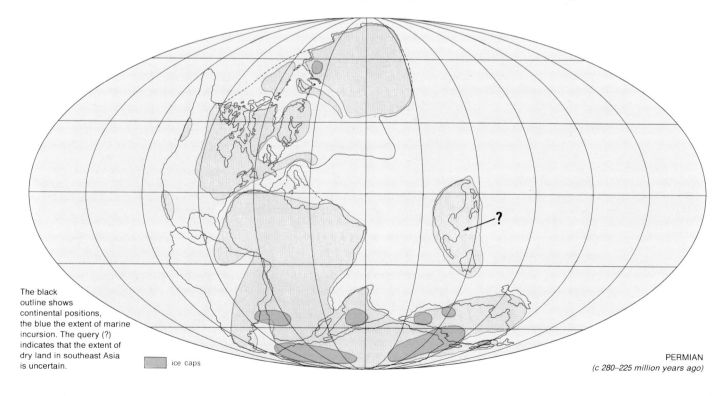

The black outline shows continental positions, the blue the extent of marine incursion. The query (?) indicates that the extent of dry land in southeast Asia is uncertain.

ice caps

PERMIAN
(c 280–225 million years ago)

Permian Kaibab limestones seen in the Grand Canyon. The limestones cap Paleozoic and Precambrian rocks and are seen on the horizon in this view. They are lighter in color than the older, redder rocks.

spanning one face of the globe from the south to the north poles.

During the opening phase of the Permian this configuration of the continents favored the extensive spread of *glaciation in Gondwanaland, matching that which was to ravage the northern continents during the *Pleistocene. The westward-flowing south equatorial warm-water current was deflected southward into the oceanic gulf between Africa and India, encouraging steady evaporation of water from the surface and subsequent snowfalls in the southern reaches of Gondwanaland. A continental ice sheet developed over Antarctica, which then as now straddled the South Pole, while a number of smaller dislocated ice caps spread from the peripheral upland regions.

The north equatorial current was deflected northward into the seas of the Cathaysian kingdom where moist, warm conditions were encountered in latitudes considerably farther north than might otherwise be expected. Hot dry conditions, with the development of extensive deserts, prevailed over much of the Euramerican kingdom and northern Gondwanaland. The southern part of Angaraland (roughly equivalent to today's Asian Russia) fell in the hot dry equatorial belt, while its northern parts lay in a warm-temperate humid zone.

The global climatic framework altered through the Permian in harmony with the migration of the united continents northward through some 15° of latitude: as one would expect, the climatic belts are generally seen to have shifted southward relative to the continents. In Gondwanaland, glaciation soon subsided and conditions became progressively warmer, while in Angara and northern Cathaysia they correspondingly became steadily cooler. The desert environment of Euramerica and northern Gondwanaland persisted throughout the Permian but shifted south with the Equator.

Flora. Global floral distribution patterns since the appearance of the first primitive land plants followed a trend of general homogeneity during the *Devonian, a gradual development of provincialism through the Carboniferous which rapidly reached a peak in the middle phases of the Permian, followed by a reversal to greater uniformity in the *Triassic and *Jurassic. The considerable pressures brought to bear on the vegetation by the development of sharply differentiated climatic belts during the early lower Permian may be invoked to explain this diversification. Four floral kingdoms (Gondwana, Cathaysia, Euramerica, An-gara), broadly reflecting the climatic zonation, can be distinguished.

Euramerican Kingdom. The earliest Permian floras are not markedly different from those of the late Carboniferous, the primary change being the decline of the arborescent lycopods and arthrophytes (*horsetails) which dominated the earlier coal swamps. The most notable newcomer was the widespread seed fern *Callipteris*, particularly *C. conferta*, whose first appearance is usually regarded as marking the start of the Permian. The *conifers, represented by *Walchia*, a forest tree uncommon earlier, became locally common.

These early floras characterized the basins associated with the Appalachian ranges and the areas bordering the Texan and Donetz seas. Inland from these vegetated areas nothing is known of the flora, which was possibly very sparse owing to the desert conditions.

The sole preserved late lower Permian material derives from the region of the Texan Sea, surrounding which there were three distinctive floral provinces: one along the western slopes of the ancestral Rockies, the other two along the southeast and northeast shores of the sea. Each was dominated by a particular genus of seed fern (*Supaia*, *Gigantopteris* and *Glenopteris* respectively). The conifer *Walchia* was still prominent in the region; while the other representatives of the floras were not dissimilar from those of the early lower Permian.

Middle Permian floras are even more scanty, being known only from fragmentary material carried into the Zechstein Sea. The flora, clearly adapted to hot dry conditions, consisted chiefly of coniferous forest with the new genus *Ulmannia* dominating.

Upper Permian floras are unknown.

Cathaysian Kingdom. The flora of Cathaysia, similar to that of Euramerica during the earliest Permian, assumed an independent character thereafter, particularly through the appearance, diversification and dominance of the gymnosperm (see *plants) *Gigantopteris* and its relatives. This group of plants clearly favored warm moist conditions. Endemic species of fern and seed fern appeared, while the conifers were virtually absent.

Cathaysian plants are known from widespread localities through all four phases of the Permian. However, the western extension of the kingdom into the Tethyan region is based on very conjectural plant occurrences.

Angaran Kingdom. This kingdom shows progressive expansion and differentiation into regional floras during the early and middle Permian, by which stage four distinctive provinces are discernible: a Siberian province forms the core, and lies surrounded by the three peripheral buffer provinces of Petchora, Ural-Kazakhstan and Far East. The warm temperate Siberian province appears to have been particularly characterized through most of the Permian by forests of *Cordaites.* Endemic species of fern, seed fern and horsetails were also much in evidence. The buffer provinces displayed features transitional in nature with Euramerica and Cathaysia.

Due to lack of information it is difficult to ascertain the situation in the upper Permian.

Gondwana Kingdom. The Gondwana flora was markedly distinct from those of the northern continents. The newly evolved division of plants, the *Glossopteridophyta,* unknown in the north, dominated the scene in the south. These plants owed their establishment to the spread of glaciation, which had almost annihilated the earlier vegetation. For a brief spell after the retreat of the glaciers the genus *Gangamopteris* stood as the chief representative of the division, but it was soon supplanted by the closely related *Glossopteris* which by the late Permian was the truly dominant element of the flora throughout the kingdom. Lycopods were not uncommon in certain areas during the earlier phases of the Permian, but became extremely rare later. The horsetails generally became more – rather than less – common, often forming dense bamboo-like stands in the swamps of the late Permian. The ferns and seed ferns were nowhere as significant as in the northern floras. The cycads and ginkgos were rare, as in the north, and only began to show their true mettle in the early *Mesozoic. The true conifers were likewise uncommon, but the

closely related Cordaitales, with large parallel veined leaves, flourished around the coal swamps during the earlier phases of the Permian. *Noeggerathiopsis* was the southern representative of this latter plant group, and has at times been considered as identical with *Cordaites,* its northern counterpart.

All woody plants of the Gondwana Kingdom exhibit annual growth rings, and this reflects the seasonal nature of the prevailing climate.

Tetrapod Vertebrates. As the curtain rose on the Permian, the *reptiles were gaining in the war for supremacy over the *amphibians; and the scene was restricted to the equatorial belt traversing the southern part of the Euramerican continent. The theme that was to unfold during the Permian was of reptilian ascendancy and of successive waves of colonization until, by the close of the period, most of Pangaea was inhabited.

Throughout the lower Permian the tetrapods (*tetra,* four; *pod-,* foot) were confined exclusively to the paleotropics of Euramerica. The aquatic fauna was probably still dominated by the amphibians, some of which were of giant proportions, though life on the land was now securely in the thrall of the reptiles.

The varied reptile faunas fall very largely into two orders; the *cotylosaurs (stem reptiles descended directly from the amphibians) and the pelycosaurs (the forerunners of the *mammal-like reptiles). A bizarre characteristic of a number of the pelycosaurs was the development of a huge sail-like structure adorning the back. One such reptile, *Dimetrodon,* was over 10ft (3m) long and had a massive skull: an active predator, it held sway over its contemporaries. *Edaphosaurus,* somewhat smaller and with a less massive head, was the herbivorous counterpart.

The only early Permian tetrapod known outside Euramerica is *Mesosaurus,* a small, long-snouted amphibious reptile that fed on small *crustaceans. This enigmatic interloper, which put in an appearance in Gondwanaland for only a brief spell, was spawned by unknown stock.

Beginning near the early/middle Permian boundary, extensive colonization and adaptation occurred for several million years. Only two assemblages of middle Permian tetrapods are known, one from the Kazanian stage of the Russian Platform and the other from the slightly younger *Tapinocephalus* zone of the Karroo Basin, South Africa. Both represent diverse faunas flourishing on broad, low-lying swampy plains adjacent to extensive inland seas. The two faunas were similar in general though quite different in detail; and they reveal very marked advances over those of the early Permian. The reptiles had by this time achieved complete supremacy, amphibians being low in both numbers and diversity. The cotylosaurian and pelycosaurian orders of reptiles were still present, but poorly represented: the *mammal-like reptiles had assumed dominance.

Colonization beyond the Euramerican and western Gondwana continents was in all probability barred during the middle Permian by the sea and mountain tracts of the Uralian and Cape/Natal geosynclinal belts.

In the upper Permian the principal fossil tetrapod assemblages derive once again from the Russian Platform and the Karroo Basin. The faunas are still superficially similar. Now, however, with the final retreat of the Uralian and Cape seas, sporadic migration occurred for the first time into Angara, Cathaysia and east Gondwana, where (very sparse) remains have been encountered.

*Mammal-like reptiles continued to completely dominate the fauna but within the order significant evolutionary advances had taken place. The Dinocephalia had died out, while the dicynodonts had flourished and diversified to fill the available herbivorous niches. Among the carnivores the most significant newcomers were the cynodonts (dog-tooths), from which progressive stock, late in the Triassic, arose the *mammals.

Marine Invertebrates. Three major faunal realms, controlled by water temperatures, can be recognized in the Permian seas – paleotropical Tethyan, northern cool-water Boreal and southern cool-water Gondwana.

Mixing of Boreal and Tethyan faunas occurred in the southern reaches of the Uralian Geosyncline during the early lower Permian. A narrow passage enabled warm Tethyan waters to enter the essentially cool-water Uralian Sea. Thereafter the passage was blocked. The Tethyan realm in the east extended far into northern latitudes indicating the circulation there of warm waters. Recognition of the three faunal realms, and correlation of strata within each or from one to the next, rests primarily on the study of three very different groups of animals – the fusulinids, ammonites and brachiopods.

The *fusulinids, a superfamily of the order Foraminifera, phylum Protozoa, appeared in the early Carboniferous and became extinct at the close of the Permian. They were abundant and widespread, evolved rapidly and attained a remarkable degree of diversity. They were small (measured in millimetres) inhabitants of the sea bottom, and flourished in relatively shallow clear water away from the shores. They dwelt principally in warm-water seas.

During the early lower Permian the fusulinids were present, often in great numbers, throughout the Tethyan and Boreal realms. They were conspicuously absent in the glacial waters of the Gondwana realm (other than for an isolated occurrence along what is now the Chilean coast of South America).

In the late lower Permian, presumably due in large measure to the northward drift of the continents, the fusuline faunas of the Boreal realm became impoverished and included only cosmopolitan genera. The

Tethyan faunas, on the other hand, became further diversified, with a larger number of endemic genera. The fusulinids still enjoyed no success in the penetration of the Gondwana realm where the waters were still unfavorably cold.

By the middle Permian, with continued northward drift, they had become extinct in the Boreal realm. They remained absent in the Gondwana realm (except for occurrences in what is now New Zealand); but continued to be abundant and still further diversified in the Tethyan realm. The Iranian and Southern China seas were the only seas of significance to persist after the widespread regressions of the middle/late Permian transition. In these last remaining oases the fusulinids became progressively less diverse and abundant, and this continued until their extinction by the end of the Permian.

The ubiquitous retreat of the seas played havoc in all walks of marine life, so that the faunas that appear in the widespread early Triassic transgressive seas were radically altered in aspect. This is in marked contrast to the situation at the onset of the Permian, when marine life (and indeed terrestrial life) continued through from the Carboniferous essentially unchanged.

Some sixteen families and seventy genera of *ammonites are recorded from the Permian. This degree of diversity is relatively low when compared to their much greater differentiation in the Mesozoic. They are presumed to have been highly mobile, free-swimming animals which inhabited primarily shallow waters in paleotropical latitudes, though a number of cosmopolitan Permian genera, of great value in global correlations, occurred.

The ammonites showed greatest profusion in the Tethyan realm. The best exposed sections, yielding abundant ammonite assemblages throughout the lower Permian, occur in the southern Uralian Sea. At the close of the early Permian the Uralian Geosyncline ceased to subside and the sea began to recede, with the resultant development of extensive *evaporite deposits. Ammonites are thereafter rarely encountered in this area.

The best developed ammonite-bearing sections of the middle Permian are to be found around the mouth of the Texan Sea, which in turn began to dry out at the close of this phase. From here we hop to the northern margins of the Iranian Sea for well exposed, well developed, ammonite-yielding strata representing the late Permian. As we have already seen, these three sections have been chosen as reference for the lower, middle and upper Permian respectively.

Ammonites occur sparsely and in low diversity in the cool-water realms. A few cosmopolitan genera are occasionally encountered at scattered levels through the lower Permian (and lowest middle Permian) in the marginal seas of eastern and western Australia. These comprise the most tangible props for establishing correlations between the sections of the Gondwana and Tethyan realms, the remaining bulk of the Gondwana marine invertebrates being essentially endemic to the realm. In the middle Permian, rare ammonite finds are made in the geosynclinal seas lining the northwestern and northern margins of Euramerica and in the Himalayan, Madagascar, and New Caledonian regions of Gondwanaland.

The *brachiopods, which constitute an independent phylum, have persisted from the *Cambrian to the present, but are now on the verge of extinction. During the Permian they occurred in great abundance and diversity in both paleotropical and cool-temperate seas, where they generally lived firmly attached to irregular rocky bottoms in the off-shore reaches of shelf seas. They are of considerable value in correlations within any particular realm but, since few forms appear to have displayed a sufficiently wide tolerance of different water temperatures to enable them to colonize beyond their parent realms, they are of little value in broader correlation.

At the end of the Permian there was a massive extinction of the brachiopods: of over 125 genera only two survived the start of the Triassic.

Conclusion. The dramatic chain reaction of change seen to reverberate through the Permian, sparked by the meeting of the northern and southern continents, brought the Paleozoic to an unequivocal close and ushered in the new Mesozoic era, during which the world was to see the beginnings of the mammals' slow rise to dominance. The true significance of the Permian's end can perhaps be seen from the name of the era which ended with it: the Paleozoic, or era of ancient life. JMA

Mesozoic

The Mesozoic, the era of "middle life", lasted some 160 million years, from about 225 to about 65 million years ago. It encompassed the Triassic, Jurassic and Cretaceous periods. Early in the era the first mammals appeared, but faunas as a whole were dominated by the reptiles, some of which achieved massive proportions. AI

Triassic

The Triassic period lasted about 30 million years, beginning about 225 million years ago and ending approximately 195 million years ago. It was the first period of the Mesozoic, an era characterized by the appearance of faunas and floras strikingly different from those of the preceding Paleozoic era, a change particularly marked among the marine invertebrate faunas, because it coincided with the widespread extinctions that took place during the late Paleozoic. These late Paleozoic extinctions and the subsequent expansion and diversification of the new marine faunas in the Triassic are generally attributed to the reduction, during the late Paleozoic, in the area of the seas covering continental margins, the principal habitat for these faunas, and the subsequent expansion of the shelves during the Mesozoic.

The changes in the faunas were also reflected in the floras. The late Triassic marked the appearance and predominance of new groups. These changes, taken together with the extinction of much of the late Paleozoic flora, were probably associated with a considerable change in climate.

Paleomagnetic and facies evidence suggests that the position and configuration of the continents changed very little from the *Permian to the Triassic period. One difficulty in proving this is that few complete late Permian to early Triassic marine successions are known, and consequently very little evidence is available on which to reconstruct the geographical details of early Triassic seas. However, two Triassic world-wide marine margins can be identified, namely the circum-Pacific and Tethys.

In absolute contrast to the marine shelves and basins around the one supercontinent, Pangaea, were the huge landmasses of its two components, called Laurasia and Gondwanaland, which were joined along the lines of the incipient mid-Atlantic ridge and western Mediterranean. These two continental masses were characterized by extensive terrestrial deposits in which the remains of reptiles and other vertebrates, and of plants, were preserved.

Biostratigraphy. In the Alpine region the marine Triassic rocks are traditionally divided, on the basis of their *ammonoid faunas, into five stages.

One of the main problems of Triassic biostratigraphers has been the lack of a marine rock succession in which there is unambiguous fossil evidence of an unbroken sequence of rocks from Permian through to Triassic. Various Tethyan localities have been investigated, especially in the Himalayas, the Salt Range (Pakistan) and eastern Iran, as well as circum-Pacific localities in northeastern Siberia, North America and the Arctic. One result of these studies has been the introduction in recent years of four new stage names, to replace the single Scythian Stage representing the lower Triassic rocks, although so far these new stages have been mainly applied to the North American and Arctic successions where they are defined on the basis of their faunal sequences.

Subdivision of Triassic rocks is further complicated by the presence of very extensive sedimentary basins in Laurasia and Gondwanaland filled with terrestrial deposits and lacking a marine fauna. The presence of land plants offers the possibility of correlating between the marine and non-marine deposits by means of their fossil microflora, but many of these terrestrial deposits have been so oxidized that suitable microfossils are rare or absent. Furthermore, the task of establishing a useful

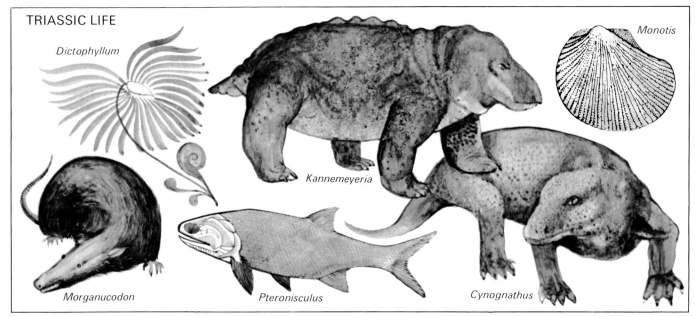

TRIASSIC LIFE

Dictophyllum

Monotis

Kannemeyeria

Morganucodon

Pteronisculus

Cynognathus

correlation scheme between Triassic microfossils and ammonoids has not yet been satisfactorily achieved: it remains a task for future biostratigraphers.

Fossils. Triassic fossil organisms valuable in providing evidence of the environment in which they lived are often much closer related to modern forms than are the Paleozoic fossils, so they can be used to interpret the environment with greater confidence.

During the Triassic the marine faunas expanded. *Mollusks were the dominant invertebrates, of which the ammonoids are undoubtedly the most useful because they became widespread and abundant and displayed great evolutionary changes in their easily recognized and preserved shell morphology. The ammonoids had become almost extinct in the late Permian, but during the Triassic they rapidly evolved and diver-

sified before approaching extinction again in the late Triassic.

After the ammonoids the lamellibranchs, a class of *bivalve mollusks, were the most widely distributed and diverse group of Triassic invertebrates. Some, such as *Monotis*, are useful as guide fossils and are widely used for correlation in the upper Triassic rocks of both circum-Pacific and Tethyan marine deposits.

The special value of colonial *corals is their toleration of fairly narrow limits of water depth, salinity and temperature; and consequently they are used to interpret the environment in much greater detail than most fossil groups permit. The Triassic corals are of particular use in this respect because during the middle Triassic there appeared in the Alps and the Mediterranean region the new order of scleractinian

corals, to which modern reef-building corals belong. The main Paleozoic coral groups became extinct at the end of that era, but curiously there is an apparent absence of any record of early Triassic corals. This may be associated with the absence of hard parts in the ancestors of the scleractinian corals, but it remains a field for future investigation. By the end of the Triassic these new corals had become widespread throughout the world.

The main terrestrial and aquatic vertebrates were *reptiles and *amphibians, and these do not appear to have undergone important evolution in passing from the Permian to the Triassic period. The reptiles, especially the *dinosaurs, increased in importance during the Triassic, becoming more diverse and numerous. *Mammal-like reptiles, whose ancestors

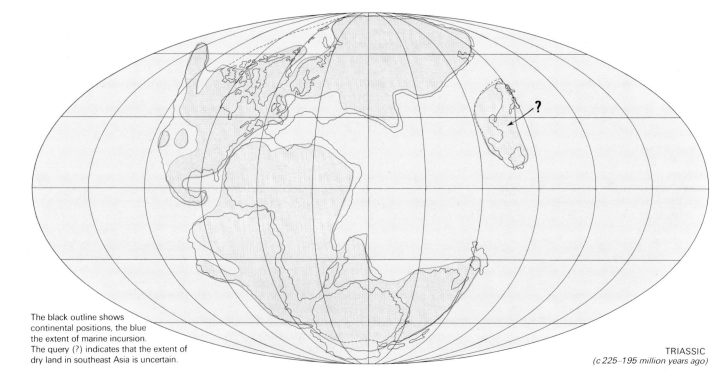

The black outline shows continental positions, the blue the extent of marine incursion. The query (?) indicates that the extent of dry land in southeast Asia is uncertain.

TRIASSIC
(c 225–195 million years ago)

Salt pseudomorphs in marls indicate the hot, dry conditions that existed in Triassic deserts. Pseudomorphs are the result of the filling of spaces left by crystals after they have been dissolved away.

can be traced back to the *Carboniferous, became widespread and common during the Triassic: they, like the ammonites, became nearly extinct by the end of the Triassic but survived to become the ancestors of the modern *mammals.

From the late Carboniferous up until the beginning of the Triassic, four floral provinces can be distinguished: the European, Angaran and Cathaysian warm provinces to the north of Tethys, and the Glossopteris cold-temperate province to its south.

The early Triassic floras appear to have been sparse and poor, and this is usually interpreted as a result of the unfavorable climate. Furthermore, they were mainly survivals from the Permian period. As many early Triassic terrestrial deposits are red beds with *evaporites, indicating arid or semi-arid hot conditions, the early and middle Triassic floras were probably concentrated around lakes and rivers where *Neuropteridium* ferns grew with conifers like *Voltzia*, while horsetails such as *Schizoneura* grew in the shallow waters. In contrast to this warm flora of Laurasia the southern continent of Gondwanaland was characterized by the cold-temperate *Glossopteris* flora.

The late Triassic floras reflect an evolutionary change by becoming more abundant and varied, with many new groups appearing: the main plant groups were conifers, ferns, cycads and ginkgos.

Paleogeographical Maps. During the Triassic period there were only two main continental margins, the circum-Pacific, which could be regarded as an external margin, and the Tethys, which appears as an internal margin, the two being separated by the huge land areas of Laurasia and Gondwanaland.

The available paleomagnetic data (see *geophysics) suggest that throughout the Triassic period there was no significant movement of Pangaea. This phase of only very slight plate-tectonic activity appears to have lasted from about 250 million years ago to about 170 million years ago.

The configuration of Pangaea during the Triassic, with Gondwanaland occupying a very southern and hence cool position, had a major influence on the world's climate. This climatic influence is recognizable in the types of rocks deposited – for example, desert dune sands and evaporites – and in the distributions of fossil animals and plants. Another major paleogeographical influence of this supercontinent was the greatly reduced length of coastline throughout the world: this had the effect of restricting the total area and distribution of marine shelves along the coastlines of the Pacific and Tethys, and influenced the distribution of faunas because marine shelves were the principal habitat of the great majority of the creatures that

have come down to us as fossils.

One of the complicating factors that have affected the interpretation of Triassic paleogeography is the widespread effects of the late *Mesozoic and *Cenozoic orogenies, resulting from the convergence and in places the eventual collision of parts of the north and south margins of the Tethys ocean. This collision resulted in the Alpine, Himalayan, IndoBurman and Indonesian *mountain chains, where most of the evidence of the Tethyan marine Triassic rocks is exposed.

Triassic Paleogeography, Tectonics and Igneous Activity. Although most of the circum-Pacific continental margin of Pangaea remained mobile throughout the late Paleozoic and Mesozoic, the Triassic was a particularly quiet period. Much of the Tethys margin remained passive throughout the period. On a world-wide basis the tectonically quiet Triassic separates the late Paleozoic orogenic events that characterize the Pacific margin of the continents from the next major tectonic phase of the middle and late Mesozoic, when the conglomerated continent of Gondwanaland was split up by the opening of the new Atlantic and Indian Oceans.

There were three Triassic major paleogeographical provinces, namely the huge land area of Laurasia and Gondwanaland, and the two ocean margins of circum-Pacific and Tethys.

The Circum-Pacific Margin. In North America the geosynclinal belts that con-

Buttes formed by the remains of the Jurassic Navajo sandstone deposits overlying Triassic red beds in Utah, USA.

stitute the Triassic margin pass into the Canadian Arctic region where the Svedrup Basin contains thick Triassic miogeosynclinal facies (see *geosyncline): the same is true of Triassic deposits on the eastern side of the Siberian platform. The Cordilleran belt of North America must have represented an active continental margin during the Triassic, as indicated by the volcanic rocks, which were important in the central sector, where *andesite, *rhyolite, *dacite and pyroclastic deposits are preserved. Some small Triassic *granite intrusions represent an early stage of plutonism.

In the Antarctic peninsula (West Antarctica) there appears to have been strong *folding and some metamorphism (see *metamorphic rocks) during the Triassic. This orogenic phase may be related to the history through the Triassic of eugeosynclinal deposition and volcanism in New Zealand, when it was adjacent to West Antarctica: during the Mesozoic New Zealand was much closer to eastern Australia and the Tasman Sea had not yet formed.

The circum-Pacific margin of Gondwanaland extended around eastern Australia into New Guinea where it connected with the Tethys ocean margin of Gondwanaland. The continental margin of New Guinea seems to have been, like all of the southern margin of Tethys, a tectonically

passive feature throughout the Triassic.

The Northern Margin of Tethys. The Alpine cycle, representing the accumulation of sediments and igneous rocks and resulting in their deformation and uplift into the Alpine mountain chain, began in the Triassic period. It started with marine transgressions over the eroded Hercynian mountain complexes and with the development of marginal troughs within and adjacent to the continental margin. The marine deposits are mainly *limestones, *dolomites, *sandstones and *shales. The transgressions which characterized the Alpine Triassic marine deposits occasionally invaded the continental hinterland of Laurasia, where the "Germanic Trias" facies of red beds and evaporites accumulated. By the end of the Triassic the Tethys sea had extended over the adjacent forelands covering the older Triassic red-bed facies.

In the Himalayas there appears to be an important gap in the sedimentary sequence at the Permian-Triassic boundary. Extensive carbonate and shale deposits, with some volcanics, represent shelf and deeper basinal sediments that accumulated on the northern margin of Tethys.

Unlike the quiet shelf and basin deposits that characterize much of the northern margin of the Alpine-Himalayan Tethys, the Triassic deposits of the IndoBurman ranges, Indonesia and the Philippines contain unmistakable evidence of an active continental plate margin (see *plate tectonics). This Triassic convergent plate

margin extended around southeast Asia from Burma through the Philippines and the Ryuku arc to Korea and Japan.

It is in the Japan region that the northern margin of Tethys met the circum-Pacific margin.

The Southern Margin of Tethys. On the southern side of the present Mediterranean, in the Atlas mountains of Morocco and Algeria, are found Triassic rocks very similar to those of the Alpine mountain chain. As on the northern margin of Tethys, Triassic marine transgressions also invaded the older "Germanic Trias" red-bed facies, which was deposited on both the African and European continental blocks.

The correlation of the Atlas mountains to the east is uncertain. They may belong to the facies belts that pass through the Apennines, Southern Alps, Dinarides and Hellenides. It is not easy to determine what elements belong to the southern part of Tethys. In Libya, Egypt, northern Israel and on the Arabian peninsula Triassic marine-shelf deposits accumulated, and the sea probably extended onto the Ethiopian shield.

The southern margin of Tethys can also be identified in western Australia and on the present northern Australian shelf, where land-formed deposits lie in alternating layers with open marine-shelf sediments that accumulated around this part of Australia and New Guinea.

Laurasia. Much of the North American continent was above sea level, and suffered active *erosion during the Triassic. In late Triassic times, fault-bounded troughs formed in eastern North America in which great thicknesses of terrestrial sediments accumulated together with some basic volcanic rocks. The interior lowlands also preserve some records of the terrestrial deposits that accumulated thinly over large areas during the Triassic. In the west, along the margins of the present Cordillera, thin sequences of non-marine red beds with evaporites are found.

The European landmass, like that of North America, consisted of the eroded late Paleozoic mountain ranges as well as extensive lowlands, such as the North Sea Basin, where the detritus accumulated mainly as red beds with evaporites. Many, but not all, of the basins of *deposition were fault-bounded troughs. There is evidence that these Triassic sediments accumulated under hot arid and semi-arid conditions, which in northwest Europe gradually diminished in aridity during the Triassic, a waning perhaps associated with the encroachment of Tethys from the south.

The Siberian continental block, unlike the European region, was the site of an important igneous episode during the Permian and Triassic. *Plateau basalts and associated basic dikes and sills were erupted, forming a layer up to 0.6mi (1km) thick and covering about 575,000mi^2 (1,500,000km^2). These Siberian "Traps" may be compared with the roughly contemporaneous plateau basalts of southern Africa, which then formed part of Gondwanaland.

Gondwanaland. Thick Triassic Gondwanaland deposits are found in large basins and in thinner widespread sequences. Large basins of terrestrial facies were developed in the late Triassic in northeastern and eastern South America, and are present in southern Africa where they consist mainly of sandstones and shales. Late Triassic plateau basalts have also been identified in South Africa. In India extensive continental red beds with a fauna of reptiles and amphibians have been dated as Triassic. In Antarctica, similar facies of terrestrial sandstones with reptile and amphibian fossils have been dated as Triassic on the basis of the plant remains that they contain.

Very similar facies were deposited in Australia, especially along the eastern margin, where sandstones of river or stream origin are known with *coals. Some volcanic activity of Triassic age is reported from the hinterland of eastern Australia. In early Triassic times small marine transgressions reached into the western and eastern margins of Australia. The present wide northwest Australian shelf region was, during most of the Triassic, the site of Tethyan marine infiltrations with the typical "Gondwana" facies.

Summary. Much of the circum-Pacific margin of Pangaea was an active plate margin during the Triassic, and consequently the site of tectonic and igneous activity, as was the northern margin of Tethys, east of the Himalayas and extending from Burma to Japan. The southern margin of Tethys and most of the western part of the northern margin of Tethys appear to have been a passive margin during the period, and so this region was tectonically quiet, with only a very little in the way of volcanic activity.

Within the continental blocks of Laurasia and Gondwanaland, very little igneous activity has been dated as Triassic. One exception is provided by the late Triassic volcanic rocks and dikes of the fault troughs of eastern North America. Parts of some dike swarms in west Africa and northern South America may also be of Triassic age and are possibly associated with the activity in eastern North America; and all this may be related to doming in the incipient mid-Atlantic ridge that was to form in the late Mesozoic. Other igneous activity on the continental blocks was concentrated in the two widely separated areas of southern Africa and Siberia, where plateau basalts were erupted.   MGA-C

Jurassic

The Jurassic, named for the Jura Mountains of Switzerland, began about 195 million years ago and ended about 135 million years ago. There were then only two major continents, Laurasia in the north and Gondwanaland in the south. During the early part of the period these were united at their western end and separated by a major equatorial ocean called Tethys, which widened towards the east.

Late in the early Jurassic, that section which we now know as northwestern Africa moved away from North America, so creating a narrow sea, the precursor of the modern Atlantic, which continued to widen throughout the remainder of the period. It was not until the Cretaceous that the North and South Atlantic and Indian Oceans came into existence.

Sea-floor spreading (see *plate tectonics) almost certainly took place in the Pacific region, but the evidence is largely lost today because the present Pacific floor is underlain by *basalt generated later.

Sea-level was comparatively high in the Jurassic: large areas of the present continents were inundated by shallow seas, and the land appears in general to have been fairly low-lying. Early in the period sea-level was at its lowest: subsequently the sea advanced more or less progressively to flood more and more of the lower-lying continental areas, reaching a maximum toward the end of the period when something like 25% of the present continental area was covered. However, in the very final stages of the Jurassic, the sea withdrew markedly from the continents, a process which continued into the Cretaceous. There are no reliable estimates of the precise range of sea-level differences during the Jurassic, but it was probably no more than about 660ft (200m). The basic cause of these changes was probably vertical movements of the mid-ocean ridge systems, resulting in the displacement of seawater (see *ocean floor).

Most of what is now Western Europe was covered by sea for almost the entire period, and the same is true for what are today the margins of the Pacific. However, much of Gondwanaland was never flooded, the sea being restricted to shallow bays or straits. Most of North America also remained uncovered, but a shallow sea spread from the Pacific into the Western Interior of the United States and Canada during the middle and early part of the late Jurassic. Another area of persistent land was what we now know as Eastern Asia.

The climate of the Jurassic was appreciably more equable than that of the present day. There were probably no polar icecaps, temperate conditions extending as far as the Arctic and Antarctic. Similarly, the climatic conditions which today characterize the tropics extended well north and south spreading as far as, for example, Western Europe.

However, it should be borne in mind that details of climate zones, or for that matter of wind and ocean current distributions, have not yet been adequately worked out.

Vertebrate Fauna. The vertebrate terrestrial life of the Jurassic period was dominated by the reptiles. The *dinosaurs had first appeared late in the Triassic from a *thecodont stock which also gave rise to *pterosaurs and, later, birds. From small bipedal animals such as *Coelophysis* there evolved the huge, spectacular creatures familiar to us all. These include the herbivorous *Brontosaurus*, *Brachiosaurus*, *Diplodocus* and *Stegosaurus* as well as the carnivorous, bipedal *Allosaurus*.

Only two rich dinosaur faunas are known from Jurassic deposits, the Morrison Formation of the American Western Interior and the approximately contemporary Tendaguru Beds of Tanzania. The two faunas are strikingly similar at family and generic level, which would suggest rather strongly that free land communications existed between western North America and East Africa until quite late in the period – a fact that is not easy to reconcile with some modern paleogeographic reconstructions.

Flying animals include the truly reptilian pterosaurs and the first animals that could be called *birds as distinct from reptiles, as represented by the pigeon-sized *Archaeopteryx*.

There were two important groups of reptiles which lived in the sea, the dolphin-like *ichthyosaurs and the long-necked *plesiosaurs. Both of these groups, specimens of which are displayed in many natural history museums, had streamlined bodies and limbs beautifully adapted to marine life. *Turtles and *crocodiles are also found as fossils in Jurassic deposits.

Jurassic mammals, known mainly from their teeth alone, were small and obviously did not compete directly with the dinosaurs. They included a number of biologi-

A Jurassic landscape:
1 *Rhamphorhynchus*
2 *Conifers and ginkgoes*
3 *Brachiosaurus*
4 *Dicraeosaurus*
5 *Megalosaurus*
6 *Kentrosaurus*
7 *Elaphrosaurus*
8 *Dysalotosaurus*
9 Crocodiles
10 Ferns, tree-ferns, cycads
11 Horsetails

JURASSIC LIFE

Rhamphorhynchus

Archaeopteryx

Gryphaea

Williamsonia

Arnioceras

Antrodemus

Stegosaurus

Macroplata

Cuspiteuthis

cally primitive groups such as the triconodonts, docodonts and multituberculates (see *primitive mammals). The fish faunas were dominated by the holosteans, characterized by heavy rhombic scales. Their evolutionary successors, the teleosts, probably appeared shortly before the end of the period (see *actinopterygians).

Invertebrate Fauna. Because they are far more abundant, the invertebrate fossil faunas of the sea are of more importance to stratigraphers and paleoecologists than are the vertebrates. By far the most useful for stratigraphic correlations are the *ammonites, a group of fossil *mollusks. They were swimmers that lived in the open sea, only rarely braving the fluctuating salinity and temperature of inshore waters. They are characteristically most abundant in marine *shales and associated fine-grained *limestones.

From a solitary family that recovered from near extinction at the close of the Triassic, there radiated an enormous diversity of genera. Many of these were worldwide in distribution, but increasingly throughout the period there was a geographical differentiation into two major realms. The Boreal Realm occupied a northern region embracing the Arctic, northern Europe and northern North America. The Tethyan Realm, with more diverse faunas, occupied the rest of the world.

Taking into account the evidence of the whole invertebrate fauna, together with the paleogeographic picture that can be deduced from the sedimentary rocks, it looks as though the differentiation into Tethyan and Boreal realms most probably developed as a result of the operation of a number of independent factors, of which possibly the most significant was irregular fluctuations in the salinity and temperature of the shallow seas close around the shores of the continents. In other words, the Tethyan Realm was marked by more environmentally stable open-sea conditions than was the Boreal Realm.

During the Jurassic, the ammonites evolved rapidly and had a high rate of extinction. No fewer than 65 zones of fossil ammonites are recognized in northwest Europe, which has become the classic region for study of this period. As the Jurassic lasted for some 60 million years, it would seem that each of these zones represents, on average, a duration of the order of a million years.

Where ammonites are absent, as in all

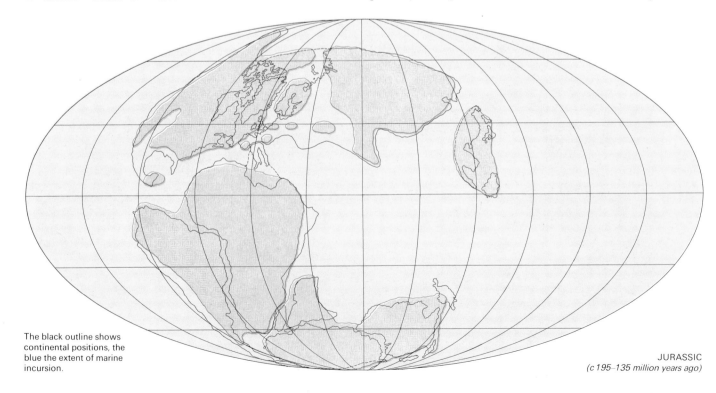

The black outline shows continental positions, the blue the extent of marine incursion.

JURASSIC
(c 195–135 million years ago)

Limestone concretions in shales deposited during early Jurassic (Liassic) times on the coast of Yorkshire, England.

non-marine and certain shallow inshore marine deposits, or where the rocks are known only from boreholes, a variety of other fossils have had to be used for correlation: of these, the most useful have proved to be *foraminifera, *ostracods, plant spores and *dinoflagellates.

In most facies the *bivalves, which flourished in shallow, muddy sea bottoms, are the most abundant and diverse of the microfauna. They included many cemented forms such as Ostrea, recliners like Gryphaea, swimmers such as the pectinids and limids and rock borers such as Lithophaga. However, the majority were burrowers; either relatively mobile, shallow burrowers or forms occupying deep, permanent burrows and normally found still in their positions of growth.

*Brachiopods were much more abundant and diverse than they are today. The range of depths below the surface which they occupied is far wider than for the bivalves, and a definite depth zonation can be established in Europe, just as with the ammonites.

*Echinoderms are best represented as fossils by the crinoids and echinoids, and were all inhabitants of shallow seas, unlike some of the modern representatives of this class. The echinoids include both primitive regular forms, like the cidaroids, and irregular forms, such as Clypeus and Pygaster.

*Corals belonged to the still extant Scleractinia group, and included reef builders such as Isastrea and Thamnasteria. Calcareous and siliceous *sponges are also quite common locally, even forming reefs. It seems likely that these sponge facies developed in somewhat deeper water than did the corals.

The invertebrate microfaunas are represented by abundant foraminifera, ostracods and radiolaria – foraminifera and ostracods are of great value to oil companies in correlation studies.

Not all Jurassic invertebrates lived in the sea. Some lived in continental environments such as lakes and rivers; they include a few genera of bivalves, gastropods and arthropods. These faunas are far less diverse than their marine counterparts.

Flora. With regard to the plant kingdom, the Jurassic might well be called the age of the gymnosperms, the non-flowering *plants, forests of which covered much of the land. They included the conifers, gingkos and their relatives, the cycads. *Ferns and *horsetails made up the remainder of the land flora. These and others of the Jurassic flora are still extant today in much the same forms.

Remains of calcareous *algae are widely preserved in limestone. Besides the laminated sedimentary structures produced by blue-green algae and known as oncolites and stromatolites, there are skeletal secretions of other groups. Many pelagic limestones have revealed themselves under the electron microscope to be composed largely of tiny chalky plates, known as coccoliths, which are secreted by certain planktonic algae called *coccolithophores.

It seems highly likely that the late Jurassic saw the emergence of the *angiosperms, the flowering plants, since well-developed flowering plants existed in the very early Cretaceous. However, it is not yet understood quite how they emerged, and a satisfactory direct evolutionary ancestor has yet to be identified with any degree of certainty.

Stratigraphy. Most of the Jurassic sedimentary rocks that can be observed today were laid down in the extensive shallow seas that flooded parts of the continents.

Western Europe has become classic ground for Jurassic stratigraphers because of the widespread development of marine and non-marine strata that are extremely rich in fossils. The succession in England is probably the most celebrated. This succession consists of an alternation of soft-weathering *clays or *shales with more

Reefs form in warm conditions. The reef deposits in northern European Jurassic strata show that equatorial conditions prevailed there.

resistant formations of limestones and sandstones. This alternation gives rise to a characteristic scarp and vale topography.

Only in the south of England is the Jurassic succession complete, with an unbroken transition to the Cretaceous, but even here the boundary beds are nonmarine, a local expression of the worldwide regression, mentioned earlier, of sea from land in the late Jurassic.

Looked at geographically, the principal facies change in Western Europe and Britain is from sandstone and sandy shale with subordinate bands of *ironstone in the north (Scotland, Scandinavia, northern England, northern Germany) to limestone and marls further south. This implies that the major source of land-produced sediment was in the north – probably one or more land masses including the Scandinavian Shield. Islands further south – such as the old Paleozoic horsts of the London-Brabant Platform, the Massif Central and the Brittany Massif – do not appear to have been major sediment sources.

The vertical sequence of alternations of clays with sandstones and limestones signifies changing depths of sea. The clays were laid down in relatively deep (around 325ft (100m)), quiet water and include thin layers of shale, rich in organic matter, which were deposited in stagnant or near-stagnant water. Sandstones and limestones

were laid down in shallower water.

The extent to which the inferred changes in depth of water signify local tectonic subsidence or worldwide sea-level changes is still in dispute. However, evidence is accumulating to suggest that some of the major changes in the classic European sequences were controlled primarily by eustatic uplift.

For the countries around the Mediterranean an interesting history of tensional tectonics has recently been worked out. In the late Triassic an extensive carbonate platform had developed, somewhat resembling the Great Bahama Bank. On this were laid down several thousand yards of extremely shallow-water deposits of limestone. These conditions persisted – everywhere from southern Spain and Morocco to the southern Alps, Austrian Calcareous Alps and Apennines to Greece – until late in the early Jurassic. A widespread collapse then took place and extensive sectors subsided considerably, resulting in the formation of deeper-water deposits. The thicker, more basinal deposits are marly limestones with *trace-fossil mottling; the thinner deposits were laid down very slowly on structural highs (probably seamounts). These deposits were from deeper water than any known further north in Europe, and probably were laid down in depths of several hundred yards. They are overlain by even deeper-water deposits of middle to late Jurassic age, thought by many to have been laid down at depths of several thousand metres. The youngest Jurassic de-

posits are fine-grained pelagic limestones composed largely of coccolith debris. They have hardly any benthonic fossils but contain the aptychi of *ammonites. Traces of vulcanicity and sedimentary fissure fillings, together with dramatic lateral changes in sedimentary thickness, provide additional support for a general, self-consistent interpretation of Jurassic geological history.

The zone of Jurassic limestone facies continues eastward into the Middle East – as exemplified by the Zagros ranges of Iran and their continuation into Saudi Arabia. Here, however, the whole sequence is of shallow-water carbonate-platform type. Thick upper Jurassic limestones are also known in the southern part of European Russia and around the Gulf of Mexico. Elsewhere in the world, limestone facies are subordinate to sandstone and shales.

Another well-studied region of epicontinental sea deposits is the American Western Interior, embracing the Rocky Mountain states. Here the lower Jurassic is represented by several hundred yards of flat-lying red or yellow *sandstones, known in different states as the Navajo or Nugget Sandstone, that was laid down in hot desert and forms some of the more spectacular landscape features of that part of the world, such as Monument Valley. These are overlain by a series of shallow marine sandstones, shales and limestones with layers of gypsum and salt, of middle and early late Jurassic age, and mark the influx of the sea from the northwest. As with the lower Jurassic, deposits were much thicker in the

Badlands composed of Jurassic deposits in Arizona, USA.

west and were derived at least partly from tectonically rising land still further west.

The youngest Jurassic deposits of the Western Interior are a group of non-marine multicolored shales, siltstones, sandstones and subordinate limestones known as the Morrison Formation, celebrated for the rich dinosaur faunas it has yielded.

The fauna of freshwater *gastropods and bivalves and the flora of charophyte *algae (stoneworts) indicate that these are mainly the deposits of lakes. As in Europe, therefore, the late Jurassic was marked here by a withdrawal of the sea from the land, in this area beginning perhaps rather earlier.

The strata described so far were laid down mainly in areas of tectonic stability. However, around the margins of the Pacific – for instance in parts of California, Japan, New Zealand, Chile and Argentina and in the Caucasus and Balkan Mountains – the deposits contain a fair deal of volcanic material and the rocks are frequently folded, sheared or even metamorphosed. All this points to regimes of great tectonic instability and probably signifies the proximity of these areas to Jurassic subduction zones (see *plate tectonics). It seems likely that much of the old Tethys ocean floor was consumed along the line including the present Caucasus ranges.

One other part of the world that warrants mention in a regional survey is the Karroo Plateau of South Africa. Here there are thick basaltic and associated *igneous intrusions. This part of Gondwanaland witnessed huge outpourings of lava from late Triassic into middle Jurassic times. (The Tasmanian dolerites and Ferrar dolerites of Victoria Land, Antarctica, are essentially contemporaneous.) Extensive outpourings of plateau basalt indicate the onset of a tensional regime which anticipated the breakup, during the Cretaceous, of Gondwanaland.

Conclusion. The Jurassic was a period of relevance to us in several ways. Economically important deposits such as coal and ironstone were laid down. In the animal kingdom, the precursor of modern birds appeared, and creatures familiar to us, such as turtles and crocodiles, coexisted with the giant reptiles, doomed to become extinct late in the Cretaceous. It was also a period of notable plate tectonic activity, as the land continued its slow evolution toward our modern continents.   AH

Cretaceous

The word "Cretaceous" is derived from the Latin word *creta*, chalk, and indeed it is the Chalk Formations of Western Europe that are the best known part of the Cretaceous stratigraphic sequence. The sequence was christened *Térrain Crétacé* by J. J. Omalius d'Halloy in 1822 on the basis of his study of the chalky sediments of the Paris Basin and

adjacent areas; and our name for it is an anglicization of this.

The Cretaceous is the third and last period of the *Mesozoic era and lasted from 135 to 65 million years ago, a span of 70 million years. It followed the Jurassic and was succeeded by the Paleocene, the first period of the *Tertiary era. From our point of view, the most important Cretaceous products are coal, oil and gas, but many Cretaceous rocks are also of economic significance: they are used in, for example, ceramics, building and in the making of cement. From the paleontologist's point of view, the Cretaceous marks an important transitional stage in the evolution of life, from the ancient forms of the Jurassic to the

"modern" forms of the Paleocene, the ancestors of the lifeforms we know today.

The Cretaceous World. The distribution of continents and oceans during the early Cretaceous resembled that during the Jurassic, but sea-floor spreading during the Cretaceous produced fundamental changes (see *plate tectonics). The North Atlantic opened progressively throughout the period, with rifting extending to the north of Britain. To the south, during the middle Cretaceous, rifting along the margins of what was to become the South Atlantic produced extensive salt basins and a seaway (if not actual oceanic crust) appeared. The principal breakup of Gondwanaland, with the northward movement of India and the

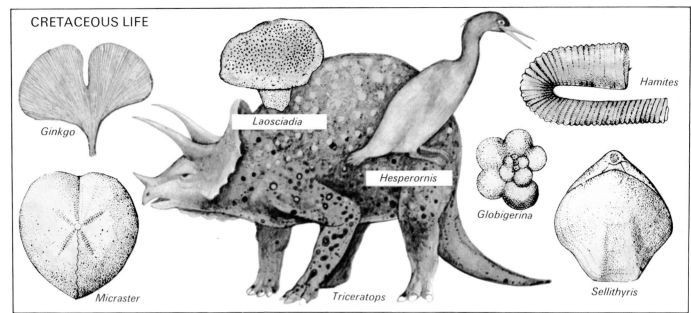

CRETACEOUS LIFE

Ginkgo

Laosciadia

Hesperornis

Globigerina

Hamites

Micraster

Triceratops

Sellithyris

separation of Antarctica, began during the period, while the floor of wide areas of the Pacific is also of Cretaceous date. Towards the close of the period the old seaway of Tethys was progressively eliminated as the African plate moved northwards to impinge upon the Asian plate, while the anticlockwise rotation of the Iberian peninsula produced the precursor of the Bay of Biscay.

Regression, the withdrawal of sea from the land, had begun in the late Jurassic, and it continued into the early Cretaceous. In many parts of the world, therefore, this is a time marked by *erosion or non-marine sedimentation. But renewed and progressive transgressive pulses, beginning during the late early Cretaceous, caused a cumulative rise in sea level of 2000–2300ft (600–700m) at minimum: this was a result of the construction of extensive mid-

ocean ridge systems and a surge in sea-floor spreading. By the end of the period wide areas of continental crust, including some which had not been submerged since the Precambrian, were flooded in the greatest marine transgression since the Ordovician – perhaps the greatest at any time of the Phanerozoic. Most of what is now Western Europe was covered by epicontinental sea, as were the margins of all of the other continental blocks: a seaway extended across the Sahara, central Europe was an archipelago with a gulf extending north to the Arctic ocean, while a major seaway extended the length of the Interior of the USA and Canada.

Cretaceous climates were equable and warm compared with those of the present. There appear to have been no polar icecaps – indeed, the poles probably experienced

warm, temperate conditions. Large reptiles were present close to the north pole, according to *fossil evidence in Alaska, while marine fossil faunas include forms which range from the then north pole through the tropics to high southern latitudes, suggesting mild climatic gradients. Reef-building *corals extended far to the north of their present ranges, as did giant *foraminifera, rudist *bivalves, and other warm-water indicators. Floras from Alaska include remains of cycads, palms and figs.

Flora. The land floras of the earliest Cretaceous, like those of the Jurassic, are dominated by gymnosperms – conifers, cycads and the like, resembling closely their living relatives. Late in the early Cretaceous, however, *angiosperms (flowering plants) became prominent and, by the close of the Cretaceous, forests in many areas were

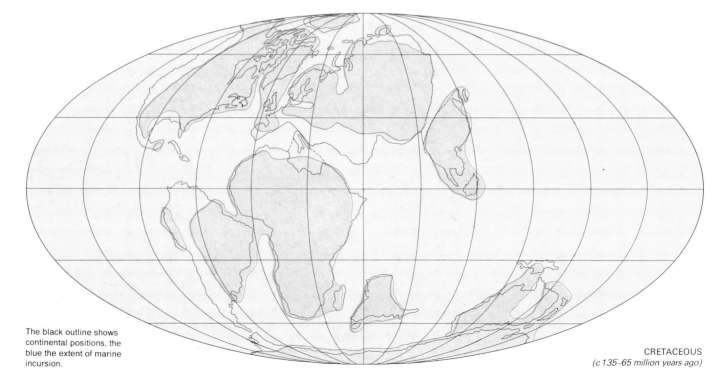

The black outline shows continental positions, the blue the extent of marine incursion.

CRETACEOUS
(c 135–65 million years ago)

Cliff dwellings built in Upper Cretaceous sandstones, Mesa Verde, New Mexico, USA.

dominated by deciduous, broad-leaved trees. By the middle Cretaceous up to 90% of floras consist of angiosperms with leaves which resembled modern beech, oak, maple, walnut, plane and magnolia, along with broad-leaved shrubs and the like. Cycads remained prominent in some upland floras, as did conifers. Various groups of marine calcareous *algae are abundant in shallow-water limestones. The chalk-producing algae (*coccolithophores) reached their peak in the late Cretaceous. Although known from the Jurassic onwards, it is only during the Cretaceous that coccolith sediments come to dominate deep-sea carbonate sequences, and only in the upper Cretaceous do they spread onto shelf areas. Chalk sedimentation spread over wide areas of Europe and North America, while chalks are known also from South America and Australia, indicating an extraordinary abundance of these microscopic organisms.

The late Cretaceous saw also the acme of the *dinoflagellates, another group of single-celled plants.

Fauna. The broad composition of Cretaceous invertebrate faunas resembles that of the *Jurassic. Protozoans are represented by *radiolarians and *foraminifera, the late Cretaceous seeing the diversification of the planktonic *globigerinids. *Sponges are a common element of the fauna of much of the European Cretaceous, and *brachiopods are in many places abundant. Coelenterates are also widespread, and the coelenterate faunas began to approximate to their modern appearance by the end of the period. *Gastropods spread during the late Cretaceous. Cretaceous *ammonite faunas were dominated by desmoceratids, acanthoceratids and diverse heteromorphs. The largest ammonite known is a late Cretaceous *Pachydiscus*. The first octopus (*Paleoctopus newboldi*) comes from the upper Cretaceous of the Lebanon.

Amongst the arthropods, many groups of crustaceans and many insects appear in much their modern forms; while the interdependence of insects and flowering plants probably developed early in the period. *Echinoderms are diverse and widely varied, with many irregular echinoids, asteroids and crinoids. Triconodont and symmetrodont *mammals died out during the Cretaceous, as did several groups of *birds. Fish faunas include chondrosteans, holosteans and cartilagenous sharks, while the teleosts undergo a major radiation during the period.

However, the most spectacular Cretaceous vertebrates are without doubt the *reptiles. Marine forms include *plesiosaurs up to 50ft (16m) long, and short-necked forms such as *Kronosaurus*, whose skull was some 13ft (4m) long. *Ichthyosaurs occur, but are far less significant than they were in the Jurassic; while a new group appeared, the mosasaurs, rather similar to the popular conception of sea-serpents, with paddle-like limbs and an array of sharp teeth. They reached sizes in excess of 32ft (10m). In addition, giant turtles (*Archelon*) with a carapace up to 13ft (4m) long have been found.

Also occurring in marine sediments, and best known from the chalks of Kansas in the US Western Interior, are the last of the flying reptiles, the *pterosaurs. One of the largest of these was *Pteranodon*, some species of which had wing-spans over 33ft (10m), the largest flying animals of all time. On land, the *dinosaurs dominated, with giant herbivores such as *Iguanodon*, the armor-plated *Ankylosaurus* and the horned *Triceratops*; and *Tyrannosaurus*, the largest known terrestrial carnivore, which reached heights of 48ft (15m).

The end of the Cretaceous, like the end of the Permian some 160 million years before, was a period of widespread extinction. At least sixteen higher taxa of animals died out by the close of the Cretaceous, including the rudistid *bivalves, the euomphalacean, trochonemalacean and nerineacean *gastropods, all *ammonoids, the *ichthyosaurs, *pterosaurs and sauropod dinosaurs, while the belemnitids died out early in the Paleocene. At a lower taxonomic

A chalk cliff on the Dorset coast, England. The chalk was deposited in a shallow water environment, and the flints, seen in regular horizons throughout the succession, formed later as a result of water dissolving and redepositing silica.

belt are major thrusts, some up to 250mi (400km) long, with lateral displacements of up to 22mi (35km), and a total crustal shortening of up to 70mi (110km). More important is its continuation, the Laramide orogeny, first named from the Laramie region in Wyoming, which affected the area west of the Sevier orogenic belt. This orogeny was responsible for the major structure of the Rocky Mountains, although their topographic relief is largely the result of post-Cretaceous uplift and erosion. Structures include major folds, with total vertical movement in some areas of over 6mi (10km); and in places Precambrian basement has been exposed.

This great orogenic belt extends for the length of North America, and there is major associated igneous activity (see *igneous intrusion), including the intrusion of enormous granite batholiths. These include the Baja California, Sierra Nevada, Idaho, Boulder and Coast Range batholiths, the last-named having a total length of over 930mi (1500km). Evidence of *vulcanicity can also be seen in the USA: volcanic ash bands occur throughout the whole of the Interior, and are the principal source of radiometric dating of the late Cretaceous.

In South America, there was a similar phase of mountain-building during the late Cretaceous, again accompanied by major igneous intrusive and extrusive activity, along the line of the Andes and the Antillean Arc of Central America. Extrusive igneous rocks associated with the opening of the South Atlantic occur widely in the Paraná Basin of Brazil, covering an area of 400,000mi^2 (1 million km^2), with a maximum thickness of 0.93mi (1.5km). Smaller areas of similar, contemporaneous volcanics occur in Namibia.

In the Middle East, there were widespread movements in the early Cretaceous, and some granitic intrusion in Iran, with late Cretaceous ophiolites in the same area. In the Himalayan region, there was major submarine *vulcanicity at this time. Late Cretaceous volcanics are known from western Australia, while there were widespread volcanism and major granite intrusion in the Japanese islands. In the eastern Antarctic, there is evidence of extensive Cretaceous vulcanicity and intrusive activity.

In contrast, the deformation affecting western Europe north of the Alps was generally on a small scale. *Faulting affected the rift systems of the North Sea, while minor *folding can also be recognized. Igneous activity was also on a small scale. Bentonites (altered volcanic ashes) are known from southern England, while much of the *montmorillonite in the chalk may have a similar origin.

In the Alpine region, the initial phases of compressional deformation associated with

level, many families of forams, bivalves, echinoderms and other invertebrates went into decline or disappeared, while there was a major reduction in the diversity of many planktonic micro-organisms, including *dinoflagellates, *coccolithophores and *radiolaria.

The cause of the late Cretaceous extinctions is not fully understood, and many suggested mechanisms – such as variations in solar radiation, or epidemic disease – are of course untestable. It is, however, obvious that whatever mechanism was responsible, it affected not only marine organisms but also terrestrial forms – from coccolithophores to dinosaurs. Among recently advanced hypotheses are: reversals

in the Earth's magnetic field, which might temporarily reduce protection from cosmic radiation; fluctuating climatic conditions associated with global sea-level changes; or even phases of mountain building.

Tectonic and Igneous Activity. The best known Cretaceous orogenic (mountain-building) areas are in the Americas. The first of these in North America was the Sevier orogeny, which takes its name from the Sevier arch in southwestern Utah. Beginning in the early Cretaceous, and extending to the close of the period, it affected a belt running from southern Nevada across Utah into the southwestern corner of Wyoming and southeastern Idaho. The most notable features of this the closure of Tethys, precursors of the main Tertiary deformation phase, appear during the Cretaceous.

Northwestern Europe. The earliest Cretaceous paleogeography of northwestern Europe, the type area for the period, closely follows that of the late Jurassic. As a result of continued regression, non-marine deposition occurred in areas such as southern England, northern France and northwest Germany. Marine deposits of the Boreal Sea extend over northern England to the Soviet Union, while to the south, in southern France and parts of the Alps, are marine sediments laid down on the northern margins of Tethys. Land areas at this time included the Paleozoic blocks of the Anglo-Brabant Massif, Massif Central, Armorica, Vosges, Hartz, Baltic Shield and much of Wales, Scotland and Ireland.

Uplift during the early Cretaceous ended deposition of fine-grained clays and limestones in areas of non-marine deposition, and these are succeeded by a thick (up to 2700ft (800m)) sequence of fluvial and deltaic *clays and sandstones, best known from the Weald of southeastern England.

The English Lower Greensand, dating from a little later, marks a transgression by the sea, and takes its name from the widespread occurrence of the mineral *glauconite; and although most of it is neither green nor a sand, its name stresses one of the features of the northwest European Cretaceous, the wide occurrence of glauconite sediments. This, together with the widespread occurrence of *chert and sedimentary phosphates, is believed to be a reflection of changing patterns of ocean currents, and upwelling associated with the initial opening of the North Atlantic.

By the early late Cretaceous, a combination of transgression, reduced relief, and perhaps low water run-off had resulted in a great reduction in supply of land-derived sedimentary material. This, combined with a peak in diversity and abundance of the *coccolithophores, led to the widespread deposition of chalks, which dominate upper Cretaceous sedimentation in an area extending from Ireland to the Caspian. Many of the land areas were greatly reduced in size by this time. Non-chalk facies are chiefly known from areas such as the southern Paris Basin, Ireland, and parts of Germany: they included cross-bedded sandstones, greensands and calcarenites.

The European Chalk was originally regarded as a deep-sea deposit, comparable to *globigerina ooze. It is now known to have accumulated at comparatively shallow depths, between 160 and 975ft (50–300m), although the closest modern counterparts are deep-sea oozes (see *ocean floor). One of the most striking features of the sequence are flints, horned nodules of black silica with white rinds of partially siliceous material. Once regarded as some sort of a primary precipitate, they are now known to be diagenetic in origin, the silica being derived from sources such as *sponge skeletons, and possible *diatoms and *radiolaria (see *diagenesis).

In the North Sea area, drilling has shown that chalk sedimentation extended into the early Tertiary. In Denmark also some Paleocene chalks occur.

Conclusion. The Cretaceous was a period of evolution rather than of revolution. At its end, which signified the beginning of the Cenozoic and the end of the Mesozoic, dramatic changes took place. It was the end of the age of the giant reptiles, the beginning of the era of modern life. The dinosaurs and the ammonites were extinguished, but the first true birds appeared. The mammals, one day to give birth to man, had remained small and shrew-like throughout the Cretaceous, but their inexorable rise was to come with the beginning of the Cenozoic.

Perhaps it would not be too much to say that the most significant element of the Cretaceous was its ending. WJK

Cenozoic

The Cenozoic is commonly described as "The Age of Mammals", and as one might expect from this nickname its most important characteristic has been the evolution of modern forms of life.

The Cenozoic has lasted for around 65 million years, and is commonly subdivided into two periods, the *Tertiary and the *Quaternary, each of which is further subdivided. The latter period, the Quaternary, is of special interest as it has seen the rise of modern Man.

Many of the major mountain ranges of the world have formed during the Cenozoic. Early in the era the Indian subcontinent was pushed against Asia, the crumpling of the land resulting in the Himalayas; and rather later the similar thrust of Italy, then part of Africa, against Europe resulted in the formation of the Alps. The later part of the era has been characterized by a series of Ice Ages from which, there is good reason to believe, we may not yet have emerged. AI

Tertiary

The name "Tertiary" was introduced by Arduino in the middle of the 18th century to denote the various rock types younger than the Mesozoic, the "Secondary". It became an internationally recognized time-stratigraphic unit when Desnoyers, in 1829, distinguished the *Quaternary as a separate period. Together Tertiary and Quaternary comprise the Cenozoic Era.

The Tertiary had a duration of about 63 million years, beginning around 65 million years ago and ending only 2 million years ago. *Lyell in 1833 subdivided the period into four epochs, the Eocene, Miocene and the Older and Newer Pliocene, later substituting the name Pleistocene for the last of these. (The *Pleistocene is now more usually considered as part of the Quaternary.)

Further subdivisions, the Paleocene for the earlier part of Lyell's Eocene, and the Oligocene for the earlier part of Lyell's Miocene, were contributed by later workers to complete the modern subdivision of the period.

The first part of the Tertiary, up to the end of the Oligocene, is sometimes called the Paleogene; and the later part, the Miocene and Pliocene (and sometimes the Pleistocene) are by some workers referred to as the Neogene.

The Tertiary can be thought of as the period characterized by the rise of modern *mammals. At the beginning of the period archaic forms predominated, but rapidly these were superseded by more and more modern forms. By the end of the Tertiary there were certainly man-apes in Africa. But the end of the period was characterized by cooling climates and a massive extinction: the emergence of modern Man himself was a matter retained for the Quaternary.

Paleocene
The Paleocene was named by W. P. Schimper in 1874 for continental and brackish-water beds in the Paris Basin. The beds chosen as typical of the Paleocene are, in actual fact, of early *Eocene age, and this has led to some problems concerning the real meaning of the term Paleocene. The Paleocene is now accepted as spanning the time between 65 and 54 million years ago, approximately.

The epoch is generally agreed to have two stages: the earlier Danian, named in 1847, the type area being Denmark; and the Thanetian, named later in 1873, the type area being the Isle of Wight, England. The Danian type area consists of limestones developed in a variety of facies, such as coral reefs, *bryozoan mounds (bioherms) and coccolith chalks (see *coccolithophores). The Thanetian type area is in contrast developed in a silty, glauconitic facies. (The Montian and Landenian stages of Belgium, used in parts of Europe as standard stages, may be considered chronologic equivalents of the Danian and Thanetian, respectively.)

A major floral and faunal discontinuity occurred between the end of the *Cretaceous and the beginning of the Paleocene: important elements of oceanic plankton disappeared, as did many ammonites, belemnites, mollusks, marine reptiles, and so on.

Significant paleogeographic changes occurred in the world during the Paleocene. The Norwegian Sea began to form as a result of the separation of Greenland and Scandinavia along the axis of the Reykjanes Ridge, a northern extension of the Mid-Atlantic Ridge. During the Cretaceous, the Atlantic Ocean, its borderland margins and large parts of the surrounding low-lying continents which were covered by shallow inland seas, had been characterized by widespread deposition of calcium carbonate under climatically equitable conditions; but, in the Paleocene, local mountain building accompanying the birth of the northeast

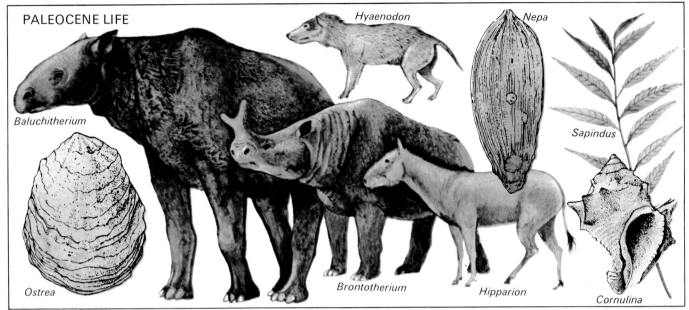

PALEOCENE LIFE

Baluchitherium

Ostrea

Hyaenodon

Brontotherium

Hipparion

Nepa

Sapindus

Cornulina

Atlantic changed the sedimentation patterns considerably, particularly in the marginal areas, with land-derived sediments becoming an important factor.

The North and South Atlantic had respectively opened to about 95% and 75% of their present-day width through sea-floor spreading (see *plate tectonics). The Atlantic and Arctic oceans were separated from each other, and a northward-flowing, warm "proto-Gulf Stream" brought subtropical faunal and floral elements as far north as the Labrador Sea and Rockall Bank. The Atlantic and Pacific were linked by the westward-flowing North Equatorial Current through the straits of Panama, which separated North and South America; it contributed to circumglobal transportation of tropical marine faunal and floral elements. In the southern hemisphere, Aus-

tralia separated from Antarctica and began its northward flight.

Climate was rather equitable all over the Earth, with evidence of subtropical floras and faunas as far north as the present-day latitude of London. Evidence of climatically controlled cycles is seen, however, in the deep-sea record of the Atlantic Ocean, with alternate equatorward and poleward expansion and retreat of high-latitude and low-latitude oceanic planktonic floras and faunas. There is no evidence of polar icecaps.

Significant changes in the organic realm distinguish the Paleocene from the Cretaceous. Paleocene mammalian faunas were characterized by multituberculates, creodonts, condylarths (see *primitive mammals) and the earliest prosimians (ancestral forms of the *primates). Migration of mam-

malian faunas between Europe and North America occurred *via* a polar route between Spitzbergen and Greenland, and this resulted in virtually identical faunas in these two areas. However, trans-Eurasian migration was inhibited as a result of a north-south interior seaway – the Uralian Sea – which connected the polar regions with the equatorially situated Tethys Sea.

The marine realm was characterized by a rapid radiation of calcareous plankton following their virtual extinction at the close of the Cretaceous. Large (0.2–0.4in (5–10mm) diameter) tropical shallow water *foraminifera – known as *Nummulites* – evolved within the Paleocene and continued to flourish throughout the *Eocene; they were to decline in the early *Oligocene and become extinct at the end of the middle Oligocene.

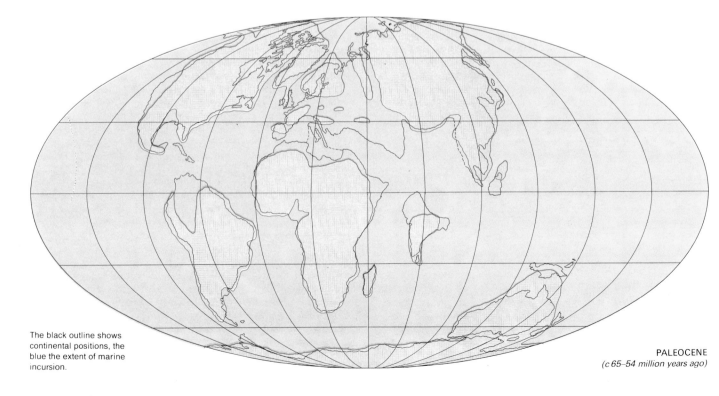

The black outline shows continental positions, the blue the extent of marine incursion.

PALEOCENE
(c 65–54 million years ago)

Eocene

*Lyell, in 1833, originally introduced the term Eocene to describe the lowest subdivision of the Tertiary, including the rocks between the *Cretaceous and *Miocene in which only a small (less than 5%) number of living molluscan species were believed to occur.

Numerous stage terms have been introduced over the years to correspond to a threefold subdivision of the Eocene. The most commonly accepted stages include (from oldest to youngest) the Ypresian, Lutetian and Bartonian. The Cuisian and Priabonian are commonly used synonymously with upper Ypresian and Bartonian, respectively.

The sediments of the type areas of the Eocene stages of northern Europe are deposited in shallow-water environments of the continental shelf. These sediments are generally characterized by abundant molluscan faunas, using which local stratigraphic correlations are possible. Faunas of nummulites, an extinct group of *foraminifera, are locally abundant at certain stratigraphic levels and enable regional correlation to be made.

The stratigraphic position of the Paleocene/Eocene boundary is controversial because of confusion surrounding Schimper's original characterization of the former epoch (see *Paleocene). He appears to have considered parts of the Ypresian as Paleocene in age in one instance, whereas in another he included them in the Eocene. As a result the Paleocene/Eocene boundary is drawn by some stratigraphers at the base of the Cuisian. This results in the stratigraphically undesirable practice of having the Ypresian stage straddle the boundary, its lower part being of Paleocene age.

In his original concept of the Eocene, Lyell included in its upper part the marine sands of Fontainebleau (Paris Basin). He subsequently extracted these rocks from the upper Eocene and included them in the lower *Miocene. In 1854 the term "Oligocene" was introduced for the time-stratigraphic interval between the Eocene (as modified by Lyell) and the Miocene and this term naturally included the sands of Fontainebleau and their equivalents.

The stratigraphic position of the Eocene/Oligocene boundary is also controversial. This stems from the recent, somewhat contradictory, evidence that the sands of Lattorf (East Germany), commonly assigned to the early *Oligocene, may in actual fact be of late Eocene age.

With these qualifications the Eocene is generally accepted as spanning the time between approximately 54 and 38 million years ago.

The final fragmentation of the Eurasian continent occurred about 50 million years ago with the separation of Greenland and Scandinavia near Spitzbergen. It is still uncertain whether there was communication between the Atlantic and Arctic oceans at this time, or whether a land barrier extended transversely from Greenland to Scandinavia in the vicinity of present-day Iceland and the Faeroe Islands.

One of the outstanding characteristics of the Eocene record in the oceans is the formation of extensive deposits of organically-derived silica, which implies the presence of waters rich in nutrients and a high marine population at this time. The distribution of these deposits in the Atlantic is primarily along the continental margins and across the Atlantic and Pacific along the (paleo)latitudes of the (paleo)equatorial belt, implying transportation by the warm-water oceanic current systems of the time.

Extensive areas of the continental margins – particularly in the Tethys Sea, which extended from the Indo-Pacific region to the Atlantic Ocean – were developed. The extraction of large amounts of silica by the oceanic plankton was balanced by the carbonate-rich environment developed in the shallow, marginal areas of Tethys, in which the developing nummulite faunas flourished (see *foraminifera): over 5000 years ago the Egyptians quarried the extensive deposits of these rock-forming fossils, which are exposed in the vicinity of Cairo, to build the pyramids.

During the middle and late Eocene the Pyreneean orogeny led to the formation of the east-west mountain range, the Pyrenees, between Spain and France. Although subtropical conditions existed in Europe as far north as the Paris and London Basins, the first evidence of (at least) minor *glaciation in the southern hemisphere is seen in the oceanic record near Antarctica. A significant worldwide cooling event occurred about 38 million years ago (Eocene/Oligocene boundary) with the formation of significant sea-level glaciation on Antarctica. The temperatures of the deeper-water layers (below 3300ft (1000m)) were lowered by several degrees, and as a result the thermal structure of the oceans as we know it today was essentially formed at this time. This played a significant role in climatic modification, as the movement of water masses over the surface of the globe is one of the major factors affecting climates.

In addition to the proliferation of the shallow-water, tropical faunas of nummulites, the Eocene is characterized in its early part by a great diversification of marine planktonic faunas and floras, followed by a gradual but inexorable decline in diversity, and the extinction of various lineages in the middle and later parts.

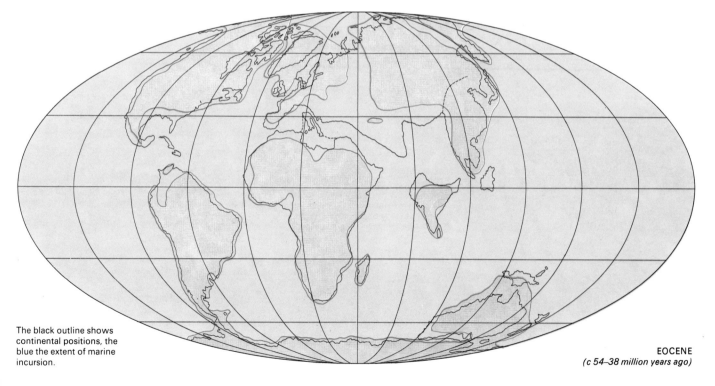

The black outline shows continental positions, the blue the extent of marine incursion.

EOCENE
(c 54–38 million years ago)

Flysch deposits consisting of shales and sandstones at San Sebastian, Spain. These rocks were deposited in the Tethys Sea during Eocene times.

Among the *mammals the Eocene is characterized by the initial appearance and rapid radiation of such groups as *rodents, *artiodactyls, *perissodactyls, *carnivores and certain *subungulates (elephants and related forms), *edentates, and *whales; and the extinction of amblypods, multituberculates, creodonts and condylarths (see *primitive mammals). Early Eocene mammalian faunas in Europe and North America were virtually identical; but from the middle Eocene onward the two faunas were totally isolated, a reflection of the disruption of the polar communication route by the separation of Greenland and Scandinavia. The continued presence of the north-south Uralian Sea in Eurasia, running from the polar regions to the equatorially situated Tethys Sea, resulted in continued separation of European and Asian land-mammal faunas. Current studies suggest that limited exchange of land mammals between the southern and northern shores of Tethys took place.

Oligocene

The term Oligocene was introduced in 1854 to describe strata intermediate in age and position between Lyell's *Eocene and *Miocene. These Oligocene strata were originally believed to be the result of a marine transgression which had covered a large part of northern Europe, but in fact the early Oligocene is characterized by world-wide regression – probably due, at least in part, to extensive glaciation on Antarctica – and much of the Oligocene is missing, or present only in marginally deposited shallow-water facies over a large part of the Earth.

The Oligocene, which covers a span of roughly 12 million years, from 38 to 26

million years ago, was a time of significant geographic, climatic and faunal changes. Isotopic studies indicate that major climatic cooling occurred at the Eocene/Oligocene boundary, 38 million years ago, and again during the mid-Oligocene, from 32 to 27 million years ago; and these events are reflected in significant invasions of equatorial latitudes by normally high-latitude calcareous plankton floras. The Oligocene was a time when the diversity of oceanic planktonic faunas and floras was generally low, and it represents a transitional period during which early Tertiary faunas and floras were gradually dying out or evolving into the late Tertiary, modern faunas and floras. The once prolific nummulitic fauna (see *foraminifera) became extinct at the end of the early Oligocene, and its ecologic niche was occupied later in the epoch by another group of "larger foraminifera" – the miogypsinids – which were to flourish in the Miocene.

In the southern hemisphere the separation of Tasmania and the South Tasman Rise from Antarctica, about 30 million years ago, removed the last barrier to what is now one of the major factors governing global oceanic circulation and climatic conditions because of the way that it mixes the waters of all the oceans, the circum-Antarctic Current. It appears to have remained relatively stable since its inception in the mid-Oligocene.

The epoch was characterized by the continued rise of the *mammals. There were, for example, the appearances of *Anthracotherium*, an *artiodactyl similar to the wild pig, with strong incisors and large canines; the rhinoceros (*Aceratherium*); and the tapir. Also in the Oligocene occurred the expansion of the prosimians and the disappearance, at the close of the epoch, of the titanotheres, a group of large

*perissodactyls with concave skulls and prominent horny protuberances above the nose. The closure of the Uralian Sea in Eurasia permitted trans-Eurasian migration of mammalian faunas; and, at least intermittently, migration to and from North America *via* the Bering landbridge was possible.

Miocene

A time-stratigraphic term created by *Lyell in 1833, Miocene describes those strata in Europe and equivalents of the same age elsewhere which were believed to contain 20–40% of the species of *mollusks that are still extant. Numerous stage names have been applied within the epoch, but the following (from oldest to youngest) are these in most widespread use at present: Aquitanian, Burdigalian, Langhian, Serravallian, Tortonian and Messinian. The Miocene lasted some 19 million years, from about 26 to about 7 million years ago. Most of the major aspects of contemporary Earth history can be traced to this epoch.

Major Miocene Paleogeographic Events. The junction of Eurasia and Africa about 18 million years ago resulted in the interruption of the east-west Tethyan seaway and the origin of the Mediterranean Sea as we know it today. The immigration into Eurasia of African elephants, bovids and pigs in the early Miocene was the result of this dramatic closure of the Tethys seaway. The eastern part of Tethys evolved into what is now the Indian Ocean as India collided with Asia and the Himalayas were formed. In Europe this was the period of major Alpine orogeny, leading to the present-day Alps and related mountain chains to the east.

A major East Antarctic Ice Sheet formed in the late Miocene about 10 million years ago, and subsequently expanded, about 6 million years ago, to a size considerably in

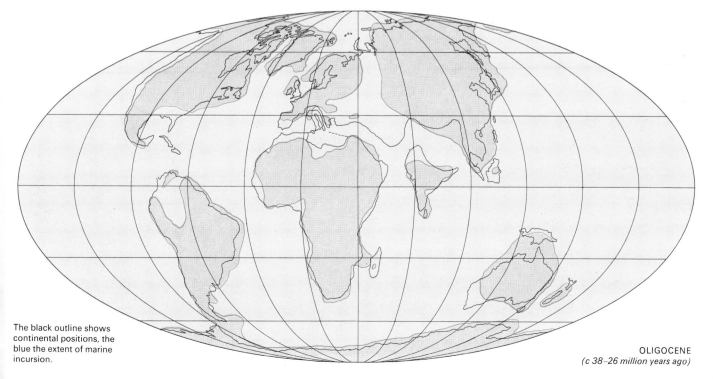

The black outline shows continental positions, the blue the extent of marine incursion.

OLIGOCENE
(c 38–26 million years ago)

excess of its present-day dimensions. This latter event was linked with the isolation of the world's oceans and the evaporation and desiccation of the Mediterranean Sea in what must be considered one of the most dramatic events in the history of the Earth: the opening of the Straits of Gibraltar 5 million years ago marked the end of the "salinity crisis", as Atlantic waters were able to flow once more into the Mediter-ranean Basin. However, the once rich marine fauna and flora of the Mediter-ranean Sea, which had migrated southward along the west African Coast after having been expelled as the Mediterranean grew ever saltier during the late Miocene, never completely succeeded in reestablishing it-self, and the Mediterranean today contains only an impoverished representation of the luxuriant life that thrived there during the

An eroded volcanic landscape in South Yemen. The peaks seen here are the remains of volcanoes that were active during late Tertiary times.

Miocene.

The initial appearances of the planktonic globigerina (see *foraminifera) and the lar-ger benthonic foraminiferal group of miogypsinids which replaced ecologically the *Nummulites*, occurred rather before the

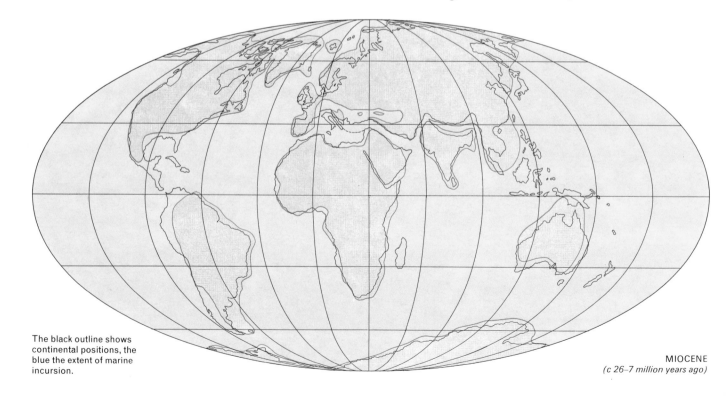

The black outline shows continental positions, the blue the extent of marine incursion.

MIOCENE
(c 26–7 million years ago)

beginning of the epoch. The upper limit of the Miocene is characterized by the extinction of a number of marine microfaunal taxa, but it is more significantly denoted as a major paleogeographic boundary: in the Mediterranean area the youngest Miocene is characterized by *evaporite deposits (anhydrite, gypsum and salt) which were formed in deep basins isolated from the world ocean. This evaporative phase, which lasted less than 1 million years, is known as the "salinity crisis" because of the extreme effect which it had upon the marine fauna and flora present in the late Miocene Mediterranean. A return to normal marine conditions denotes the base of the Pliocene in this area.

Life. The Miocene is characterized by the appearance and radiation, or continued development, of faunal and floral elements that were gradually to become our contemporary fauna and flora. Calcareous planktonic microfaunas and microfloras became important once again following their decline in the Oligocene, and their diversity has been shown to bear a close relationship to the temperature of the oceans.

Among the plants, sequoia, taxodium, cypress, poplars, oaks, laurels, camphor and palms thrived in central Europe. *Mammals reached their height during the Miocene, in particular the elephants, which underwent a remarkable diversification: the epoch witnessed the appearance of mastodons with four tusks (*Tetrabelodon*), and of *Deinotherium*, a gigantic, 16ft-high aberrant elephant with lower incisors recurved towards the rear, which persisted in Africa up to the Pleistocene. Deer, anthracotheres and pigs frequented the oak-forest environment while tapirs and rhinoceros wallowed in low-lying swamp areas. Ruminants with twisted horns (such as antelopes) appeared among the *artiodactyls and occurred together with the simple-horned deer and giraffids. Monkeys appeared by mid-to-late Miocene time and the early separation of the basic primate stock towards the hominoid branch, which was eventually to lead to the *hominid lineage and Man himself, can be traced to within the epoch. Hyaenids, civets and cats lived in the forests and prairies. Crocodiles, tortoises, large salamanders and a variety of fish (e.g., perch, eels) inhabited inland waterways.

The horses continued their evolutionary trend towards modern forms, gradual reduction of the lateral toes occurring along with the development of teeth with a high crown and deep socket. The early Miocene *Merychyppus* and its late middle Miocene descendant *Hipparion* appeared in North America and emigrated to Eurasia *via* the Bering landbridge. The latter form appeared about 12 million years ago, and its appearance is one of the most useful and widespread stratigraphic indicators in mammalian biostratigraphy.

Pliocene

The name Pliocene was introduced by Sir Charles *Lyell in 1833 to denote those European strata (and, by extension, their equivalents elsewhere) in which more than half the species of *mollusks are still to be seen alive today. He changed his mind in 1839, and created the term *Pleistocene for the "Newer Pliocene", in which 90–95% of the various species of mollusks are still extant. The name Pleistocene is still with us, even although Lyell himself later tried to suppress the term in favor of "post-Pliocene" or "post-Tertiary".

In terms of geologic time, the Pliocene was an extremely short epoch. Its start can be considered as around 7 million years ago, and its end, and the beginning of the Pleistocene, as around 2 million years ago; so its total duration was only some 5 million years – little longer than some of the stages of other Cenozoic epochs. But, despite this, it was an epoch of marked, and comparatively rapid, change.

There were several major paleogeographic events during the Pliocene, each of which affected the global distribution of both plants and animals.

The Gibraltar Straits opened up, and so marine connections between the Mediterranean and the Atlantic were resumed.

The uplift of the Isthmus of Panama some 3½ million years ago resulted in a cessation of the exchange of marine fauna and flora between the Atlantic and the Pacific, an interruption of the connection that had continued, essentially undisturbed, between the two oceans for some 125 million years. The Isthmus of Panama provided a major migration route for North and South American mammals, allowing interchange between two mammal faunas that had been isolated from each other throughout the Cenozoic. This migration was predominantly southward from North America, with forms such as equids, mastodons, tapirs and llamas successfully colonizing the South American continent. In contrast to this general trend, such forms as sloths and armadillos made their way northward into North America.

About 3 million years ago polar glaciation began to develop in the northern hemisphere, and this resulted in the appearance of the Labrador Current, which displaced the Gulf Stream to its present position, south of latitude 45°. For over 100 million years before this the Gulf Stream had flowed into the Labrador Sea carrying tropical-water elements from the Caribbean. The glaciation also caused the formation of a Polar faunal province, completing the process of faunal localization which

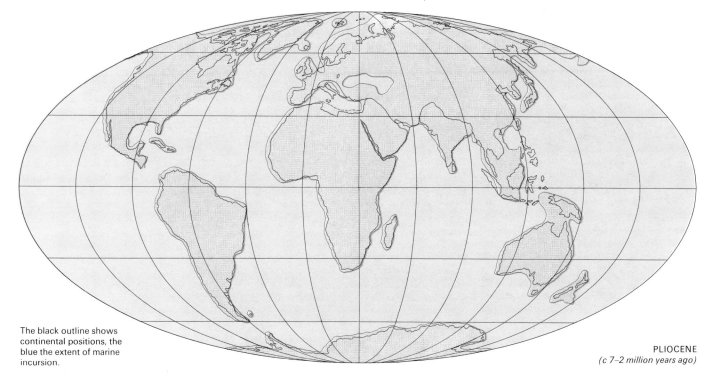

The black outline shows continental positions, the blue the extent of marine incursion.

PLIOCENE
(c 7–2 million years ago)

had begun millions of years before in the Paleocene and Eocene.

This marked deterioration in climate which characterized the Pliocene resulted in the extinction of numerous marine *plankton. In fact, the species of plankton alive today represent essentially no more than a relict fauna and flora that survived – and adapted to – the "ecologic trauma" that they experienced during this brief epoch.

The Pliocene also witnessed the demise of numerous elements of the prolific, if somewhat bizarre, mammalian fauna of the Miocene. Small mammals like the rodents continued to proliferate, and their fossils are extremely useful in making correlations over large distances.

The evolution of the elephant has been traced back as far as the early Pliocene in Africa, and mastodons and mammoths made their initial appearance in the late Pliocene and the early Pleistocene.

But among the mammals of the Pliocene, the most interesting to us is surely *Australopithecus*, Man's earliest definite ancestor. Fossil australopithecines dating back at least four million years have been found in East Africa. This comparatively recent discovery has, effectively, doubled the age of Man because, before it, the oldest known fossil men were those found in the Olduvai Gorge, dating back only two million years. (See *hominids.)

Major tectonic activity during the Pliocene occurred within the Mediterranean Basin: there was a significant downwarping of the sea floor, particularly in the Tyrrhenian Sea. There were also major orogenies, notably a continuation of the building up of the Andes and the Himalayas, as well as along the west coast of North America, giving rise to the features we now know as the Cascades, Olympic Ranges and California Coast Ranges.

The Pliocene can be viewed as the last epoch before the world became very much as we know it today, the end of the past and the beginning of the present. The Pleistocene would see the emergence of modern Man and most of the mammals that we are accustomed to. And with the Pleistocene, too, would come the Ice Ages and the uncountable changes they wrought – both in the patterns and families of life and in the very shape of our planet Earth.   WAB

Quaternary

From time to time during its history, the Earth has been subject to ice ages during which ice sheets have expanded to cover large areas of its surface. We know of several such episodes during the late *Precambrian, an ice age during late *Paleozoic time, and lastly an ice age during the Quaternary, a period which commenced about 2.5 million years ago and which includes the present.

The base of the Quaternary is normally defined on the basis of a worldwide cooling, and during the period large ice sheets

have expanded (glacial periods) and contracted (interglacial periods) on many occasions. The onset of the Quaternary ice age was probably initiated by the drift of the Antarctic continent into a polar position, thus allowing a large sheet to build up. The evidence of fossil plants suggests that before the *Miocene the Antarctic enjoyed a temperate climate, but during the late Miocene we find, in deep-sea cores from the southern oceans, evidence of a great increase in iceberg-dropped detritus, suggesting that ice sheets on Antarctica were releasing large icebergs carrying glacially eroded material. By the beginning of the Quaternary, this cooling appears to have become global.

The existence of large ice sheets on Earth exerts a fundamental influence on climatic and oceanic circulation, the distribution and nature of terrestrial environments and the distribution and evolution of animals and plants. The fluctuating nature of these ice masses can be established in a variety of ways, but perhaps one of the most informative is the study of oxygen-isotope ratios in the tests of benthonic *foraminifera found in deep-ocean cores (see *geochemistry). During the onset of a glacial period, water is progressively lost from the oceans and stored in growing ice sheets. At the present day, the isotopes O_{18} and O_{16} occur in seawater in a roughly constant ratio; but when water is lost to growing ice sheets, less of the heavier isotope, O_{18}, is transferred and thus the O_{18}/O_{16} ratio in the oceans increases. This increase depends upon the amount of water lost to the ice sheets, and thus, if we determine the progressive change in the O_{18}/O_{16} ratio in the tests of deep-water foraminifera which have slowly accumulated on the deep ocean floor, we can deduce changes in the volume of ice on Earth. From such studies it has been shown that the last glacial period ended about 10,000 years ago, and that the warmest part of the present interglacial occurred about 4–5000 years ago. Since then our climate has been generally cooling.

The Frozen World. How do environmental conditions on Earth change from periods of maximum ice-sheet exten-

sion to periods of minimum extension? A wide variety of geological and biological techniques applied to sediments in the sea and on land enables us to reconstruct environmental conditions during that period of the last glaciation when ice sheets were at their most extensive.

Most of North America was covered by an ice sheet, as was much of northwest Europe and northern Russia. Most of the world's great highland areas bore ice caps, and extensive areas of floating pack ice blocked the Atlantic to north and south. As a result of the loss of oceanic water to the ice sheets, worldwide sea levels were lowered by about 300ft (90m), leading to the exposure of large areas of shallow continental shelves and thus to an enlargement of many land areas.

The polar fronts migrated in an equatorwards direction, so that latitudinal temperature gradients in middle latitudes were increased, thus increasing oceanic and atmospheric circulation intensity: this led to increased storminess in middle latitudes. The changed pattern of climatic circulation also led to desiccation in the equatorial zones of Africa.

In addition, the compression of climatic zones between expanded polar fronts led to a contraction of floral zones on land. Extensive areas of tundra, underlain by permafrost, lay to the south of the northern European ice sheet as far as the northern shore of the Mediterranean. To the south of this lay the forest zones, first birch and pine and then broad-leafed forest, all displaced some 1250mi (2000km) to the south of their typical interglacial positions.

The enormous changes in climatic and vegetational environments during a glacial period produced concurrent great changes in the distribution of animals. The expansion of tundra to the south enormously extended the range of the great tundra vertebrates, such as reindeer, mammoth, woolly rhinoceros and musk ox, many of which are now extinct – their bones may be found in glacial river gravels throughout much of the modern temperate zone, fossil evidence of earlier glacial conditions.

Chronology. The passage of Quaternary

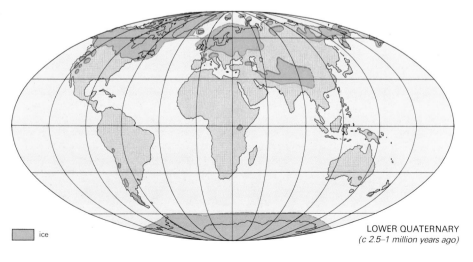

ice

LOWER QUATERNARY
(c 2.5–1 million years ago)

A satellite picture of the Sierra Nevada. These mountains are the result of uplift and faulting during late Pliocene and Pleistocene times.

time is measured by a variety of means. Absolute dates can be obtained from many materials: fossilized organic matter can be measured by carbon-14 dating provided that it is not older than 50–60,000 years; igneous rocks can be dated by the potassium-argon method; and some sediments can be dated by magnetic means (see *age of the Earth). When fine magnetic particles fall out of suspension in still water to be deposited as sediment, they tend to adopt orientations that are dictated by the direction of the Earth's magnetic field. Recent sediment studies have shown that over the last 12,000 years the Earth's magnetic pole has moved from an extreme easterly to extreme westerly position about every 2000 years. From dated lava flows it has also been shown that from time to time the direction of the Earth's magnetic field has reversed. The time-scale of these changes has now been used to date sedimentation in the deep oceans and in other areas of quiet sedimentation (see *geophysics).

Much of the history of the Quaternary can be seen as one of enormous fluctuation between the extremes of environment we have described. Because of these strongly marked environmental changes, the basis of stratigraphic subdivision is different from that of other geological systems and eras: relatively cold glacial stages are interspersed with relatively warm interglacial stages – although a glacial stage may not be without warmer periods, and an interglacial may have cold periods within it.

Plant remains comprise the most important fossil assemblages used for relative dating and correlation of these stages. Because of the relatively short duration of the Quaternary, plants show little evolutionary change and thus assemblages of plants rather than successive species are used to characterize particular periods of time: organic beds within Quaternary sequences may be ascribed to the appropriate interglacial by the similarities in the composition and sequence of the whole floral assemblage.

Animal Life. The Quaternary history of

As the ice retreated during Holocene times, the removal of weight from the Earth's crust led to uplift. Features such as shorelines moved upwards, resulting in raised beaches such as this one on the coast of East Greenland.

vertebrates strongly contrasts with that of the plants in that there are very striking evolutionary changes. These are probably the result of intense selection pressures during this period of rapidly changing environment when, in as little as five thousand years, areas which had been adjacent to the northern hemisphere ice sheets could change from treeless arctic tundra to temperate broad-leaved forest. We see evidence of rapid evolution, especially in the large vertebrates which adapted to a very varied series of ecological niches. Among the elephants we see the evolution of the steppe mammoth, and its disappearance about 12,000 years ago – probably as a result of human predation. Among the others we see the giant Irish deer with its antler span of 13ft (4m), and forms such as the woolly rhinoceros and the saber-toothed tiger.

In the gravels associated with the valleys of many modern rivers of the temperate zone of the northern hemisphere, the teeth and bones of mammoth, reindeer, bison and many other large vertebrates are commonly found. From such deposits as this, and from a study of pollen, beetles, snails and countless other organic remains, the environment in which many Quaternary strata have been deposited can be reconstructed in very great detail.

The vertebrates of, perhaps, greatest in-terest to us are the *hominids. The earliest known fossil hominids date from the Pliocene; but the Quaternary can be regarded as the true "Age of Man". In particular, its latter part – the Holocene – has seen the rise of civilization, as Man has learned to alter and, to some extent, to control his environment.

Tectonics. In geological terms the Quaternary period is of very short duration (2.5 million years), hardly enough for tectonic activity such as plate movements to produce substantial changes in the Earth's surface configuration and structure. Some of the most dramatic tectonic changes reflect the rhythmic growth and decay of the great ice sheets of the northern hemisphere and the concomitant changes in sea level. For instance, large areas of northwestern Europe and North America are currently rising at a considerable rate – 0.35in (9mm) per year in the Gulf of Bothnia between Sweden and Finland, and 1.17in (30mm) per year around the Hudson Bay. Both of these areas lay beneath the centers of ice sheets, which finally disappeared only about 7000 years ago. The effect of loading the Earth's crust with these enormous masses of ice was to depress it, probably by as much as 2300–2950ft (700–900m) beneath the center of the 8200ft (2500m) thick Scandinavian ice sheet and 2600–3300ft (800–1000m) beneath the 9500ft (2900m) thick North American ice sheet. The crustal material displaced from beneath the ice sheet was pushed outwards and caused the crust to rise beyond the margin. After the

retreat of the ice masses, the Earth's crust rebounded – upwards beneath the ice sheet and downwards beyond it. The current upward movements of Scandinavia and northern North America are a continuation of this process, although the rate has been decelerating for several millennia.

These glacially induced crustal disturbances have also influenced igneous activity. In Iceland, the frequency of volcanic activity increases strikingly during glacial periods, the volcanoes rising up through the ice sheet. It is probable that magma is squeezed upwards through the crust because of the additional load of the ice cap.

Pleistocene

The Pleistocene is a subdivision embracing the period from the beginning of the Quaternary until 10,000 years ago. The latter boundary marks a period of rapidly rising temperature – the end of the last glacial period – and the beginning of the present interglacial, called the Holocene.

Holocene

The Holocene is that period of Quaternary time from 10,000 years ago until the present day. It begins with the final decay of the great ice sheets in Scandinavia and North America, and is generally regarded as an interglacial period, on the assumption that it will be followed by yet another glacial period. The warmest part of the Holocene was some 5000 years ago and, since then, substantial changes in climate have occurred, such as the post-medieval cooling – known as the "Little Ice Age" – which ended at the end of the last century.   GSB

The History of Life on Earth

The Origin of Life

Despite its diversity, living matter is characterized by an astonishing biochemical uniformity. All known forms of life have two features in common: they have a cellular structure, in which the cells are bounded by membranes; and they are composed of two kinds of macro-molecule, nucleic acids and proteins. The combination of all these features is a certain indication of life, quite apart from the consideration of func-

tion. It is thus possible to define "life" without having to define the difference between "living" and "dead".

Most theories for the origin of life presuppose that life has evolved from simpler organic entities. The investigation of the origin of life seeks to differentiate true life from some precursory, prebiological entity which may be called "protolife". The most direct evidence for the origin of life would be the discovery of protolife among the early fossils.

Early *Precambrian fossils are found in two situations. Macroscopic fossils are found in the form of stromatolites, formed in dolomite or limestone, and interpreted as blue-green algal reefs. Microscopic fossils of two kinds, filaments and spheres, of

The results of some experiments support the idea that life could have originated under conditions similar to those found today in volcanic environments. Here, gases are brought together at high temperatures in thermal springs of New Zealand.

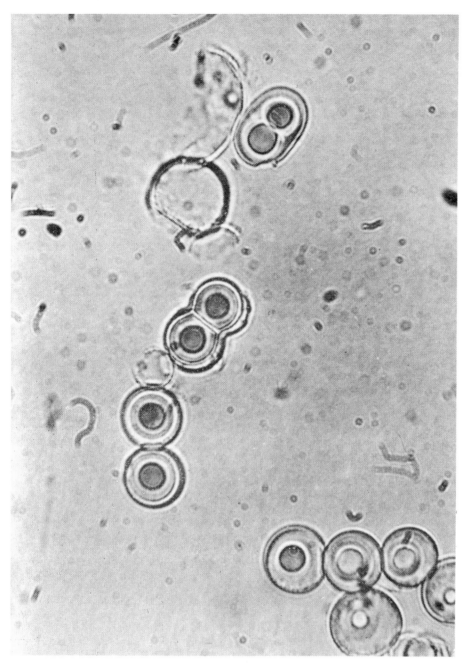

Cell-like structures called "proteinoid microspheres" have been produced by evaporating organic chemicals on hot lava beds. These resemble what were probably the first living organisms.

diameters in the range 10–20μm are found in *cherts.

The oldest stromatolites occur in the Bulawayan Formation and have been dated at 2900 million years. The oldest cherts with microfossils are from the Onverwacht Formation and are over 3300 million years old. The stromatolites are universally regarded as the remains of true life: the earlier microscopic fossils may well also represent the remains of blue-green *algae, but it is perfectly probable that they represent some form of primitive protolife.

The oldest known rocks bear a metamorphic imprint dated at 3760 million years, and are therefore considerably older than the Onverwacht fossils. These rocks include metamorphosed water-laid sediments, some of which have been claimed as derived from biological sources. There are three kinds of such rock: marbles claimed as metamorphosed stromatolites; graphitic schists claimed as metamorphosed oilshales; and quartz magnetites claimed as banded ironstones, which are in turn postulated as oxygen receptors for photosynthetic organisms. If these claims are admitted, life cannot have originated after about 4000 million years ago. As the *age of the Earth is supposed to be only about 4600 million years, the origin of life must have been a very early event in the Earth's history.

Experimental evidence has shown that some kinds of protolife could form even before the planets themselves in the solar nebula. It could also form within planetary atmospheres, and on the land-surface of planets in a volcanic environment.

Experiments designed to test the hypothesis that organic synthesis could occur in the solar nebula have been mounted by E. Anders and his collaborators from Chicago. He has shown that, when gases containing hydrogen, methane and ammonia are heated in the presence of powdered refractory catalysts, the organic products include most of those found in carbonaceous *meteorites, which are therefore postulated by Anders as having formed in this way. Notable among such products are amino acids, which have been found as racemic mixtures in several carbonaceous chondrites and which, if polymerized, could give rise to proteins. Biologically produced amino acids are never racemic when fresh, so these must be indigenous to the meteorite. Carbonaceous meteorites also contain organic spheres, and mineral grains coated with organic sheaths, that have been likened to "protocells".

Experiments designed to test the hypothesis that organic synthesis can occur in primitive planetary atmospheres have been mounted by several biologists and exobiologists. An electric spark (designed to simulate lightning) is passed through a gas mixture which is kept circulating through hot water. Amino acids and other organic compounds have been identified among the products, and it has since been shown that cell-like bodies are also produced among the insoluble organic products.

Experiments designed to show that polymerization of organic compounds produced in these ways can occur in certain environments have also been mounted, by Sidney Fox of Miami. He has shown that if solutions of amino acids are evaporated on a bed of hot lava, and subsequently heated to the point of fusion before quenching with cold water, cell-like structures are produced which possess a double-layered membrane. Some degree of polymerization has occurred, and they are referred to as "proteinoid microspheres". They can be manipulated in certain ways (e.g., by changing the acidity of the solution) so that they grow and divide.

These experiments suggest that life could have originated in any one of three environments. The first suggestion is that some form of protolife synthesized in the solar nebula infected the atmosphere of the primitive Earth and subsequently invaded a primeval broth, where it evolved into life.

The second alternative is that protolife formed in the atmosphere of the primitive Earth as the result of thunderstorms. This protolife was washed into the sea, which became the primeval broth that gave rise to true life. Objections have been raised that such a broth would be incredibly dilute, but it has been suggested that one form of protolife could have been oil, with the consequent production of an oil-slick which would float on the seas and thus embody its own concentrating device.

The third possible environment would be a volcano in its later eruptive stages. Thunderstorms would occur during the eruptions, which would provide gases rich in carbons. Amino acids and other simple organic compounds would be washed down onto hot lava, and subjected to the processes invoked by Fox. Later the combined effects of heat and water would produce sugars and polynucleotides, which could invade the proteinoid microspheres and produce the first living organisms.

Convincing evidence in support of these theories is not easy to come by. Some Russian observers claim to have recognized racemic mixtures of amino acids among the products of volcanoes, but these observations remain to be confirmed.

The most speculative hypothesis of all is the celebrated "bootstraps" theory, that a visitor from elsewhere arrived on Earth, walked around for a while, and then left. However, microorganisms that were brushed off his boots contaminated the surface of the planet, and it was these that evolved toward modern terrestrial life. Of course, this theory begs the question, "What did the spaceman evolve from?", and is unprovable. Nonetheless, some scientists bear it in mind as a remote possibility.

Early stages in the production of protolife could still occur on Earth, although later stages are not likely to survive biological attack from contemporary life. Hydrothermal environments have been explored with such a possibility in view, and it has been claimed that oil and bitumen found associated with hydrothermal mineral veins are non-biological products. It has also been claimed that hydrocarbon globules found in fluid inclusions within vein-quartz may similarly be non-biological in origin, and these may contain associated proteinoid microspheres. Others believe that all these products are the result of contamination by biological products.

PCSB

Evolution

The living world comprises several million plant and animal species, all distinct, and all characterized by the ability to produce fertile offspring. Like gives rise to like, yet at the same time there are always subtle differences that distinguish individuals within any given species; but, despite this variety, the species itself appears immutable.

From this it was until quite recently concluded that all animals and plants were the product of a single act of creation, and destined to last for all time. Early doubts were occasioned by the discovery during the 18th century of the remains of giant animals (e.g., mastodon) that had once existed but did so no longer.

Development of the Theory. Perhaps the most significant contribution to 18th-century evolutionary ideas was made by Linnaeus (1707–78). In 1735 he published his first classification, the 7-page *Systema Naturae*: by 1758, in its 10th edition, this had expanded to 823 pages. The fact that

one could erect a hierarchical scheme of all living things suggested certain groups owed their similarities to descent from common ancestors. Many 18th-century scientists assembled a vast amount of data which they claimed demonstrated the divine wisdom of the Creator; but as the evidence accumulated it became apparent that the observations could be better explained by the evolution or transformation of species through time.

*Darwin's great contribution was to assemble the evidence in such a way that it led inevitably to the conclusion that evolution was the only possible rational explanation for the origin of living animals and plants. Darwin served as naturalist on board *H.M.S. Beagle* in its 5-year voyage round the world. The myriad observations that he made could only be understood on the grounds that evolution must have occurred: the succession of life recorded in the rocks, where ancient forms of life became extinct and were replaced by the appearance of more modern; the curious distribution of animals and plants; embryology, which emphasized the basic similarity of fish, reptiles, mammals and Man; the modifications of the vertebrate limb which all possess an underlying basic plan; the existence of vestigial organs such as the pelvic girdle in snakes and whales – and the fact that a hierarchical classification could be erected.

Darwin was well aware of the work of animal and plant breeders in developing new strains by artificial selection. The problem was to discover a mechanism of natural selection. Malthus' essay on population provided the clue – offspring are produced in far greater numbers than their parents yet populations remain relatively stable; i.e., a large proportion of the young cannot survive to maturity. Since all individuals vary from one to another, it seemed evident to Darwin that those better suited to the conditions in which they found themselves stood a better chance of survival than those less suited. Hence the popular notion of Darwinism as "the survival of the fittest".

Natural selection was a process that was easy to grasp and it established an overwhelming case for evolution. The theory of evolution, moreover, coincided with the prevailing philosophy of the new industrial society. Darwin himself was the first to acknowledge that evolution was only a theory, albeit the most reasonable one to account for the natural world. He conceded that the proof could only be provided by the *fossil record and that at the time he was writing such proof was not yet forthcoming.

The key objection to Darwin's theory was that selection could only be on variations that already existed. There was no explanation as to how these variations arose in the first instance, and certainly no suggestion as to the origin of the new characteristics they possessed. Darwin came to believe that characteristics acquired during the lifetime of an animal could somehow be

transmitted to the succeeding generations: this belief in the inheritance of acquired characteristics is popularly associated with *Lamarck. While Lamarckism is today generally discredited, it is not unreasonable to imagine that the response of an organism to its environment is in some way built into the hereditary system.

Genetic Basis. Paleontologists record the succession of phenotypes, the structures that are developed during an organism's lifetime, often as a response to the environment. To an extent this must be an expression of the genotype; that is, the hereditary make-up. The hereditary potential may or may not find its full expression in the phenotype. For example, if food is scarce individuals' growth may be stunted, but with the return of optimum conditions they will achieve their full stature: a gradual increase in size may be an evolutionary change or it may be merely a reflection of an improvement of the food supply.

The consensus among biologists is that random changes in the genetic material, "mutations", occur and that these are then subject to natural selection. Normally mutations are disadvantageous and, being recessive, do not find expression in the phenotype unless they occur in both male and female gametes of the zygote. Should circumstances change and the mutation become advantageous, in time it will be favored and become dominant, so that even if present in only one of the contributing gametes it will find expression in the phenotype.

It was recognized that the genetic material was situated in the chromosomes of the cell nucleus and that these could be mapped so that the position of the genes for particular features could be located at a particular position on the chromosomes. But the nature of the gene eluded biologists and no evidence was forthcoming with regard to what constituted mutations.

The nature of the gene and mutations came to be understood once Watson and Crick had elucidated the structure of deoxyribonucleic acid, DNA. This molecule comprises a double helix formed of two complementary strands of purine and pyrimidine bases strung along a phosphate-sugar backbone, each strand acting as the template for its opposite number, thus providing the basic copying mechanism required of any genetic material. Subsequent researches established that, although there were only four bases, their sequences along the DNA molecule formed the genetic code which contained the instructions for protein synthesis. The nature of a protein is a consequence of the sequence of the amino acids. There are only twenty naturally occurring amino acids and these are coded for by triplets of bases. Since there are 64 possible combinations, several triplets will code for the same amino acid: the triplets are the "words" and there are codes for "capital letters" and "full stops".

A mutation consists of a change in the

base on the DNA molecule, changing the genetic code but not necessarily the resulting amino acid for which that triplet coded. Even if a different amino acid is substituted, it may not affect the structure and functioning of the final protein. Each protein has its own shape or configuration – its tertiary structure, which is a consequence of its amino acid sequence. Within certain limits there can be amino acid substitutions at particular places that still allow the protein to function adequately. The sequencing of amino acids in particular proteins such as hemoglobin, the respiratory pigment in the blood of vertebrates and some invertebrates, allows direct comparisons to be made between the same protein occurring in different animals. For example, the beta chain of hemoglobin of the gorilla differs from that of Man at only one amino acid locus out of about 150, but differs in 17 sites from that of the pig. This indicates that Man is more closely related to the gorilla than to the pig – a conclusion that can be supported on other grounds! By such studies one can draw up family trees of modern animals to show their relationships and hence possible evolution.

At the cellular level, it is not yet feasible to deduce how a simple animal or plant cell first evolved. The origin of the variety of complex organelles, each with their own specialized functions, still awaits an explanation, but it is already clear that this history is likely to be more complex than previously imagined. Recent evidence suggests that one of the key organelles of all animals and plant cells, the mitochondrion, which is concerned with energy transfer, was originally an independent organism: it still retains its own DNA and the capacity to synthesize protein, and reproduces independently of the rest of the cell. Mitochondria seem to be related to the modern bacterium *Paracoccus*, and it has been postulated that initially mitochondria were parasites, or were perhaps ingested as food by the host organism: now they have become endosymbionts, with the processes of both host and guest so integrated that it is hard to imagine one existing independently

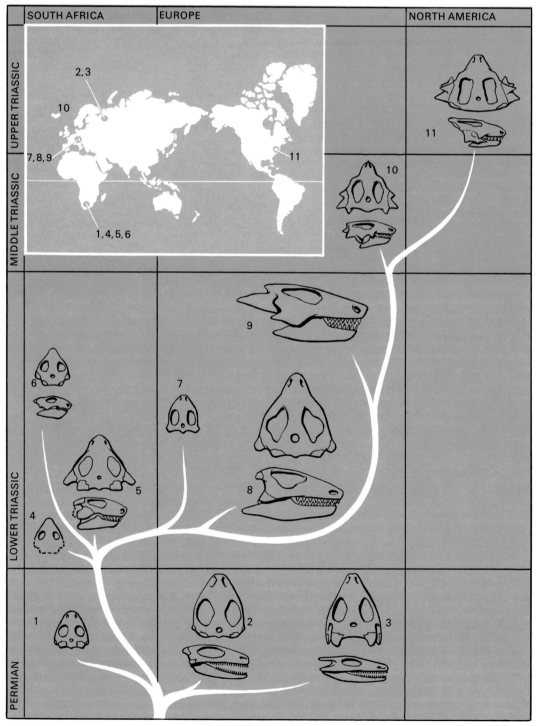

Fossil skulls of small reptiles called procolophonids arranged according to the age of the rocks in which they occur and the continents on which they have been discovered. Paleontologists are able, by comparing the anatomy of related animals or plants, to construct family trees in which the lines linking each type represent directions in which evolution is thought to have taken place.

of the other. A surviving example of this is with the giant freshwater amoeba *Pelomyxa*, which has no mitochondria but instead houses symbiotic bacteria.

There have been few evolutionary studies undertaken at the tissue level, and they are almost exclusively concerned with hard tissues. One such study has documented the gradual evolution of one type of hard tissue into another. The first vertebrates possessed a bone-like tissue, aspidin: this can be traced in the fossil record over a period of 150 million years. In early examples there were no cell inclusions, but eventually cells became incorporated and organized in the same way as in bone. The evolution of the organization of the organic matrix of collagen can be similarly traced. In the early types of aspidin the collagen fibers were laid down as parallel mats of criss-crossing fibers, as in dentine, the material that makes up the bulk of human teeth; but as time progressed they were organized into alternate layers with the fibers orientated as in modern bone. This sequence of changes illustrates a possible way that bone could have originated from a dentine-like tissue.

Evolutionary Histories. By far the best documented accounts of evolution are those of the vertebrates, from fish to Man, taking in such groups as the *dinosaurs. The evolution of the vertebrate skull, teeth and limbs are described in numerous texts on the evolution of the vertebrates, and in all cases it is possible to relate such structural changes to changes in behavior, such as modes of locomotion and feeding habits. From the discovery of fossils and their detailed analysis, evolution by natural selection has become established as fact.

Some of the most remarkable and seemingly mysterious evolutionary events, such as the change from *reptile to *mammal, have recently been elucidated. For example, the bones of the reptilian jaw joint became incorporated into the middle ear of the mammal, and this involved the reduction of the bones of the joint and their migration into the ear apparatus. The reduction of the bones of the jaw joint was the result of the split of the old jaw-closing muscle into two major parts, one with a forward component and the other with a backward, so that there was no force exerted at the joint. The bones, which were now taking no strain, simply shrank in size over the generations. The eardrum was situated close to the joint, and the spike of the articular bone of the lower jaw would have come into contact with the eardrum, automatically amplifying sounds impinging on the membrane. The three-bone system would have given the animal improved hearing – an obvious advantage in life. This remarkable change occurred several times in different evolutionary lines of true mammals.

An equally surprising development is recorded in two quite separate evolutionary lineages – the *dinosaurs and the mammals. Mammals evolved muscular cheeks, which are important in chewing, and a bony

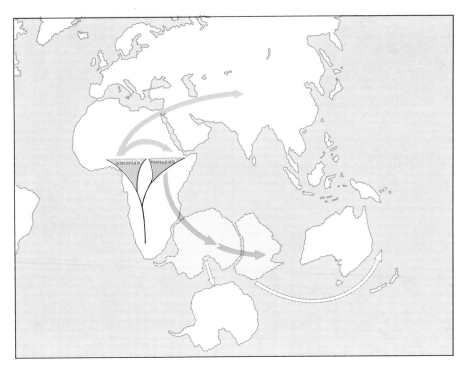

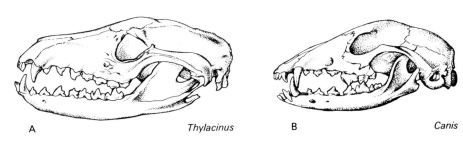

A   *Thylacinus*   B   *Canis*

Plate tectonics has had a profound effect on the evolution and distribution of organisms. Marsupial and placental mammals evolved in Eurasia or possibly Africa. Because marsupials diverged first, they could spread across Antarctica to Australia. By the time the placentals had evolved, continental drift had occurred and Antarctica and Australia had separated from Africa, leaving a marine barrier that could not be crossed. As a result, marsupials (A) and placentals (B) evolved similar forms in regions that are widely separated today.

secondary palate to separate the air and food passages and so allow breathing at the same time as food is retained in the mouth and chewed. In parallel, the herbivorous ornithischian dinosaurs became adapted to deal with the new, tougher plant materials that evolved during the latter part of the *Mesozoic era: unique among all the reptiles, they developed muscular cheeks, a chewing dentition and bony secondary palates.

There are numerous examples of animals evolving similar features which allow them to fill comparable ecological niches. A familiar example is the reptilian marine ichthyosaur that fed on fish and cephalopods, and which had the overall proportions, even to the extent of the triangular dorsal fin, of the modern mammalian dolphin. Both groups display the habit of accumulating the chitinous hooks from cephalopod tentacles in their stomachs and then regurgitating them to dispose of them.

The isolation of South America during most of the *Tertiary resulted in a number of mammalian types which paralleled forms

evolving elsewhere. There was a *marsupial sabertooth cat; and a small horse-like animal, the proterothere *Thoatherium*, in which the reduction of the digits exactly paralleled that in the true horses.

Although evolution can be shown to have taken place at all levels of organization, from the molecular to the whole animal, there is a further way in which it can be seen to have occurred. The entire community of living things can be shown to have undergone significant evolutionary changes. The food chain or web in the different environments has itself evolved from earlier patterns. The first reptiles that ventured onto dry land during the early *Permian fed exclusively on animal protein, the smallest feeding on *invertebrates: there were no vertebrates able to feed directly on plants. The gradual evolution of herbivores eventually allowed the land to support a large population of herbivores preyed upon by a smaller number of carnivores. When the dinosaurs replaced the dominant paramammals or *mammal-like reptiles during the Triassic, the modern-type food chain

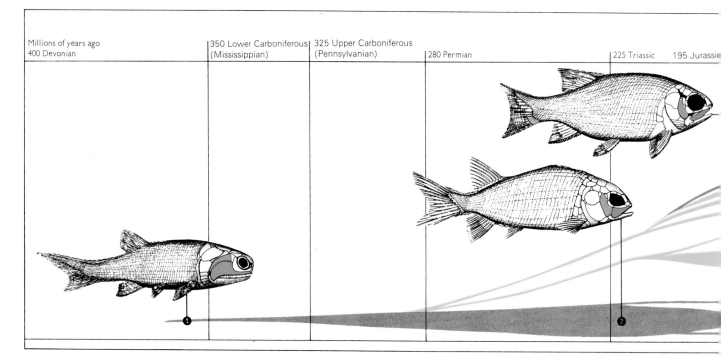

| Millions of years ago 400 Devonian | 350 Lower Carboniferous (Mississippian) | 325 Upper Carboniferous (Pennsylvanian) | 280 Permian | 225 Triassic | 195 Jurassic |

An example of evolutionary trends in a group of animals is seen here in the evolution of actinopterygian fishes. The first well preserved fossil *Moythomasia* (1) occurred **360** million years ago. Two important evolutionary trends are seen in the fossil record. The body lobe of the tail (yellow) became progressively shorter, and the mouth-parts changed considerably. In *Moythomasia*, a bone called the preopercular (red) was firmly attached to the upper jaw or maxilla (blue); the jaws functioned like a pair of scissors. In later chondrosteans such as *Pseudobeaconia* (2) the preopercular slanted forward and jaws became shorter. In the holosteans, for example *Parasemionotus* (3), the maxilla was no longer attached to the preopercular, enabling the mouthparts to function with greater flexibility. This trend culminated in the teleosts, for example *Elops* (4), in which the maxilla was firmly attached to the skull only at its front end. This enabled the whole jaw apparatus to be thrust forward in order to engulf prey.

established by the paramammals was destroyed and initially the land was dominated by exclusively carnivorous dinosaurs. In time there evolved plant-eating forms, so that once again a familiar type of food chain was established.

Radiations and Extinctions. One of the most striking features recorded in the fossil record is the pattern of radiation followed by extinction. From humble beginnings there is a rapid efflorescence and then, more often than not, a sudden decline until the group vanishes from the Earth: time and time again, large groups of highly successful and seemingly well adapted animals suddenly go into decline and disappear.

At the beginning of each major radiation are a number of simple primitive forms: for example, if one considers the vast radiation of the archosaur reptiles which produced the gigantic dinosaurs, one finds that heralding the age of dinosaurs were primitive *crocodiles. But today the only living archosaurs are those selfsame crocodiles; and this is the paradox of evolution. Natural selection appears to favor those animals that become well adapted to their environment – the better this adaptation the more successful the group. The trend is towards greater and greater specialization, greater efficiency and hence greater success. But, by the same token, with environmental change comes disaster. The primitive forms that have not become highly specialized, but have retained a degree of adaptability, are the ones

that survive. In the final analysis the fittest, the survivors, are those forms that have remained variable. Many modern species are polymorphic, the shapes, sizes and colors varying so that, although circumstances may alter to the disadvantage of one form or other, the chances are that at least some will survive.

Evolutionary Centers. The process of evolution is a fundamental feature of the living world. However, one of the curious aspects of the fossil record is that, wherever a paleontologist finds himself, it is obvious that evolution has always taken place somewhere else. Geologists use fossils to distinguish strata from one another, fossil faunas being usually quite distinct from one stratigraphic level to another. But the intermediates are somehow always missing. Most of the time the fossil record documents a succession of migrations.

If all the fossils of any particular group are examined from all over the world, it does become possible to discover where evolution was actually taking place – usually in a single faunal province situated in tropical or subtropical latitudes. From here there were periodic waves of migration, the emigrants then establishing themselves in new areas and continuing with little or no modification until the next wave of immigrants invaded the region.

At the present day the greatest genetic variety of animal and plant life is to be found in tropical latitudes, whereas in more

temperate latitudes the variety is less although the numbers of the forms that are present are greatly increased. Away from the tropics, natural selection undoubtedly operates, but this is essentially a negative process – it eliminates.

The most dramatic evolutionary events seem to have occurred when natural selection was in abeyance. The radiation of the *amphibians during the *Carboniferous took place in a swampy environment that was highly favorable, so much so that virtually *any* new variety was viable. The radiation of the mammal-like reptiles during the Permian and Triassic and the evolution of the Jurassic and Cretaceous dinosaurs also represent times when a new group of animals found itself in a position to exploit a new environment. Once the new environment was fully occupied, and all the available niches had been taken, then and only then would natural selection come into play.

Conclusion. Though the fossil record provides overwhelming proof that evolution has occurred, it does not give any indication as to the mechanism. This is the domain of the geneticist, but any account that he produces of the process of evolution will only be viable if it can explain what the fossil record establishes has actually happened – and when, and where. (See also pp. 751–66.)   LBH

The Fossil Record

The term "fossil" has subtly changed in meaning over the centuries. Until the 18th century it was used to describe any rock or mineral dug up from the Earth, but since then its use has become more and more confined. Today, any relic or trace of a formerly living organism may be called a fossil, from the perfectly preserved insect in amber or Woolly mammoth in ice to the

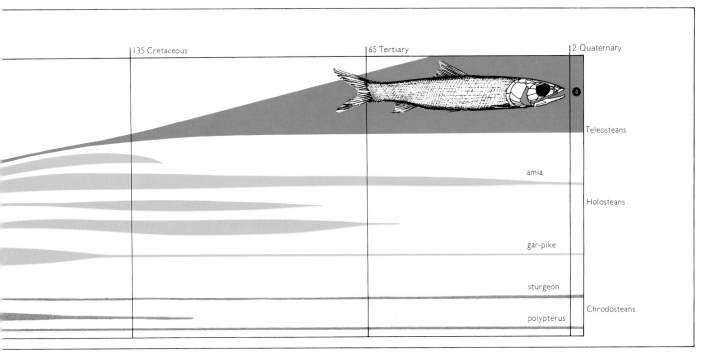

135 Cretaceous   65 Tertiary   2 Quaternary

Teleosteans

amia

Holosteans

gar-pike

sturgeon

Chrodosteans

polypterus

crawling trails of snails and the excrement of crabs. We should also include the faintest traces of all, chemical imprints of organic molecules left in the rocks.

Whether or not an organism is preserved as a fossil depends primarily on the nature of the materials of which it is made up. Most tissues comprise complex organic molecules that are either consumed after death by other organisms or readily broken down by chemical action. Soft tissues, therefore, leave little for the fossil record.

However, these customary processes may be bypassed in some way by the embalming resins of amber, the refrigerating action of ice or the antibiotic conditions of some stagnant lakes and ocean basins. Occasionally, the soft tissues of plants or animals may be petrified (i.e., their places may be taken, after death, by minerals that were initially dissolved in water which has permeated the organism). More usually, however, only the most resistant and stable organic materials can survive long after death, as with the lignified tissues of fossil land plants and the scleroprotein skeleton of the extinct fossil *graptolites.

Fortunately, a great many animals and plants have developed the ability to mineralize their own tissues. Familiar examples of such mineralization are the silica (SiO_2) and calcium carbonate ($CaCO_3$) spicules of sponges, the calcium carbonate shells of mollusks and skeletons of corals, and the calcium phosphate ($Ca_3(PO_4)_2$) of vertebrate bones and teeth. Not only are these mineral skeletons relatively resistant to decay in comparison with the soft tissues, they may also encapsule a complete life-history of the organism from birth to death, allowing us all fashion of valuable insights.

Despite the preservation potential of skeletons, only a very small proportion are ever fossilized. Fossilization depends on the creature either living in, or being trans-

ported to, an area of active sedimentation, circumstances that are rather unevenly distributed about our planet. Most favored for a continuous fossil record are those regions of the seabed below the zone of wave disturbance (the more one approaches the strand line, the more frequently are the sediments reworked or eroded and so the less complete will be the fossil record). Terrestrial environments experience such a dominance of the processes of decay and erosion that our knowledge of terrestrial life at any one time may rest on no more than a few relics washed into rivers or the sea or lodged in the deposits of cave *tufas and fissure fillings.

Changes following death and burial can lead to considerable transformations in the appearance of plants or animals. Not only may bacterial decay and groundwater solutions leach away organic and mineral parts, but the cavities so formed can later fill with new and uncharacteristic minerals. Alternatively, these minerals may replace the original skeletal parts. More usual, though, is a recrystallization of the original materials into more stable forms of the same or similar minerals, with preservation of the fossil's original microstructure if conditions are suitable. In addition, a considerable burden of sediment on top of the fossils will cause compression, and they may be further distorted by folding of the rocks during Earth movements.

Worse can happen. The high temperatures and pressures of metamorphism invariably cause recrystallization of the fossil materials and obliteration of their diagnostic characteristics. For these and many other reasons, the fossil record is neither complete nor easy to interpret.

It should not surprise us, then, that until the 17th century most naturalists were perplexed by the stony nature and curious shapes of many fossils, embedded – as they often are – in hard rocks from outlandish

places. Common opinion classed them with meteorites and gemstones, strange manifestations of cosmic forces. Without knowing either the meaning of shape in living organisms or the nature of the geological column, a correct interpretation remained impossible; and although *Steno and *Hooke had by 1667 argued for a natural organic origin of fossils, it was almost 200 years before an acceptable correlation of the fossil record and its meaning was arrived at.

A widely held misconception that persisted for some time took fossiliferous rocks to be antediluvian relics washed up by the Flood. It is to *Cuvier that we owe the demonstration (1801) that more than one "flood" was involved. By 1808 he had sufficient data to outline the basic biological and geological changes involved in the fossil record and he went on to suggest its value to stratigraphy.

However, it was a humble civil engineer called William *Smith who put fossils to the test. In 1815 he published a geological map of England, compiled from many years of study, which traced strata of similar age right across the country by recognition of their similar fossil content. Many years of similar intensive and thorough work followed, so that by 1914 all the geological periods and many of their subdivisions were firmly grounded on a paleontological basis.

WWI saw an increased demand for oil, and the development of subsurface drilling techniques became a priority – to the paleontologist's profit. As the recovered rock chips from such boreholes are rather small, a new field of enquiry, that of micropaleontology (the study of microscopic fossils), was initiated on a grand scale and still forms a considerable proportion of present-day research: the abundance, variety and rapid evolution of tiny fossils such as pollen grains, *ostracods and

How animal remains become incorporated into the geological record. A dinosaur is drowned in a flooded river, and its body comes to rest on the river bed where it is rapidly covered with sand and mud. These sediments form the layers of rocks called sedimentary rocks. In this example the rock strata were tilted before erosion took place.

*foraminifera render them ideal time-markers in rocks of Cambrian age and younger.

As well as being restricted to rocks of a certain age, fossil species resembled their living descendants in being adapted to a restricted range of environmental conditions (see *paleoecology). Information about past environments is not just interesting for its own sake: it provides a useful guide for the economic geologist in search of mineral reserves like oil which tend to accumulate only in rocks formed in certain environments.

Paleontological research has contributed in this way to knowledge of ancient shore-lines, ocean currents, climates and latitudes. It has also helped to reveal more remarkable phenomena, including *plate tectonics and the gradual reduction through time of the number of days in the year. But perhaps most significant is the support lent by the fossil record to the hypothesis of *evolution. Family trees have been worked out for a great many organisms, both living and extinct. The rates of evolutionary change for these different lineages have been assessed, and related where possible to the major controlling factors. We are now in a position to reveal the outline of the history of life on this planet, deduced almost entirely from the fossil record.

Although we have evidence that oceans existed at least 3750 million years ago, the first organic remains are much younger. These are unicellular bacteria and blue-green algae an estimated 3100 million years old (though there are earlier microfossils – see *origin of life). At this time the Earth's atmosphere was probably almost devoid of oxygen and the surface itself was bombarded by harmful ultraviolet rays from the Sun and outer space. Possibly because of these adverse conditions, primitive plant cells were the dominant form of life on Earth for at least another 2400 million years.

Nonetheless, considerable advances were

Once discovered, fossils must be protected from damage. Here a specimen is covered with layers of cloth soaked in plaster prior to its removal to the laboratory.

made in the organization of the cell itself. The nucleus appeared about 1600 million years ago and served as an information store – it enabled the cell to function more efficiently. First steps in sexual reproduction were taken between that time and about 900 million years ago: sexual reproduction allows useful information for survival of the organism to be passed on and distributed in time as widely as possible.

This lengthy algae-dominated period was terminated by a series of world-wide glaciations about 700 to 600 million years ago. It is possible that these glaciations, together with the advances already made, may have been responsible for the revolution that followed.

Fossil animals are first known from about 700 million years ago. They are found as impressions left by soft-bodied creatures in shallow-water sediments. Jellyfish and wormlike creatures seem to have predominated, though there is evidence of a planktonic and benthonic flora. After a period of about 100 million years there is clear evidence of a dramatic rise in sea level, possibly the result of melting polar ice caps, so that continents were flooded to an extent which has barely been matched since.

This event heralds the beginnings of the

*Paleozoic. The rapid expansion of sea-floor area was accompanied by the first occurrence of animals with mineral skeletons; and both of these factors contribute to the absolutely staggering increase from this time in the number of known plant and animal groups. Thus the number of invertebrate phyla rises from two in the late Precambrian (Coelenterata and Annelida) to at least twelve in the early *Cambrian.

From that time onward the fortunes of the various plant and animal groups appear to have been linked to changes in geography. Humid land areas became widespread in the *Devonian, providing a habitat for early vascular plants and land arthropods. Fish were also evolving rapidly in lakes and coastal waters, seasonal desiccation of which advanced the development of fish with lungs. By *Carboniferous times, certain of these had all the characteristics of *amphibians and were thriving in the coal-swamp forests of tree ferns, giant clubmosses and horsetails.

The ensuing *Permian was extremely hot and dry in many parts of the world so that those groups which were more or less independent of standing water found themselves at an advantage. Most notable of these were the *reptiles and the seed-bearing plants. The withdrawal of the seas in the Permian is attributed to continental collisions and a major glaciation. Many marine organisms characteristic of the Paleozoic became extinct, especially the more

specialized forms. The ecological niches left vacant by this extinction were gradually filled in the *Triassic by a less varied and less specialized fauna that had managed to hang on. As the seas began to flood back onto the much eroded continents, marine life of a new order began to diversify again – the *Mesozoic had arrived in no uncertain terms.

Cold climates were virtually unknown in the *Mesozoic era, so the radiation of warmth-loving reptile groups went on more or less unimpeded. Mammals are not very significant in the Mesozoic fossil record, possibly because they inhabited cooler, upland areas; their early remains are known from Triassic fissure fillings. Birds are likewise scarce, but they did not appear until late in the era, in the *Jurassic, evolving from either *dinosaur or *crocodile ancestors.

Flowering plants are known from the early *Cretaceous and seem to have dominated land floras by the late Cretaceous. At the same time, both plant and animal plankton were undergoing a revolution that led to the almost world-wide deposition of chalk sediments. (See also p. 740ff.)

Associated with all these changes is the gradual dwindling of characteristic Mesozoic elements, such as dinosaurs and ammonites. Their final replacement by the new Cenozoic plants and animals was hastened further by global climatic and geographic changes, in turn brought about by

Earth movements. Nevertheless, this late Mesozoic extinction was not as drastic as that at the end of the Paleozoic; and it was followed by a much more rapid and spectacular radiation of plants and animals. The radiation can be explained both by the great variety of habitats that resulted from geographic isolation of the continents and by the development of distinct climatic belts. Mammals, birds, gastropod *mollusks and foraminiferid *protozoa are among those groups which evolved rapidly and spread widely in the early Cenozoic. (See p.745.)

Climatic differentiation led gradually to climatic deterioration. About one million years ago, the ice caps at the poles began to expand considerably, and since that time rapid (in geological terms) oscillations between glacial and temperate climates have led to the extinction of a great many plants and animals.

The extremely adaptable *hominids were presumably in a position to take advantage of this. Unfortunately, hominid behavior was such that there is a scarcity of human bones in the fossil record, and so our knowledge of this most interesting period is very incomplete. Nevertheless, the rather slight differences between recent Man and the fossil remains of about 2.6 million years ago seem to·suggest that Man's evolution has been, for at least that time, psychological and social rather than biological.

Obviously the study of ancient life from fossils preserved in the rocks has great bearing on our understanding of Earth history, as well as of the evolution of life itself: it follows that this study has more to contribute to our knowledge of Man's true place on the planet than almost any other branch of learning. There cannot, for example, be any support today for the old line of thought which saw Man as the final and glorious culmination of the evolutionary process, atop the tree of life. The fossil record is full of biologically comparable "success" stories, and some of those were very short-lived.

The present-day disturbances of the delicate ecological balance brought about by the activities of Man are also not entirely novel. Geological and biological revolutions of this kind have taken place a great many times. Some geologists have even claimed that these revolutions occur rhythmically through time, being controlled by fluctuations in solar or cosmic energy. We shall be able to confirm this only if similar patterns are observable in the fossil records of other planets. Even the dead planets could well possess a fossil record almost as revealing to us as the discovery of living cosmic neighbors. (See also pp. 765–6.)   MDB

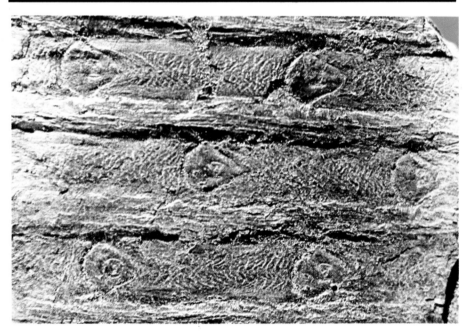

Fossils preserved in a variety of ways. *Above*, a Jurassic nautiloid seen in section clearly shows how mineral replacement has led to the preservation of internal structures. *Center*, a mold of a Jurassic gastropod in which sediment has filled the space once occupied by the mollusk. *Below*, an impression of a fern from the Carboniferous in which only surface features are preserved.

Paleoecology

Ecology is the study of the relation between living organisms and their environment, where they live and how they interact with other organisms and with the environment. Organisms and their environment together make ecosystems. Paleoecology is concerned with the ecosystems of the past, and with their evolution.

The problem is immense, for while we can closely study living organisms and determine modern environmental parameters, the evidence for the past is in the unwieldy form of rocks and fossils. Firstly, the environment must be reconstructed from the evidence remaining in the rocks; and secondly the fossils revitalized by making comparisons or analogies with living forms, or by constructing models. The geologist has only one advantage over the ecologist, that he may have evidence of evolutionary and ecological change with time as represented in a succession of sediments.

Problems. The *fossil record is very incomplete and, clearly, it is absolutely impossible to fossilize completely a community of living things: the nearest that can be achieved is a Pompeian-type catastrophe, but even there many people as well as birds, insects and other animals managed to escape. Little remains of the contemporary vegetation and much is lost of physiological and behavioral details. Nevertheless, the degree to which fossil environments can be reconstructed is often surprisingly good. The paleoecologist has to be paleobiologist, sedimentologist and biologist. In addition to trying to understand the biology of fossil species it is important to appreciate how death occurred, and the events that followed, leading to decomposition of the soft parts, disarticulation and breakup of the skeleton and eventual burial and potential fossilization.

As in ecology, the concern is first with the individual or individual species (autecology), and then investigation proceeds to the assemblage as a whole (synecology). Often, much information can be obtained before the fossil is freed from the sediment, and a determination of whether or not the organism was fossilized in life position is particularly important. The orientation of fossils in the sediment not only reflects changes of orientation that may have taken place after death in response to currents and waves but also orientations adopted by the living organisms themselves in respect to feeding currents, gravity and light. Epizoans, such as parasites, encrusting on other organisms may provide physiological information by indicating, for instance, the region on a brachiopod valve where nutrient-bearing water entered.

As with an ecological study, the way in which sampling is tackled can be critical to results. The problem is complicated in that invariably one is sampling organisms which lived at different times. There are obvious difficulties in determining the diversity,

AGE	DEPOSITS	ENVIRONMENT AND FAUNA	
UPPER TRIASSIC	Sandstones	DESERTS	
MIDDLE TRIASSIC	Sandstones and shales	RIVERS AND DRY LAND	*Scaphonyx*
LOWER TRIASSIC			*Euparkeria* / *Dicellopyge*
PERMIAN	Shales, siltstones and fine sandstones	LAKES AND SWAMPS	*Muchocephalus*
UPPER CARBONIFEROUS	Glacial deposits	GLACIERS	NO FOSSILS

The Karroo deposits of southern Africa provide one of the best examples of a sequence of rocks that indicate a gradual change of climate. Evidence from the sediments is confirmed by the fossils preserved in them. Examples of the fauna are *Muchocephalus*, an aquatic amphibian; *Dicellopyge*, a fresh-water actinopterygian fish; *Euparkeria*, a thecodont that lived on dry land; and *Scaphonyx*, a ground-dwelling mammal-like reptile.

abundance and nature of the coexisting fauna, though some indication of the soft-bodied fauna can be obtained from the form, frequency and abundance of their burrows and other *trace fossils.

The recognition of distinct associations of species which were probably part of an original community is an obvious goal. A number of fossil communities have been described but few if any of these would approach the ecological definition of a community – this may be defined as an assemblage in which the sum of interactions between elements within the assemblage is greater than the sum of those between the assemblage and its surroundings. Fossil communities can be reconstructed with a fair degree of certainty from fossil coral reefs and similar units where a high proportion of the fauna is in life position: fairly good estimations of density and diversity can be made in cases like these. Communities have also been reconstructed, though with less certainty, from shell beds where the organisms have clearly been physically aggregated.

Where fossils are found essentially in life position it is possible to determine substrate preference and also trophic (feeding) position by comparison with living representatives. But extinct groups of organisms pose problems as in some cases we're not certain to which phylum – or even kingdom – they belong. In the Mesozoic the *ammonites probably occupied a number of ecological niches, but unfortunately so little is known of their arm form and jaws that only generalizations can be made. On the other hand, individuals have been found of their contemporaries, *Ichthyosaurus*,

whose digestive systems contain large numbers of fossil undigested hooks from squid arms. This establishes a major food-chain link. The determination of food chains and food webs in fossil marine environments is difficult because of the open nature of the marine system: food webs can be more readily deduced for terrestrial environments. The densities of the fossil remains of any one trophic stage reflect, of course, preservation potential and not necessarily original abundancies.

As with living organisms, every fossil once lived under the constraints of various physical, chemical and biological factors, any one of which may have been limiting. In reconstructing the environments of the past we must attempt to determine these factors. Most have not changed appreciably with geological time but other factors may have: for example the length of the day (which may be recorded in the daily growth bands of some fossil corals and bivalves) has been increasing and it is extremely likely that the nature and amount of the Sun's radiation has changed through geological time. Other factors such as temperature, salinity, oxygen and carbon dioxide content of air and water, and trace element concentration all vary locally and may vary periodically. It is not possible to determine any of these chemical and physical factors with anything approaching the precision we might want. For instance, the heavier oxygen isotope O^{18} tends to concentrate in the sea since the generally more common O^{16} can escape more readily. The proportion of O^{18} in calcium carbonate shells tends to increase with rising temperature so that knowing – or at least having an estimate of – the

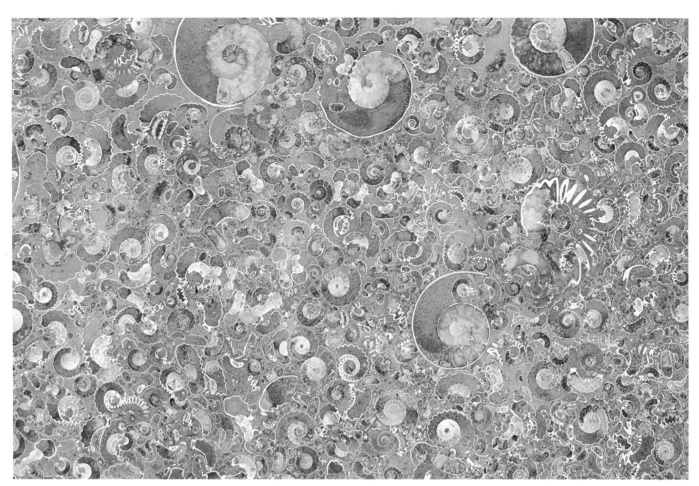

A section through a limestone composed almost entirely of mollusk shells. Such rocks indicate shallow water or shore conditions. Banks of shells are commonly seen on beaches of the present day.

composition of the seawater in which a particular creature lived, the temperature of the water can be estimated.

Depth under the surface of the sea is not in itself a limiting factor although it does, of course, affect pressure and light penetration. However, in reconstructing the geographies of the past it is very useful to be able to draw profiles and show depths with a reasonable degree of certainty. Thus paleoecologists are somewhat mesmerized by depth and, unfortunately, there are few satisfactory criteria that can be used for its determination. Since they require light, marine algae are important: fossil green algae in life position almost certainly indicate depths less than 230ft (70m). Certain bed forms such as underwater sand ripples and dunes may be useful, since the depth of water under which they lay does affect some of the superficial patterns of marine beds. Depth (pressure) has an effect on the solubility of calcium carbonate – but this is

A group of actinopterygian fish preserved in sandstone. Their abundance indicates a sudden change of conditions that led to the simultaneous death of large numbers of individuals, and their exquisite state of preservation is evidence that they were not transported prior to being covered with sand. If they had been transported by currents after their demise, fragile structures such as fin-rays would certainly have been damaged.

also dependent on the amount of dissolved carbon dioxide, so that the relationship is complex. Large eyes or blindness in fossil creatures can be correlated with depth by observations of similar characteristics in creatures alive today.

A major factor affecting nearly all fossils is provided by the changes that may take place after the organism's death and burial by later sediment. Apart from the decay of soft-bodied elements, shells too may undergo change, particularly in porous sediments. More soluble minerals, such as *aragonite, tend to be lost first; in contrast, *calcite is relatively stable. Post-Paleozoic corals which have aragonitic skeletons are generally not nearly so well preserved as *Paleozoic corals which had a calcitic skeleton. All is not gloom: aragonite, including the pearly layer of shells, may well be preserved even from the Paleozoic in muddy and relatively impermeable sediments.

Goals. Most of the world's most famous fossiliferous deposits contain a very biased fauna because of the special conditions of fossilization. It is important to understand how such deposits arise, not only to discover how they themselves were formed, but also to predict where similar deposits might occur elsewhere.

The revolution that has taken place over the last few years in our understanding of the changing distribution of continents and oceans – the concept of *plate tectonics – has provided paleontologists with a basic

key to the distribution of organisms about the Earth during the geological past. Since different groups of organisms react differently to barriers inhibiting gene-flow, communities also change. Faunal and floral provinces similar to those existing today can be recognized in the past. In the geological record, geographical *connections* that led to important faunal change – such as took place when the Americas were linked up by the Panama isthmus – are mostly easier to detect and appreciate than are the effects of *separation*, though there are exceptions; for example the isolation of the Australian *marsupial assemblage.

Other barriers leading to speciation may be climatic (the creation of a desert), ecological (the growth of a forest) or physiological; and the effects of these in the past are difficult to determine. Moreover, the relative importance of different types of barriers in geological evolution is not known.

Conclusions. *Evolution has not proceeded at an even pace, and "crises of evolution" must ultimately have had an ecological cause. For instance, the appearance of calcareous skeletons early in the Cambrian may well be associated with the level of atmospheric oxygen (and hence the level of oxygen dissolved in the seas) having reached about 10% of the present atmospheric level: below this level of concentration, secreted calcium carbonate tends to be easily redissolved. The widespread extinctions at the end of the Paleo-

Dinosaur footprints preserved in mudstone. The presence of infilled cracks indicate a lake bed in the late stages of drying out.

zoic may be largely due to the continentalization and reduction in area of shallow marine shelves, and the extinctions at the end of the Mesozoic to the general climatic deterioration that took place towards the end of the *Cretaceous. In contrast, the widespread decay among the *stromatoporoids and *corals and the temporary termination of reef-building activities towards the end of the *Devonian have not been satisfactorily explained.

As we can never hope to learn the complete story of evolution we can never recover in full its ecological accompaniment, but any information that helps fossils "live again" is worth pursuing. Determining the likely porosity and geographical boundaries of a fossil reef, and hence its *petroleum prospects, is an ecological exercise. Paleoecology is a growing subject, and its significance has extended far beyond the bounds of academia into areas that affect, in terms of simple economics, all of us today. It would appear that this is a trend that will both continue and accelerate in the future.

RG

Plants and Animals

The vast array of species in the *fossil record is the result of the process of *evolution. A classification of plants and animals that reflects the evolutionary process consists of a hierarchy of groups or taxa. Small taxa such as families or genera contain closely related species, that is, species that are thought to have evolved from a common ancestor. Closely related families are classified in larger taxa such as orders or classes and so on. The largest taxa, except for the Plant and Animal Kingdoms, are called phyla.

The entries that follow correspond in most cases to phyla, but for groups that are better known or are of more general interest, entries are based on smaller taxa, usually orders. Each is illustrated with a drawing of a member of the phylum or order concerned. The date of this representative is shown by a red spot on the scale,

600　　　　400　　　　200　　　　0
millions of years ago

and the range of the taxon as a whole by a colored strip. In the example above, the taxon has a range of 500–100 million years ago, and its representative occurred 300 million years ago.

AI

Plants

Algae

The algae are an exceedingly diverse group of plants, ranging in size from single cells measuring just a few thousandths of a millimetre to giant seaweeds 160ft (50m) long. They are usually found in aquatic habitats, both marine and freshwater, but also occur on the surface of soils and on tree trunks. Although they show such variation in external form, internally they all have a simple, rather uniform structure, usually consisting of only soft tissue.

Algae are subdivided into at least six major groups on the basis of the pigments they contain (often reflected in differences in their color; red, green, etc.) together with the nature of the stored food and of the cell wall and, on motile forms, the structure of the hairs (flagella).

The presence of single-celled plants, filaments, plates or complex branching forms in almost every group of the algae makes identification of fossils, which lack their original color, a hazardous process – indeed, the soft nature of most algal tissues mitigates against preservation. Thus, for example, the brown algae (Phaeophyta), which show the most highly differentiated internal vegetative structure of living algae and are the very common and familiar seaweeds of temperate regions, have little or no fossil record. There are notable exceptions: certain Precambrian *cherts contain exquisitely preserved single cells and filaments, while some algae have silica or lime skeletons and were important "rock-builders" in the past. As these latter are overrepresented in geological history, it is impossible to assess the time of maximum diversity of the group. (See also p.18.)

Blue-green algae (Cyanophyta). These, the most ancient of all plants, show the simplest forms of construction: single cells, clumps of cells, or chains (filaments) of cells. Like the bacteria, they have no well defined nucleus within the cell, a feature that contrasts with all other plants and animals. Living blue-greens have the widest habitat range of the algae – indeed, of all plants – surviving such extremes as snowfields and hot springs. Simple spherical cells, attributed to the blue-greens, are recorded from rocks over 3000 million years old (see *origin of life). The younger Bitter Springs Chert flora (800 million years old) contains both single-celled and filamentous types closely resembling living forms, excellent illustrations of the extreme evolutionary conservativeness of the group. Of some stratigraphic importance in the Precambrian are stromatolites, columnar to dome-like structures built around sheets of blue-green algae, which still occur in some intertidal regions. (See also p. 50.)

Green algae (Chlorophyta). These are of enormous importance as they gave rise to all other green plants. Living examples include single cells, filaments, sheets and complex branching forms, sometimes composed of giant cells with a plurality of nuclei. Their fossil history is sporadic except for those which had lime or silica skeletons; for example, *Ordovician representatives added lime to tropical reefs just as *Halimeda* does today. Another calcareous group, with an intricate whorled arrangement of branches (Dasycladiaceae), can be traced from the *Cambrian to the present and shows an increase in complexity and regularity of branching, so that by the end of the Paleozoic the modern verticillate arrangement had evolved. The stonewort *Chara*, which also has whorls of branches and a skeleton of silica, has more limited importance as a rock-builder, but is common in *Chara*-marls from the *Silurian onwards.

Red algae (Rhodophyta). Predominantly deepwater seaweeds, especially in warmer areas, the red algae range in structure from sheets of cells to elaborate branching forms, and have complex life-histories. Their geological history centers on calcified types: *Corallina*-like forms, abundant today, have been reef builders since the late *Carboniferous, while the extant *Lithothamnion* is first recorded from the *Jurassic.

Golden-brown algae (Chrysophyta). Living golden-browns exhibit a range of forms paralleling that of the green algae, but it is the unicellular types, important constituents of modern planktonic plant life, which are of greatest geological significance. The most familiar are the *diatoms. Another single-celled kind had minute plates of calcium carbonate incorporated into the cell wall: microscopic studies have revealed that the vast *Cretaceous deposits of chalk were built up of countless numbers of these plates (coccoliths – see *coccolithophores). Acritarchs, small hollow bodies (0.8–2in) often brightly ornamented with spines, found in marine sediments from the Precambrian to the present day, are thought to be the reproductive stages (cysts) of planktonic algae. Because of their abundance and wide distribution, they are gaining importance in biostratigraphy. Some of the more recent examples are known to be related to the golden-brown *dinoflagellates and are called hystrichospheres. DE

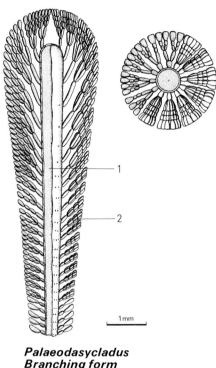

Palaeodasycladus
Branching form

1 Central axis
2 Branch

600   400   200   0
millions of years ago

Diatoms

Diatoms are a group of microscopic, single-celled golden-brown *algae. The group are known from the early *Cretaceous to the present, with dubious records from the *Jurassic. They reached their maximum diversity in the *Miocene. Most modern diatoms live in marine or fresh waters, although some live in soil. Again, most are solitary, but some occur associated in filaments or adjoined in colonies. Many are planktonic, but others live attached to other plants.

The cell wall is siliceous and consists of two pieces, the one fitting within the other like a pill-box and lid. Form and sculpture are diverse and variable, and diatoms are among the most beautiful microscopic objects.

They are important contributors to sediments, and diatomaceous oozes are an important category of deep-sea deposit, although shallow-marine and even lake diatom-rich sediments, or *diatomites*, are known.

The group are of considerable stratigraphic value, especially in deep-water late *Mesozoic and *Tertiary successions. They are widely used in the correlation of deep-sea cores. WJK

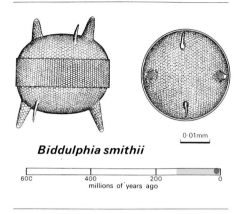

Biddulphia smithii

0·01mm

600   400   200   0
millions of years ago

Dinoflagellates

The dinoflagellates are microscopic single-celled plants, members of the phylum Pyrrhophyta. One of the chief characteristics of the group is the two flagella, long thin appendages, one band-like, extending

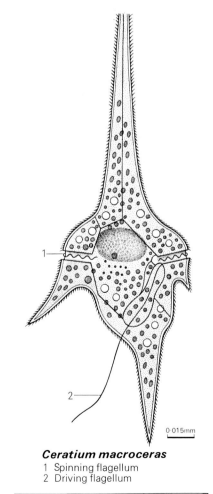

0·015mm

Ceratium macroceras
1 Spinning flagellum
2 Driving flagellum

600   400   200   0
millions of years ago

around the cell and able to spin it about its axis; the other attached by one end, and serving to drive the organism forward.

Most are marine and planktonic, causing so-called Red Tides when abundant, although a few inhabit fresh waters. Others, called zooxanthellae, are important symbionts, living in the tissues of various protozoans, sponges, worms and mollusks.

The earliest record of the group is a cyst (many dinoflagellates produce resistant resting cysts) from the *Silurian. They reached their maximum diversity in the late *Cretaceous, with minor peaks in the *Eocene and *Pliocene. They have great stratigraphic value in the *Mesozoic and *Tertiary.

Morphology is highly variable, with needle-like, globular and top-shaped forms, the theca (outer case) being made up of many plates fused and separated by prominent walls. The surface of the theca is generally ornamented by a network of thickened ridges.

Many marine sediments, from the late *Precambrian onward, yield hollow, organic-walled microfossils generally thought to be cysts of *algae. Almost 3000 species have been described, and referred to an informal group, the *acritarchs*. Many show features in common with dinoflagellates, and may be a related group.   WJK

Coccolithophores

This unique group of microscopic single-celled golden-brown *algae have an excellent fossil record from the late *Triassic right up to the Holocene, with possible records as far back as the *Carboniferous. Recent coccolithophores are mostly marine, although at least two genera are reported from fresh waters. They are typically planktonic at some stage of their life cycle, and constitute nearly half of ocean plankton in temperate waters.   WJK

Psilopsids

The psilopsids, or psilophytes, often considered as a completely extinct group, were the earliest vascular plants: a vascular plant is one possessing water-conducting tissue consisting of dead tubular cells (xylem), as well as a food transporting system (phloem): present-day examples include ferns, clubmosses, horsetails and flowering plants. Xylem is an important structural adaptation for life on land, and indeed *Silurian psilopsids were among the pioneer colonizers of land surfaces.

The psilopsids were strikingly simple plants, just tufts of branching stems, some erect and above ground and the rest horizontal and buried. They lacked leaves and roots, although some of the aerial parts were covered with spines. Each stem had a central rod of xylem tubes (tracheids). Two living rootless genera, *Psilotum* and *Tmesipteris*, were once classified with the psilopsids, but are perhaps best considered as living plants which in overall appearance closely resemble the earliest vascular plants.

Psilopsids are subdivided into three major groups, depending on the complexity of the stem-branching pattern and on the position and number of sporangia (globose or elongate sacs containing spores). The earliest and simplest forms had sporangia on the tips of smooth forking stems (Rhyniophytales) and include the earliest vascular plant, the Silurian *Cooksonia*. In the second group (Zosterophyllales), which appeared at the beginning of the *Devonian, the sporangia were attached to the sides of either spiny or smooth stems – sometimes, as in *Zosterophyllum* itself, forming compact terminal spikes or cones. It was from plants such as these that the *clubmosses are thought to have evolved. The third and youngest group (Trimerophytales) had repeatedly branching stems ending in grapelike trusses of sporangia. Such plants are considered ancestors of the *pterophytes and *horsetails.   DE

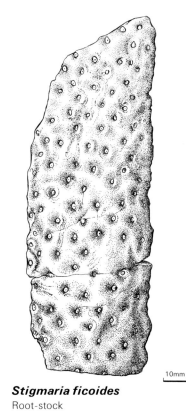

Rhynia major   25 mm
1 Sporangium
2 Stem

600   400   200   0
millions of years ago

Clubmosses (see also p. 94)

The clubmosses (lycopsids), together with the *horsetails, are truly plants of the past. Today they are rather inconspicuous herbaceous plants, but at their time of maximum diversity, in the *Carboniferous, clubmosses were dominant trees of the swamp forests and important ground-cover plants. Lycopods are characterized by numerous, usually small, moss-like leaves crowded on above-ground stems and sporangia (globose or elongate sacs containing spores) aggregated into cones, each sporangium attached to the base of a special leaf.

There are three types of living lycopods: the clubmosses themselves (Lycopodiales), the spikemosses (Selaginellales), and the rushlike aquatic quillworts (Isoetales). The most important extinct group is the Lepidodendrales. All, except the clubmosses proper and some early representatives from the *Devonian, have two kinds of sporangia, one containing a few large spores and the other numerous small ones. The earliest lycopods, recorded from the early Devonian, were herbaceous, but soon afterwards the forerunners of the Carboniferous trees appeared and evolved alongside the herbaceous forms.

Lepidodendron itself was a tree some 100ft (30m) tall, with a straight columnar trunk up to 3.25ft (a metre) wide topped by a dense crown of forking branches, some ending in small cones. The terminal branches were covered with small elongate leaves, but the trunk and larger branches bore characteristic diamond-shaped scars evidencing the loss of leaves through abscission. The base of the trunk was divided into four main branches which subdivided repeatedly and formed a ramifying root system.

Herbaceous lycopods were important ground-cover plants in the Carboniferous, perhaps forming extensive heathland vegetation, and persisted throughout the *Jurassic and *Cretaceous in similar habitats. *Lepidodendron*, however, did not survive the drier conditions at the end of the

Stigmaria ficoides   10mm
Root-stock

600   400   200   0
millions of years ago

Paleozoic. Some authors consider *Isoetes*, a plant less than a metre tall with squat fleshy root-stocks bearing crowns of quill-like leaves, the living descendants of these Carboniferous giants. DE

Horsetails (see also p. 180)

The horsetails (sphenopsids), very conspicuous members of the Carboniferous swamp forests, are represented today by a single surviving genus, *Equisetum*. Living horsetails rarely exceed 5ft (1.5m) in height. Deep subterranean rhizomes produce upright, usually ridged, green stems, which are jointed and bear whorls of small scale-like leaves. Distinct cones are present in which sporangia (sacs containing spores), are borne on the lower surfaces of umbrella-like structures (sporangiophores). The jointed nature of the stem and the whorled arrangement of both leaves and sporangiophores are characteristic of all horsetails.

A Equisetum telmateia
B Equisetum palustre

1 Jointed stem
2 Leaves arranged in whorls
3 Cone

600   400   200   0
millions of years ago

Plants very similar to *Equisetum* are recorded from *Carboniferous rocks, but far more spectacular were its close relatives, giant *Equisetum*-like trees (*Calamites*) up to 60ft (18m) tall with trunks sometimes 1.3ft (40cm) wide and whorls of prominent, elongate leaves. There are internal similarities, too: both have hollow stems with a cylinder of strands of dead tubular cells (xylem), although in *Calamites* a further layer of xylem was present.

Not all Carboniferous sphenopsids were trees. *Sphenophyllum* was a scrambling herbaceous plant, an important constituent of the undergrowth. Its slender stems, with whorls of wedge-shaped leaves, were probably supported by surrounding vegetation.

Early sphenopsid history remains uncertain. Possible middle *Devonian members are included in the Hyeniales. *Hyenia* itself was a small herbaceous plant in which a horizontal rhizome gave off slender upright branches, covered with forking appendages some of which were fertile. *Calamites* and *Sphenophyllum* disappeared when the climate became drier during the *Permian, but *Equisetum* persisted and formed extensive stands at the edges of lakes and rivers in the *Jurassic and *Cretaceous. DE

Pterophytes (see also p. 140)

The pterophytes are the true ferns, in some classifications placed with the *clubmosses and *horsetails in the Pteridophyta, or vascular cryptogams (i.e., seedless vascular plants). Today they are found in a wide variety of localities and climates, though particularly abundant in the tropics. The majority are herbaceous perennial plants, but a few are aquatic and some tree ferns may reach 20ft (6m) in height. Most possess a stem that bears roots and large, often much-divided leaves, or fronds.

Mariopteris nervosa

Frond

600   400   200   0
millions of years ago

Reproduction is by spores which form inside tiny spore-capsules borne on the edges or undersides of the fronds. Each spore grows into a minute, green free-living plant (prothallus), quite unlike the parent fern and bearing the sex organs. External moisture is essential for the male gamete to swim to the immobile egg cell to effect fertilization. After fertilization, a new fern develops.

The leaves of the earliest pterophytes,

Cladoxylales (Devonian) and Coenopteridales (Devonian to Carboniferous), were three-dimensional structures but, by the middle of the *Carboniferous, pterophytes with flattened fronds had appeared (Marattiales). Specimens of fern-like foliage are a conspicuous feature of Carboniferous plant-bearing rocks, and the period has often been referred to as "the Age of Ferns"; but the attribution of these specimens to a particular group of plants is often impossible. Some certainly belonged to ferns, but it is now generally acknowledged that most represent the similar-looking "seed-ferns" (see *cycadophytes).

Living ferns do not inhabit dry arid areas where lack of moisture would prevent completion of the life-cycle. Fossil ferns may, therefore, if their affinities with living forms can be demonstrated, provide clues to paleoclimatic conditions. AW

Cycadophytes

The cycadophytes are the oldest group of gymnosperms, only the cycads (Cycadales) surviving today. The earliest, Pteridospermales or "seed-ferns", combined characteristics of true ferns (*pterophytes) and seed plants, their seeds and pollen-bearing organs being produced on the margins of large fern-like leaves.

Most cycads resemble palmtrees (though not related), having a stout unbranched trunk with a crown of once-divided, leathery evergreen leaves. Their seeds and pollen-bearing organs are borne in separate cones, those of the female often being exceptionally large, as are the seeds. Coexistent with cycads during the Mesozoic, but much more widespread, were the Bennettitales. These cycadophytes were remarkably like cycads in appearance, but bennettite reproductive structures were quite different, being flower-like and usually hermaphrodite. Each "flower" had an axis covered with a large number of naked seeds and intermingled sterile scales, below which was a ring or cup of pollen-bearing organs, the whole being surrounded by a number of protective scales.

Other cycadophytes were the Glossopteridales and the Caytoniales. Glossopteridales were ubiquitous and common in Gondwanaland during the late Paleozoic. Their fossil remains are represented by entire, tongue-shaped leaves to which were attached the reproductive organs. Caytoniales are restricted to the Mesozoic, leaves and reproductive organs alone being found as fossils. Each leaf comprised four leaflets arising from a common point at the end of the leaf-stalk, and the seeds were enclosed in berry-like structures.

Modern cycads are restricted to the subtropics and tropics, which suggests that fossil representatives lived under similar conditions. Glossopteridales occur in beds between glacial tillites. The comparative purity of the flora and paucity of species in the vegetation of which Glossopteridales formed part indicates evolution under severe, but not necessarily glacial, temperature conditions. AW

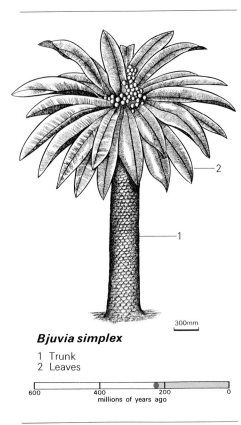

Bjuvia simplex

1 Trunk
2 Leaves

600   400   200   0
millions of years ago

up to 3in (8cm) in breadth and resembling the individual leaflets of the maidenhair fern. The reproductive structures are borne on separate trees, those of the male as catkin-like structures bearing numerous paired pollen-bearing organs, those of the female as a stalk surmounted by a pair of seeds, which after fertilization enlarge to the size of cherries. The ginkgo is remarkable in retaining the primitive feature of motile male gametes.

Cordiatales were coniferophytes which flourished during the Carboniferous. They were tall slender trees with large strap-shaped leaves quite unlike those of the living groups. Their reproductive organs were borne on catkin-like structures.

Living conifers occur in a wide range of latitudes and the usefulness of fossil forms as indicators of climatic conditions is therefore limited.   AW

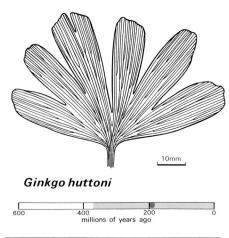

Ginkgo huttoni

600   400   200   0
millions of years ago

Coniferophytes (see also p. 100)

The coniferophytes are a group of naked seed plants classified with the *cycadophytes as gymnosperms, though the two groups have had separate past histories. Their only shared feature is the gymnospermous mode of reproduction, which could well have arisen independently in the course of *evolution. Coniferophytes have been dominant plants since the *Carboniferous, and living members still form large forests in north temperate regions. Three orders of living coniferophytes are usually distinguished: Coniferales (conifers), Taxales (yews) and Ginkgoales (maidenhair trees).

Coniferales are cone-bearing trees, much branched and often growing to a height of more than 330ft (100m). The reproductive organs are borne in separate cones, those of the female becoming at maturity either woody (as in pines, firs, western red cedars, etc.) or forming a fleshy berry (junipers). Fossil conifer remains are commonly found in plant-bearing strata from the Permian, and it seems that their evolution was complete by the end of the Mesozoic, little change having occurred since.

Though having the same growth habit and leaf-form as conifers, the yews are distinguished by the lack of female cones, having instead single seeds partially surrounded by an attractive, brightly colored cup, the aril. Fossil yews are recorded from the Triassic onwards.

The living maidenhair tree (*Ginkgo biloba*) is the sole survivor of a once much more widespread and common group. It is doubtful whether it now exists in the wild. The ginkgo is a deciduous tree with leaves

Angiosperms (see also pp. 32, 367)

The flowering plants, or angiosperms, are characterized by the production of seeds completely enclosed within the female part of the flower, the ovary. The flower is basically a reproductive shoot bearing several rings of lateral organs. At the base are several protective sepals, frequently green, forming the calyx, above which are the often brightly colored petals of the corolla. Within this are the pollen-producing organs (stamens) of the male part of the flower. The ovary, containing one or more ovules, is central. Pollen grains are carried by insects or wind to a receptive area (stigma) on the surface of the ovary: each produces a pollen tube which grows through the ovary wall and enters an ovule, so that a male gamete is introduced into a female egg cell (ovum) permanently retained with the ovule.

After fertilization the ovule develops into a seed containing, at maturity, the embryo of a new plant. The ovary becomes the seed-containing fruit, and may take one of many forms. Seeds vary in size from the microscopic (as in orchids) to the gigantic double coconut weighing up to 44lb (20kg).

Flowering plants largely replaced the gymnosperms as the dominant group of

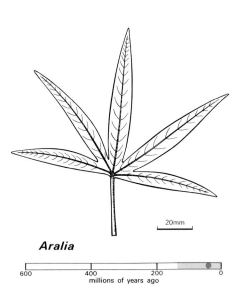

Aralia

20mm

600   400   200   0
millions of years ago

seed plants towards the end of the *Cretaceous, and this position they still occupy. They occur in every type of habitat and range in size from gigantic trees to minute plants. Some are climbers, others succulents, and a number have reverted to an aquatic habit. Most are green plants and are able to synthesize food from simple substances in the environment, but a few are partial or complete parasites.

The success of seed plants as land organisms clearly derives from the evolution of a pattern of reproduction by which fertilization can take place independently of external moisture. This has been effected by the elimination of the free-living sexual stage (prothallus) of the pteridophytic plants (e.g., *pterophytes), with retention of the egg cells within the ovule and the evolution of the pollen tube for transfer of the male gamete to the egg. Even those living gymnosperms which still retain the archaic feature of motile male gametes (cycads and *Ginkgo*) no longer require external moisture for fertilization, breakdown of certain tissues of the ovule providing liquid in which the male gametes swim.

Two divisions of angiosperms are recognized, the dicotyledons with two seed leaves and the monocotyledons with only one, other differences being that dicotyledons usually have net-veined leaves and the floral parts in fours or fives, whereas the monocotyledons usually have parallel veins and the floral parts in threes.

Being essentially ephemeral structures, flowers are much less likely to enter the *fossil record than are the more resistant parts of the plant. Knowledge of fossil angiosperms is therefore based mainly on leaves, fruits and seeds, and much can be learned from them about how modern vegetation arose. As an example may be quoted the fine and almost continuous record of fossil angiosperms in the Tertiary of Oregon. This shows a progressive change from a subtropical rain forest during the Eocene, to a temperate hardwood-conifer

Leaves of the Maidenhair tree (*Ginkgo biloba*), the sole survivor of a group of Coniferophytes.

forest during the Oligocene-Miocene, to cool temperate forests in the Pliocene, and finally to a semi-arid steppe.

The origin of the angiosperms is a continuing mystery. Perhaps their development and rapid rise was connected with the dramatic increase during the *Cretaceous in the number of insects. Equally it could have been due to the emergence of new habitats to which other plants were unable to adapt.   AW

Invertebrate Animals

Foraminifera

The Foraminiferida, commonly known as foraminifera or forams, are an order of unicellular animals of the class Rhizopoda, subphylum Sarcodina. They are related to the *radiolaria and the familiar *Amoeba*. The earliest undisputed forams are late *Cambrian, and the group survives today. Their maximum diversity has been from the late *Tertiary until modern times.

Individuals are often microscopic, but size ranges from fractions of a millimetre to four inches (10cm). All forams are aquatic and most marine, although a few occur in brackish or fresh waters. The soft tissues consist of a mass of cytoplasm, differentiated into an outer ectoplasm and

an inner endoplasm, the latter containing one or more nuclei.

Stratigraphic Importance. Most forams live on and in sediments; others are encrusting or cemented or may live on vegetation; and a planktonic mode of life has been adopted by the important superfamily Globigerinacea, which has a good fossil record from the middle *Jurassic onward.

Forams are a major contributor to Holocene sediments, the tests of planktonic species in particular forming a major category of deep sea sediment: *Globigerina* ooze. At various times in the history of the group, large benthonic forms, often several centimetres in length, evolved. These include the fusulinids (*Carboniferous to *Permian), alveolinids (late *Cretaceous and *Tertiary), orbitolines (chiefly Cretaceous) and the nummulitids (chiefly Tertiary). Nummulitid *limestone was widely used as a *building stone in the ancient world, and Herodotus, writing in the 5th century BC, noted their occurrence in the limestone of the Egyptian pyramids. Subsequently, Strabo took weathered-out specimens to be petrified lentils, dropped accidentally by the original pyramid builders! Foraminiferida are one of the most important groups of stratigraphic indicators. Being small in size, and readily extracted from well-cores and chippings, they are of prime importance in the oil industry. Larger forms with complex internal structures provide the basis for detailed subdivisions of the Carboniferous-

Permian and Cretaceous-Tertiary of many parts of the world. The planktonic globigerinids, through their widespread geographic distribution and rapid evolution, are extensively used in late Cretaceous and Tertiary stratigraphic correlation.

The geographic distribution of the Foraminiferida is influenced by such factors as salinity, turbulence, water temperature, bottom conditions and sediment type, and so they can be excellent environmental indicators. Agglutinated forms are often indicative of nearshore or brackish conditions, while faunal diversity generally increases in an offshore direction.   WJK

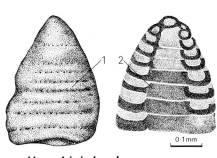

0·1mm

Howchinia bradyana

1 Test
2 Test in section

600   400   200   0
millions of years ago

Radiolaria

Radiolarians are entirely marine, commonly planktonic, microscopic protozoans of the class Rhizopoda, subphylum Sarcodina: they are close relatives of the *foraminifera. The earliest undisputed radiolarians are *Cambrian, although there are possible records from the late *Precambrian. The group are particularly diverse and abundant in the *Cretaceous and *Holocene.

They secrete a delicate skeleton, generally of silica, though members of one group (the suborder Acantharina) secrete *strontium sulfate. The skeleton is partially enclosed in soft tissue, and commonly consists of latticed spheres with radial struts, although there is an enormous variation of shape. The cytoplasm of living radiolarians is exuded outward into radiating, hair-like pseudopodia, and encloses symbiotic unicellular *dinoflagellates. Many radiolarians are dependent on the photosynthetic products of these as a source of nutriment.

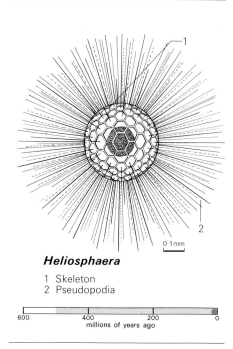

Heliosphaera

1 Skeleton
2 Pseudopodia

600   400   200   0
millions of years ago

Radiolarians inhabit waters of all depths and temperatures, although the requirements of their symbiotic zooxanthellae restrict many to the sunlit surface layers of the oceans. Their remains are an important contributor to deep-sea sediments. Ancient radiolarian-rich sediments are known as *radiolarites*, and many of these are believed to be deep-water deposits. The radiolarian silica is commonly redistributed in *cherts in these deposits.

The group are of great value as stratigraphic indicators, notably in Mesozoic and Tertiary successions, and are widely used in the correlation of oceanic cores.   WJK

Sponges

"Sponge" is the common name for members of the phylum Porifera, a group of invertebrates, predominantly marine (although members of one family are found in freshwater lakes and rivers), which first appeared in the early *Cambrian and are still extant today. They are among the simplest multicellular animals – in fact, until the 18th century they were regarded as plants. Their sizes range from less than a centimetre to several metres across. Most live attached to hard surfaces or have root-like anchorages in soft sediment, though members of the family Clionidae bore into shells and other calcareous substrates.

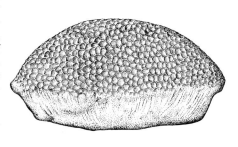

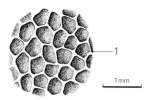

Favosites gothlandicus

1 Detail of upper surface

600   400   200   0
millions of years ago

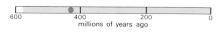

Sponges are filter-feeding organisms; many have symbiotic single-celled plants in their tissues, and may gain nourishment from them. The body is supported by slender, pointed projections called spicules, which may lie loose in soft tissue or be fused into a rigid framework. These spicules are composed of *calcite or *aragonite, of *silica, or of the protein spongin. They are commonly found as *fossils.

The main groups of sponges are: the Calcisponges (*Devonian to *Holocene), with skeletons of calcareous spicules; the Hexactinellids (Cambrian to Holocene), sometimes also known as Hyalosponges, a wholly siliceous group producing delicate, glass-like skeletons; and the Demosponges (Cambrian to Holocene), with skeletons of spongin (as in bath sponges), or of silica with or without spongin. Some organisms closely resembling *corals (*Ordovician to Holocene) as well as *stromataporoids (Cambrian to Holocene), both formerly regarded as colonial coelenterates, are now believed also to belong to the phylum Porifera.

Sponges have limited stratigraphic value, but can be important rock-forming organisms, and some are important framework organisms, building reef-like structures. Siliceous sponges are numerous in many *Paleozoic and Mesozoic sequences, their spicules being regarded as an important source of silica in *chert and *flint formation.   WJK

Corals

The word "coral" has been applied to a variety of organisms that produce calcareous skeletons, but normally it is restricted to coelenterates of the class Anthozoa which have a calcareous supporting skeleton. Many anthozoans (e.g., sea anemones) have no hard parts, and different groups of corals appear to have been derived from these soft-bodied ancestors at different times.

All anthozoans are marine. They have a nervous system, often with stinging cells, but their body consists of a single cavity with only one opening (there is no separate anus). The corals are unlike many other shallow marine fossils in that their skeleton is primarily for support, not for protection: perhaps the ability to sting was sufficient protection.

The earliest anthozoans, from the late *Precambrian, are unbranched individuals anchored by a calcareous stalk, or possibly (in the case of the late Precambrian *Charnia* and *Rangea*) by a circular calcareous disc. These early anthozoans are included in the subclass Octocorallia along with a group of corals with eight tentacles and eight fleshy partitions which extend radially into the central cavity, which appeared in the *Cretaceous. Modern octocorals are mostly shallow-water dwellers, but some have been recovered from very great depths.

The remaining three groups of anthozoan corals are of the subclass Zoantharia: they are the Tabulata and Rugosa, both extinct, and the Scleractinia.

The tabulate corals are all colonial forms in which the individual polyps (fleshy bodies) had their tubes partitioned by horizontal plates (tabulae): the vertical radiating plates (septa) seen in most other corals are absent. This group is confined to the Paleozoic, being most abundant in some *Silurian, *Devonian and *Carboniferous limestones, where they can form a large proportion of some coral reefs, though more frequently occurring as isolated colonies spread thinly over the floor of shallow seas. Some (possibly most) of this extinct group may, in fact, be not coelenterates but *sponges.

The rugose corals were the dominant corals in the Paleozoic, and are especially common from the Silurian (when the earliest coral reefs were developed) to the *Permian. Like many modern corals, they come in different shapes according to the environment: simple conical corals can occur in quite deep water, whereas the colonial corals are more typical of shallower environments. The colonial corals with loose cylindrical branches occurred either in deeper water below the areas affected by severe storms, or in quiet lagoons where they were protected by a reef or other barrier from the open sea. Many rugose corals had polygonal individuals crowded together to form a massive colony; these were capable of forming reefs in exposed sites, but more commonly occurred as isolated colonies on a flat sea floor.

The Scleractinia first appear in the Mesozoic (after the extinction of the Rugosa), and probably developed separately from some soft-bodied sea anemone. They are solitary or colonial corals with radial septa in successive cycles (starting with six in the first cycle). Abundant small plates or rods are present between the septa. Many scleractinians, which tolerate only warm subtropical or tropical waters, are dependent for their existence on the presence of a large number of single-celled *algae in their tissues; these corals have a maximum depth range of about 300ft (90m), and include most of the modern reef-builders. WSM

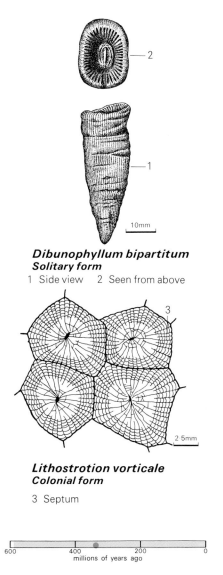

Dibunophyllum bipartitum
Solitary form
1 Side view 2 Seen from above

Lithostrotion vorticale
Colonial form

3 Septum

600   400   200   0
millions of years ago

Stromatoporoidea

The stromatoporoids are, fairly certainly, an extinct group of *sponges. They are among the most conspicuous rock-forming organisms from the middle Silurian to the upper Devonian, representing a timespan

of perhaps 75 million years; and first appeared in the early Cambrian, becoming extinct in the early Eocene. Some ten families and seventy genera have been recognized. RG

Archaeocyathids

The archaeocyathids are a group of sponge-like organisms that inhabited the shelf seas for, geologically speaking, a very short time, from the early Cambrian until the start of the middle Cambrian. They contributed extensively to carbonate sediments and in places formed extensive banks, though not reefs.

The biological affinities of the group are far from clear, but it is generally considered as an extinct phylum – possibly the only phylum ever to have become extinct. RG

Bryozoans

Members of two closely related phyla of minute colonial animals are commonly termed bryozoans or polyzoans: the Entoprocta are entirely freshwater, and have no fossil record; while members of the phylum Ectoprocta, which commonly produce a calcareous skeleton and have an excellent fossil record from the Ordovician to the present, are predominantly marine. The marine ectoprocts inhabit all depths and latitudes, with a peak in diversity during the *Ordovician, though the acme of the group is during the late *Cretaceous to present. The status of supposed *Cambrian bryozoans is equivocal: they may be ectoprocts, or entoprocts, or neither.

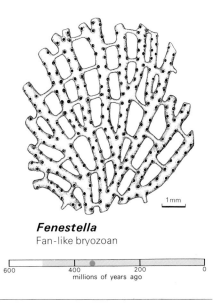

Fenestella
Fan-like bryozoan

600   400   200   0
millions of years ago

Individual animals are of millimetre size, producing a double-walled membranous or calcareous sac which contains the soft parts, including a U-shaped alimentary canal and the reproductive organs. The mouth is surrounded by a hollow, circular or horseshoe-shaped structure that bears hair-like tentacles with which the animals capture food particles and microorganisms.

Hundreds to thousands of individuals produce colonies from less than half an inch to more than a yard across. These may be like miniature plants, fan-like, or encrust-

ing on plants, rocks and the like. A few lie loose on the sediment surface, while some produce characteristic borings in shells.

Bryozoans are common fossils and may occur in rock-forming proportions, as they do in some of the Cretaceous and early Tertiary limestones of Scandinavia. They are an important contributor to carbonate sands in temperate latitudes at the present day. WJK

Brachiopods

The members of the phylum Brachiopoda are marine animals with a shell consisting of two valves, one normally much larger than the other. The name brachiopod is derived from two Greek words (*brachia*, arms; *pod*, foot), and refers to the fact that the animals have internal arms in a similar position to the feet seen in *bivalves. In most brachiopods a pedicle emerges *via* an aperture (foramen) in the larger valve near the hinge and attaches the animal to the sea floor, but some forms have lost this pedicle and rest on the sea floor directly. All brachiopods generate a current in the space between the valves by means of a fleshy arm (the lophophore); this current supplies oxygen to the gills and also carries organic matter to the mouth. Brachiopods have a free-swimming larval stage (of 1–20 days), which allows them to spread about over the sea floor.

Today, brachiopods are not very common compared with the *bivalves and other

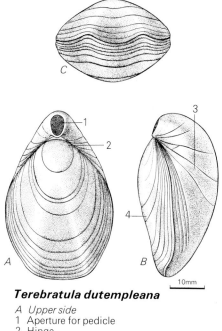

Terebratula dutempleana

A *Upper side*
1 Aperture for pedicle
2 Hinge
B *Side view*
3 Lower valve
4 Upper valve
C *End view*

600   400   200   0
millions of years ago

*mollusks. In the *Cambrian, brachiopod fossils are subordinate in numbers to the dominant *trilobites, though they can be locally abundant in some shallow marine environments. From the Cambrian onward, two classes are present: the Inarticulata, with no teeth and usually a shell composed of chitin and phosphate; and the Articulata, with two teeth in the large (pedicle) valve which fit into sockets in the smaller (brachial) valve and hold the valves in place. All articulates have a *calcite shell.

WSM

Echinoderms

The Echinodermata are an entirely marine phylum of invertebrate animals which first appeared in the early *Cambrian and range to the present day. They are important elements of many shallow-water marine Paleozoic, Mesozoic and Tertiary faunas, and include the *echinoids (sea urchins), particularly important in Mesozoic and Tertiary rocks; crinoids (sea lilies), with their acme in the *Carboniferous; asteroids (starfish), ophiuroids (brittle-stars) and holothuroids (sea cucumbers), all of which have a poor fossil record; and a number of now-extinct groups.

These diverse animals are linked by three common features: a basic five-fold (pentameral) symmetry unique in the animal kingdom; hard parts covered and permeated by soft tissues and composed of a series of plates of *calcite, each a single crystallographic unit; and a system of thin, fluid-filled tubes produced into finger-like extensions (tube feet), which generally extend through to the outside of the body and aid in locomotion, digging, gathering food, respiration and chemical sensing.

The group are of some stratigraphic value in the correlation of some Paleozoic sequences and more especially in Mesozoic rocks (in the absence of *ammonites) and in some Tertiary successions. WJK

Blastoids

The Blastoidea are a wholly extinct class of stemmed, sessile *echinoderms, rarely exceeding 12in (30cm) in total height. They range from the Silurian to the Permian, reaching their peak in the lower *Carboniferous. The group seems to have preferred shallow, agitated marine environments. They are rather rare fossils. The body consisted of a stem of thin, disc-shaped plates attached to the sea floor by a branching-system of rootlets. A cup-like calyx at the summit of the stem bore numerous threadlike brachioles ("arms") in five pairs of rows along the sides of petal-shaped ambulacra. Perforations along the sides of the ambulacra led to a complex internal pouch, made up of thin-walled folds of tissue, which served for respiration.

About 80 genera of blastoids have been described, encompassing some 380 species. The evolutionary origin of the group is unknown. WJK

A Triassic crinoid displays two features characteristic of echinoderms: five-fold symmetry, and an outer surface protected by calcite plates.

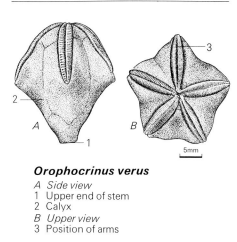

Orophocrinus verus
A Side view
1 Upper end of stem
2 Calyx
B Upper view
3 Position of arms

600   400   200   0
millions of years ago

Cystoids

The Cystoidea are a wholly extinct class of *echinoderms ranging from the lower *Ordovician to the upper *Devonian, with their peak in the Ordovician. The group are usually rare fossils, although some occur in rock-forming proportions. They appear to have favored clear, quiet-water conditions.

Most cystoids were anchored to the bottom by a short stem of disc-like plates, the summit of which bore a many-plated shell which presumably enclosed the bulk of the

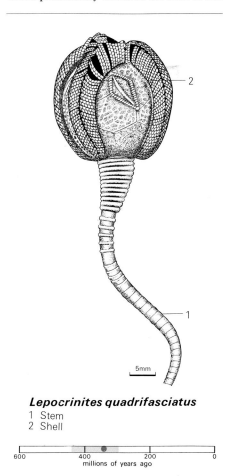

Lepocrinites quadrifasciatus
1 Stem
2 Shell

600   400   200   0
millions of years ago

soft tissues. The plates of the shell had pores, some nearly or completely closed by a thin coating of calcium carbonate, a feature which has led to debate on their precise function, although they were undoubtedly part of the respiratory system.

The cystoid shell also bore brachioles ("arms") to gather food – presumably floating organic debris or microorganisms. The food was transferred, probably via ciliated tracts, to the shell and from there to the mouth. WJK

Crinoids

The cystoid shell also bore brachioles ("arms") to gather food – presumably floating organic debris or microorganisms. The food was transferred, probably via ciliated phylum Crinozoa, and are important as the key to our understanding of the ecology and functional morphology of such extinct groups as the *cystoids and *blastoids.

Crinoids are the most diverse of the stemmed echinoderms. Typical members of the group have a basal series of root-like processes which anchor the animal to the sea bed or to vegetation, coral heads, shell debris and the like. From this arises a stem of articulated plates of diverse morphology, some disc-like, others resembling beads, and yet others taking the form of five-rayed stars. In some crinoids, there are side-branches on the stem. Adults have stems ranging up to nearly 60ft (18m) in length.

At the top of the stem, the calyx, a cup-like structure comprising a series of cycles of plates, encloses the body cavity, gut, reproductive organs and so forth. From articulatory facets at the top of the cup arise arms, in turn built of articulating plates – these arms may be built simply of rows of plates, or may branch into hundreds of branchlets, giving a crown up to 5ft (1.5m) in length. The arms bear the water vascular system and function as a feeding device: microorganisms and food particles are trapped and transferred down grooves to the mouth, which is borne on the upper surface of the calyx.

All early crinoids and many present-day forms are sessile. During the Mesozoic, however, there arose secondarily free-swimming forms in which the arms are modified to power the creature through the water. Some of these have widespread distribution and have been regarded as planktonic; others, among them the comatulid crinoids which survive to the present, have a circlet of flexible appendages called cirri at the base of the calyx, with which they can temporarily secure themselves to the bottom.

Crinoids were at their height during the *Carboniferous, and throughout the *Paleozoic were successful inhabitants of many marine environments.

They are excellent stratigraphic indicators of marine environments. They have been utilized as indicators in several areas: their plates can be used as index fossils in some of the thick Paleozoic shale sequences of the US mid-continent area, as can the microcrinoids, whose adult calyx was only a fraction of an inch across. WJK

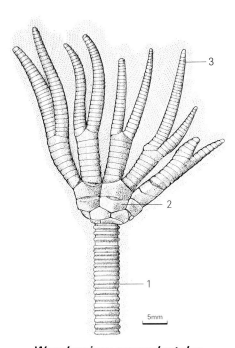

Woodocrinus macrodactylus
1 Stem
2 Calyx
3 Arms

600 400 200 0
millions of years ago

Echinoids

The sea urchins, or echinoids, are a class of benthonic *echinoderms ranging from the *Ordovician to the present day, being most abundant and diverse from middle *Jurassic times onward.

The exoskeleton (or test) is generally globular, and is built of twenty rows of interlocking calcareous plates. These are generally arranged in two sets of five pairs of plates, extending from the apex to the base of the test. The plates are either perforate, allowing access of the extensions of the internal water vascular system, the tube feet, to the exterior; non-perforate; or bear tubercles which form articulation points for spines usually modified for walking, burrowing, protection and defense.

In regular echinoids, there is a basic pentameral symmetry, with a large opening (the peristome) at the center of the lower surface of the test. This is covered in life by a leathery membrane in the center of which is the strong-jawed mouth. Regular echinoids are all epifaunal grazers, and the powerful jaws rasp at encrusting organisms such as bryozoans, algae and the like, or are used to cut vegetation. At the opposite end of the test, the anus opens in the middle of a further leathery membrane, which covers a second large opening in the test. Around it are specialized plates from which the gonads discharge. All early echinoids show this very regular symmetry, and all appear to have lived epifaunally, generally in quiet-water situations.

During the early Jurassic, however, a major radiation occurred, and forms evolved in which the anus migrated to a position away from the summit of the test. This was accompanied by a change in life habits from epifaunal grazing to infaunal deposit feeding, and specialized spines and tubercles were evolved for digging and burrowing, while the perforated plates and tube feet were modified for respiration, burrowing, crawling and feeding. The greatest specialization is shown by the heart urchins: burrowing is accompanied by assumption of a deposit-feeding habit and disappearance of a functional jaw apparatus in adults.

Echinoids are common fossils in many shallow-water Jurassic, Cretaceous and Tertiary sediments in spite of their fragile tests, and are excellent indicators of sea-

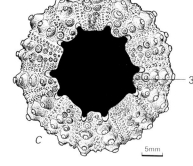

Hemicidaris intermedia
A Side view
1 Tubercle
B Upper side
2 Anus
C Lower side
3 Peristome

600 400 200 0
millions of years ago

floor conditions. In the absence of *ammonites, they have been widely used as stratigraphic indicators.　　　　WJK

Mollusks

The mollusks, the phylum Mollusca, are a major invertebrate group, in numbers second only to the *arthropods. They appear to be of almost unparalleled antiquity: *trace fossils attributed to them occur in the late *Precambrian marine sediments.

Included in the phylum are the chitons, or coat-of-mail shells (class Amphineura); elephant's-tusk shells (class Scaphoda); oysters, mussels and other shells with two movable halves (*bivalves, of the class Bivalvia); snails, slugs and limpets (class Gastropoda); squids, cuttles, octopuses, belemnites, *nautiloids and *ammonoids (class Cephalopoda); the class Monoplacophora of superficially limpet-like organisms; and a number of minor, extinct groups.

Because of this great diversity of form, it is rather hard to describe a "typical mollusk"; but the basic morphology is fundamentally similar. There is little or no segmentation; and they have bilateral symmetry – i.e., one half mirrors the other. The internal body organs (viscera) are enclosed by a body wall, the lower part of which, the foot, is modified to provide locomotion, while the upper part, the mantle, hangs down as a fold so that there is a free space between it and the viscera. This mantle cavity houses the gills and aids also in feeding and locomotion. Sensory organs are concentrated in the head region (except in bivalves).

Some secrete a shell, generally external, though in certain cases it is secondarily enclosed in tissue. When external, the shell more or less totally covers the soft tissues. In some mollusks the shell has been totally lost.

Mollusks inhabit marine, brackish, freshwater and sometimes even terrestrial environments. They are exceptionally important since many produce shells of calcium carbonate: this has often happened in sufficient concentrations to form limestones.　　　　WJK

Ammonoids

The ammonoids are a wholly extinct class of cephalopod *mollusks known from the early *Devonian to late *Cretaceous, their acme being during the *Triassic. Superficially similar to *nautiloids, they had an external aragonitic shell subdivided internally into chambers and so serving for both flotation and protection. The two groups can generally be distinguished in that ammonoids had a globular or barrel-shaped rather than saucer-shaped larval shell, and a ventral rather than sub-central siphuncle (a tissue-filled tube extending back to the larval shell). In addition, the sutures (the trace where the septa, or internal partitions, were attached to the inside of the shell) are complexly crenulated rather than broadly curving; while the shell exterior is often strongly ornamented rather than smooth.

Three broad groups are recognized, and

Jurassic specimens of the ammonite *Metophioceras* preserved on the lower surface of a limestone bed. Ammonites are sometimes over a metre in diameter and include some of the largest mollusks.

most readily distinguished on the basis of the suture lines. In the goniatites, an essentially *Paleozoic group, the lobes and saddles are simple and entire, angular or rounded. In the ceratites, essentially *Triassic, the saddles are entire, and the lobes serrated; while in the ammonites (late Triassic, *Jurassic and *Cretaceous) both lobes and saddles are subdivided.

Ammonoids were a diverse, variable and successful group of planktonic or free-swimming organisms, entirely restricted to marine environments. They were probably rather poor swimmers, being better adapted for vertical movements through the water by varying the amount of fluid within their chambers. Many possessed a well-developed jaw apparatus: some may have been carnivores and scavengers; others were probably plankton feeders or herbivores. The creatures were sexual and the sexes quite distinct: in many species the females (termed macroconchs) were often several times larger than the males (microconchs).

These later, Cretaceous ammonite faunas are notable for the diversity of straight, helical and loosely coiled or heteromorph groups, some of which in turn give rise to normally coiled descendants. These heteromorphs are definitely not "degenerate" forms or evolutionary "dead ends" as is so commonly stated, for they

Clydoniceras discus

1 Suture

15 mm

| 600 | 400 | 200 | 0 |

millions of years ago

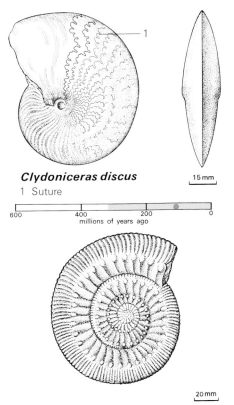

20 mm

Stephanoceras humphriesianum

| 600 | 400 | 200 | 0 |

millions of years ago

include some of the most diverse, long and widely ranging species, genera and families.

Although of limited value as environmental indicators, ammonoids are the most important group of larger invertebrates for the correlation of Devonian to Cretaceous marine sediments, forming the basis of global zonal schemes during this interval.   WJK

Nautiloids

The term nautiloid is commonly applied to *mollusks of three subclasses (Nautiloidea, Endoceratoidea, Actinoceratoidea) of the class Cephalopoda. The earliest nautiloids appeared in the late *Cambrian, and the group reached their acme in the *Ordovician. There is a single extant genus, *Nautilus*.

All nautiloids had external shells of *aragonite, consisting of a hollow cone, the regions toward the apex being divided into chambers (or camerae) by simple, transverse concave, saucer-like partitions (septa). This body chamber housed the bulk of the tissues. The foot was modified into tentacles which surrounded the head and were used in feeding, and there were well developed eyes and jaws. The mantle cavity, housing the gills, acted as an organ of jet propulsion: water was expelled through the restricted aperture to boost the creature forward.

Early nautiloids were straight or slightly curved, and maintained an equilibrium position by partial flooding of chambers or the deposition of aragonitic "ballast" in the chambers and siphuncle (a tissue-filled tube extending through the septae back to the larval shell). Coiled forms evolved independently on several occasions during the Paleozoic. Modern *Nautilus* reaches a maximum diameter of 10in (25cm), though some straight Paleozoic forms reached lengths in excess of 30ft (9m), and are among the largest mollusks.

Nautiloids are good indicators of fully marine conditions. WJK

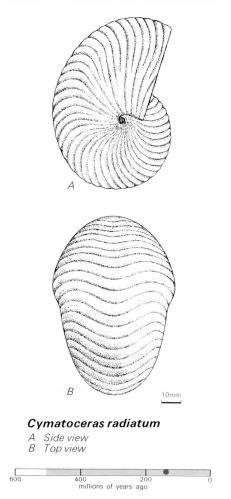

Cymatoceras radiatum
A Side view
B Top view

600 | 400 | 200 | 0
millions of years ago

Belemnoids

The belemnoids are a group of wholly extinct, *Carboniferous to *Oligocene cephalopods referred to the subclass Coleioida, order Belemnitida. The best known representatives are the belemnites of the *Jurassic and *Cretaceous, at which time the group reached the acme of its 300-million-year history. They evolved from the Bactritoida, a group of straight, *nautiloid-like cephalopods with external shells, by a process of total envelopment of the hard parts by soft tissue. They were squid-like in external appearance, with lateral fins, well-developed eyes, and tentacles. Internally there was a well-developed muscular mantle cavity, expulsion of water from which enabled rapid jet propulsion. Some possessed ink sacs.

The hard part most commonly found fossil is the guard, a tapering, bullet-shaped object composed of radiating fibers of *calcite (there may have been some

*aragonite present as well). The pointed end lay at the posterior of the body, while a conical cavity at the anterior end of the guard housed the phragmocone, a reduced equivalent of the conical, chambered, ancestral bactritid shell. The phragmocone probably acted as a buoyancy apparatus, while the guard may have served as a counterweight. In front of the phragmocone lay the proostracum, a quill-like extension which served to protect the viscera.

Belemnites have been used widely in the correlation of Cretaceous marine sediments, especially the European chalk sequences, and to a lesser degree in the Jurassic. They are excellent marine indicators. WJK

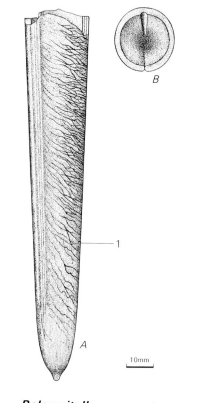

Belemnitella mucronata
A Side view
1 Guard
B Guard in section

600 | 400 | 200 | 0
millions of years ago

Gastropods

The gastropods are a class of marine, freshwater and terrestrial *mollusks typified by a single, conical, variously coiled external calcareous shell made of *aragonite or aragonite and *calcite, over whose open end there is often a calcareous or organic "door", the operculum. Some have lost the shell altogether (nudibranchs), and in others (slugs) it is internal: a good example of a gastropod with an external shell is provided by the common snail.

Gastropods show distinct anatomical

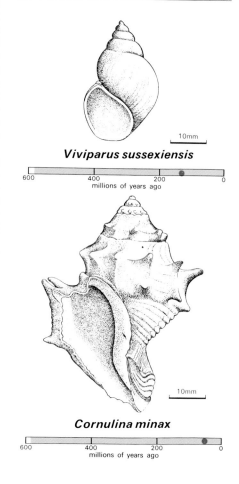

Viviparus sussexiensis

600 | 400 | 200 | 0
millions of years ago

Cornulina minax

600 | 400 | 200 | 0
millions of years ago

differences from other mollusks. The viscera are concentrated together, and there is a head with well-developed sensory organs, in which is a mouth containing a specialized radula (see below). The foot is flattened and muscular and is used in locomotion, be it crawling, burrowing or swimming. The mantle cavity contains the gills, and in some forms (the pulmonates) is modified into an airbreathing "lung".

The basic subdivision of the gastropods is made on features of the heart, gills and other soft tissues, and in many cases this makes classification of fossil material difficult. Three subclasses are generally recognized, the Prosobranchia, Opisthobranchia and Mesogastropoda.

Gastropods first appeared in the early *Cambrian, underwent a major radiation in the late *Cretaceous and have reached their peak today: the Holocene will probably be known to future paleontologists as the age of gastropods!

The group occupy both aquatic and terrestrial habitats, the first land snail (*Palaeopupa*) appearing in the *Carboniferous. Some are pelagic and most have pelagic larvae. Most bottom-living forms creep on hard or soft substrates, and their range is from the intertidal regions to the abyssal depths. Pelagic forms swim using a highly modified foot; some are epiplanktonic on *algae, while the truly planktonic *Janthina* supports itself in the water by a float of air bubbles which it produces.

A few float, others bore, are cemented, or are parasitic. The majority graze on vegetation or on encrusting animals such as *bryozoans and *sponges; but some have a long, out-thrust proboscis and become active predators on other mollusks, while others have a specialized horny, toothed band called a radula and can drill into shells. Still others have a poisonous bristle called a style, and feed on fish; while some are parasitic on bivalves or are symbionts living on the feces of *echinoderms and other mollusks: a number of fossil examples of such symbiosis is known. A few gastropods occupy a deposit-feeding niche (*Aphorrhais*), whilst *Turrilella* are ciliary feeders, living part-buried in sediment and drawing in detritus or mucus strands, or filtering such material out of seawater.

In spite of their varied habitats, little use has been made of gastropods as environmental indicators, and they have no wide application as stratigraphic markers.

WJK

Bivalves

The Bivalvia (also known as Pelecypoda and Lamellibranchiata) are an aquatic class of *mollusks ranging from the middle *Cambrian to the present. They are an important element in many shallow-water late *Paleozoic and *Mesozoic sequences, reaching their acme during the *Tertiary.

Anatomically, they have diverged considerably from the basic molluscan pattern. The mantle has expanded markedly, and is modified into voluminous folds which hang down on either side of the visceral mass. The body has become compressed laterally and the head reduced to the point of disappearance; and they have adopted a passive mode of life. The shell has two valves, or halves, joined dorsally along the hinge by an elastic ligament, and is built of layers of *aragonite, or aragonite and *calcite in separate layers.

Bivalves are superficially similar to *brachiopods. Typical members may be distinguished by, in bivalves, the lack of an opening for the pedicle and of internal calcareous supports; and by the plane of bilateral symmetry, which generally runs through the plane of contact of the valves in bivalves, but bisects the valves in a front-to-back direction in brachiopods.

Bivalves are essentially suspension feeders, the gills being expanded into a filtration device. The foot is commonly modified into a hatchet-shaped burrowing organ. Most are infaunal burrowers, living buried at various depths in sediment, although maintaining contact with the surface *via* tubular extensions of the mantle called siphons. Others are cemented; lie on the sediment surface; attach by a cluster of organic fibers secreted by a gland near the foot; or bore down into the sediment. A few can swim for brief periods, usually to escape predators.

Externally, bivalves are ornamented by diverse ribs, spines, tubercles and growth lines, which function as aids in burrowing, stabilization and attachment. Internally,

Pseudunio valdensis
A Side view of valve
B Top view
1 Hinge

20mm

600   400   200   0
millions of years ago

there are along the dorsal margin tooth- and socket-like structures associated with the articulation of the valves, and generally large scars indicating the site of attachment of the adductor muscles which work, in opposition to the elastic ligament, to close the shell.

Bivalves are excellent environmental indicators, their morphological features giving information of substrate conditions; while knowledge of modern forms allows recognition of ancient freshwater, brackish and fully marine environments. Overall geographic distribution and diversity patterns of bivalves have been used to determine climatic zonation during parts of the Mesozoic, while they have been widely used as paleoclimatic indicators for the Tertiary and Quaternary. The group are also of great stratigraphic value from the

*Carboniferous onwards. Freshwater mussels are one of the keys to the correlation of the coal-bearing strata, whilst inoceramids and the giant, aberrant rudistids are widely used in the correlation of the *Cretaceous. In the absence of larger *foraminifera or planktonic forms, bivalves form the basis for much Tertiary correlation.

WJK

Arthropods

The Arthropoda are Man's only serious competitor on this planet. As a group, they are biologically more successful than the vertebrates in being able to inhabit more extreme environments; but they are relatively small animals compared with vertebrates and mollusks, their size being limited by their characteristic exoskeleton. The largest size achieved by an arthropod was in the *Devonian, a giant *chelicerate almost 5.9ft (1.8m) in length, though the giant Japanese crabs today can, with legs outstretched, extend to 16ft (5m). About 75% of all known living animals are arthropods, most being insects: however, because of the relative paucity of fossil insects, arthropods are less dominant in the fossil record.

The fossil history of the phylum goes back at least to the early *Cambrian, and there can be no doubt that it had a long Precambrian history. The fossil remains do not demonstrate the origin of the phylum, and biologists favor the suggestion that it derived from more than one ancestral stock. The common features of arthropods (the exoskeleton – and therefore molting –, the articulated limbs and the compound eyes) are thus likely due to convergent evolution.

Nine superclasses of Arthropoda are recognized though two of these are unknown as fossils. The *trilobites are probably close

The arthropods, of which this Jurassic lobster from the Solnhofen limestone of Bavaria is a good example, are characterized by jointed limbs and an exoskeleton. Being hard, the exoskeleton is sometimes preserved in such a way as to reveal considerable anatomical detail.

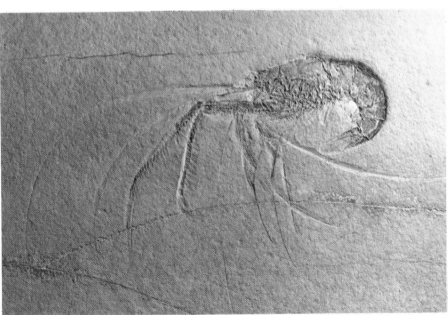

to the *chelicerates; the *crustaceans (crabs, lobsters) appear to be a quite distinct group; and the *insects can be grouped with several other, small classes into the Hexapoda (six legs). However, there are a number of fossils which do not fit into any of these groups. RG

Trilobites

This fascinating group of aquatic *arthropods appeared early in the *Cambrian, but must have been in existence long before. They reached their acme in the *Ordovician, thereafter gradually decreasing in diversity and in numbers of ecological niches occupied. Only one order survived into the *Carboniferous and the class became extinct late in the *Permian.

They are probably the best known fossil invertebrates: their relative abundance and distinctiveness, especially in lower *Paleozoic sediments, means that they are among the easiest fossils to find.

The name "trilobite" derives from the longitudinal division of the animal into three parts seen on the upper surface of the body. Apart from a narrow border zone and a large mouth-plate, the lower surface of the creature was not mineralized, and so is only rarely preserved in fossil form.

Each segment carried paired appendages, all similar except for the first two pairs behind the mouth, which appear to have carried a denticulated jaw. Each appendage is in two parts; a jointed section, which performed a walking and digging function, and a bristly section, probably used mainly for food collecting. The bristly section has often been considered as a respiratory organ, but it seems likely that respiration took place through the extensive thin integument on the underside. The organization of the appendage suggests a relationship between the trilobites and the *chelicerates.

Like other arthropods, trilobites had to molt to grow. They did not assimilate the exoskeleton as *crustaceans do when molting, and trilobite molts probably form the bulk of their fossilized remains. Molts have provided much information on the trilobite life-cycle. Shedding occurred at various places on the head-section, along the back (like shrimps) or, more frequently, along a line just behind the eye. Trilobites are relatively rarely found complete as, obviously, the highly segmented skeleton is easily dispersed.

Trilobites were essentially filter feeders, but some were probably able to deal with small prey. They show great diversity in shape and size and different forms were adapted for burrowing, swimming and many other ecological niches. Deeper-water forms often show a considerable reduction of the eye surface. The largest trilobite reached a length of 27in (70cm).

Most trilobite eyes, like those of other arthropods, have several thousand lenses covered by a single cornea. The lenses are of *calcite with the central axis normal to the visual surface, thus largely eliminating double refraction.

Apart from the more primitive forms most trilobites protected themselves like the modern woodlouse – by rolling up into a ball – and various devices were evolved to ensure a complete envelope.

The activities of the bottom-dwelling trilobites have been preserved as *trace fossils in shallow marine sandy environments (where trilobites were most common).

The reasons for their extinction are not understood. There is no obvious competitor for their ecological niches, though the crustaceans began to take their place later, in the Mesozoic. RG

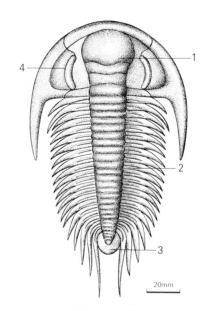

Paradoxides davidis

1 Head
2 Thorax
3 Pygidium
4 Eye

Crustaceans

The crustaceans are the major group of marine arthropods today, and rival the *insects in abundance, if not in diversity. They are distinguished from other arthropods by having two pairs of antennae on the head. The exoskeleton is generally strengthened by patches of calcium carbonate, but to a variable extent. The crustaceans were and are mostly marine, but the superclass as a whole shows an astonishing range of ecological tolerance and adaptation.

Found from the *Cambrian onward, they comprise over 900 genera in 9 classes. The more important fossil classes (apart from the *ostracods) are:

The *Branchiopoda* (which includes the brine shrimps), a relatively primitive filter-feeding group with numerous longitudinal segments, and often partially protected by a bivalved carapace. They first appeared in the early *Devonian.

The *Copepoda* are the marine equivalent

of insects. Although extremely abundant in marine waters today, the only fossils known are from *Miocene lake deposits.

Complete *cirrepedes* (barnacles) are rather uncommon as fossils, because the skeletal plates separate quickly after death. Stalked goose-barnacles are known from the late Silurian, where complete specimens were fossilized still attached to *Eurypterus* (an aquatic arachnid). Acorn barnacles are known from the *Cretaceous.

The *Malacostraca*, which includes the crabs, lobsters and shrimps, is a group known from the early *Cambrian. They show considerable diversity, though good fossils are relatively uncommon, partly due to the incompleteness of calcification. Many forms burrow into sand or mud, sometimes plugging the burrow wall with muddy pellets to produce characteristic *trace fossils. RG

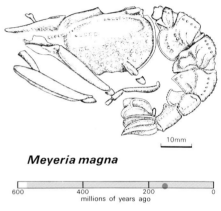

Meyeria magna

Ostracods

The Ostracoda form an extant subclass of *crustaceans. They are common fossils from the lower *Cambrian onward; and, because of their small size, often rapid evolution and the frequent environmental restriction of some groups, are important stratigraphical and environmental indicators. Of the over 900 genera which have been recognized about a quarter still survive.

Ostracods have an egg-shaped bivalved shell of calcium carbonate generally less than 0.04in (1mm) in length. This gives little indication of the form of the animal's soft parts except for the adductor muscles (used for closing the shell), eyes and certain structures which are regarded as brood chambers. Nevertheless there is considerable variation of the shell, with lobes, ridges, pits, spines and frills. Freshwater ostracods are typically smooth-shelled, whereas those of the shallow marine shelf are often deeply sculptured. Most are bottom-dwellers but a small group is planktonic.

The abundance of their shells in the fossil record is undoubtedly influenced by the fact that, like other arthropods, growth is accomplished by molting, this occurring six to nine times during the lifespan, so that each individual may be represented by several shells. RG

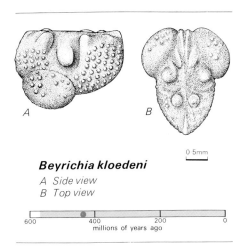

Beyrichia kloedeni

A Side view
B Top view

```
600        400        200        0
      millions of years ago
```

Chelicerates

The group of *arthropods with a pair of chelicerae, pincers in front of the mouth, is made up of the arachnids, which include spiders and scorpions, and the merostomates, which include the much less formidable horseshoe crabs and the extinct eurypterids. While the merostomes have always inhabited inland or coastal waters the arachnids are typically air breathers. They are relatively uncommon fossils.

The best-known fossil arachnids are spiders fossilized in *Oligocene amber from the Baltic coast; but the first mites are known from the lower *Devonian. Scorpions date from the *Silurian, but were then relatively large animals – sometimes attaining a length of about 3ft (0.9m) Probably such forms were aquatic, breathing through gills. Around 60,000 species of arachnids are known.

The horseshoe crabs show only minor evolutionary changes since the late *Paleozoic: fossils date from the lower *Cambrian. The broad, low-vaulted three-piece shield at the front is followed by a number of segments and a prominent spine toward the rear. Locomotory appendages are borne on this shield; the segments that follow bear the gills.

The eurypterids (represented by 30 genera) range in size from small to very large. They have an elongate body which may be as long as about 6ft (1.8m), making them the largest known arthropods of all time. The body terminates with either a spine or a spine modified to form a paddle-like tail. The last pair of locomotory appendages is often modified for swimming, and the chelicerae may be very large and obviously predatory.   RG

Insects

Perhaps the most beautiful of fossils is an insect trapped in golden *amber; and many insects are found thus in *Oligocene amber from the Baltic shores. However, in spite of their numerical abundance among living animals, insects have a rather poor fossil record. The reason is obvious: the adults are air breathers and, on death, only rarely will the intact insect sink to the substrate of a fluvial pool or lagoon.

The earliest insect known is a collembolid (springtail) from the lower *Devonian. Winged insects are known from the upper *Carboniferous, associated with *coal beds, though they had probably evolved by late Devonian times (when plants had reached tree size). The largest known insect, found in the Carboniferous, had a wing span of almost 23in (600mm) and was rather like a giant dragonfly. Insects with folded wings and fore-wings modified to become protective elytra (as in the beetles) are also known from the upper Carboniferous. They probably occupied a similar scavenging role to that of today. Butterflies, moths and ancestral dipterans (flies) are known from the lower *Permian, and thus arrived on the scene prior to the evolution of the *angiosperms (flowering plants).   RG

Conodonts

The conodont animal is one of the most elusive fossils. While the small toothed or platey structures of calcium phosphate, known also as conodonts, can be readily found in most marine sediments (especially *limestones) from the *Ordovician to the upper *Triassic, there is still no positive evidence of what their owners were like.

With their rapid evolution, the Conodontophorida are important for stratigraphic zonation, particularly during the upper *Devonian and lower *Carboniferous. Individual conodonts represent an internal secretion built up plate by plate, with a "pulp" cavity at the base. The crown varies from being fang-like to serrated blades, bars and serrated plates.

Six types of natural associations are known, though these do not particularly aid interpretation of the biological relationships between them. The six assemblages are assigned to six genera.

In the absence of the conodont animal, the relationships of the group are in doubt, but they were possibly supporting structures for teeth or, less probably, respiratory organs, of a fish-like or perhaps hagfish-like animal. There are a number of other interpretations.   RG

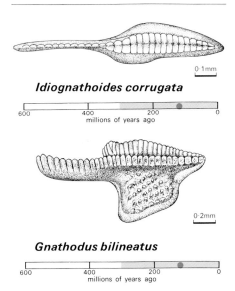

Idiognathoides corrugata

```
600        400        200        0
      millions of years ago
```

Gnathodus bilineatus

```
600        400        200        0
      millions of years ago
```

Graptolites

The name graptolite is commonly applied to members of the wholly extinct class Graptolithinia. These somewhat enigmatic fossils first appear in rocks of middle and late *Cambrian age, and finally disappear in the late Carboniferous. Graptolites (the name means literally "rock writing") generally occur as silvery carbonaceous or pyritic films on bedding planes in fine-grained black *shales. The group were originally regarded as inorganic or vegetable in origin, and have subsequently been referred to the Cephalopoda, Coelenterata and Bryozoa. We now know from detailed studies of their microarchitecture that they should be referred to the subphylum Hemi-

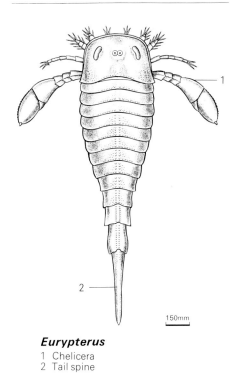

Eurypterus

1 Chelicera
2 Tail spine

```
600        400        200        0
      millions of years ago
```

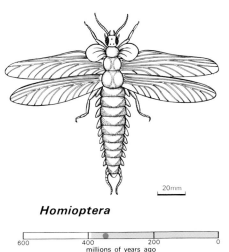

Homioptera

```
600        400        200        0
      millions of years ago
```

chordata, phylum Chordata.

Graptolites were colonial organisms: individuals secreted minute, millimetre-sized cups built up of half-rings of protein or protein-like material. Through complex budding and branching, colonies of from one to many branches were produced. In some graptoloids the contributory cups are of different shapes, suggesting several distinct types of individual were present.

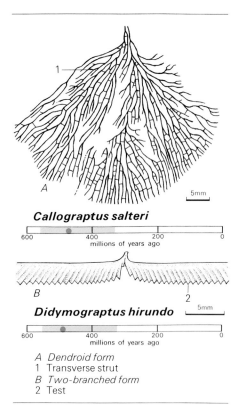

Callograptus salteri

600	400	200	0

millions of years ago

Didymograptus hirundo

600	400	200	0

millions of years ago

A *Dendroid form*
1 Transverse strut
B *Two-branched form*
2 Test

The earliest graptoloids are referred to a group known as the dendroids, which exhibit cups of differing shapes and developed into shrubby, lace-like colonies of moderate size (usually less than 6in (15cm)), in which the branches were commonly joined by transverse struts. Perhaps the best known is the many-branched *Dictyonema*, which is believed to have been either planktonic or epiplanktonic in its life habits: other dendroids seem to have been sessile, living attached to the sea floor.

From the dendroids arose the graptolites proper, again a planktonic or epiplanktonic group, characterized by colonial structures with generally only a few branches, and only a single type of cup. The earliest graptolites were many-branched, but parallel evolution led to progressive reduction in the number of branches. In addition, evolutionary studies have demonstrated progressive modification of the position of the branches and changes in details of the shape of the cups.

The graptolites are key stratigraphic indicators from the upper Cambrian through to the lowest Devonian: their distribution was very wide, and they are often common in offshore black *shales and siltstones, although generally scarce (through ecologi-

cal exclusion or non-preservation) in nearer-shore sediments such as coarse sandstones and limestones. Because nothing is known of their soft tissues, little is known of their precise life habits. They are believed to have fed on organic debris or planktonic microorganisms, by analogy with their nearest relatives, and float-like devices may have been developed. In some cases several colonies have been found associated in star formations.

Three smaller groups, the Tuboidea, Camaroidea, and Crustoidea have also been described, mostly from Ordovician rocks of the European area.   WJK

Trace Fossils
Trace fossils are structures left in sediment or hard substrates by living organisms. In a ghostly way, they indicate the presence, at one time, of an organism whose bodily remains have long disappeared. Trace fossils therefore include tracks, trails, burrows, borings, fecal pellets (either the fossil excrement itself or castings), resting impressions and other structures actively produced by animals (and, more rarely, plants).

Trace fossils thus represent fossilized behavior – they give an indication of what the animal *did*, despite the fact that only rarely can a trace be attributed to a particular genus or species.

Organisms are only rarely preserved in association with the traces they produce, and much of our inferences about the affinities of trace fossils depends on observation of modern organisms. Since trace fossils are commonly produced by soft-bodied organisms, they frequently give an indication of the presence of elements of fauna that would rarely, if ever, be otherwise preserved.

Trace fossils first appear in rocks approximately 1000 million years old, and provide the earliest evidence for the existence of metazoan (many-celled) animals; also, they give us our only evidence of the early history of several invertebrate phyla during the late Precambrian. Trace fossils are found from all ages in terrestrial, marine and freshwater sediments. Tracks and trails attributed to groups as diverse as polychaetes and dinosaurs, trilobites and fish, have been recognized, and in the case of wholly extinct groups such as the trilobites provide our only concrete evidence of the behavior of the living organisms.

Most trace fossils cannot be attributed to particular organisms, or even to groups of organisms. They can, however, be divided into various behavior categories. These include: *Domichnia*, simple dwelling burrows, more or less permanent habitations of the animals producing them; *Fodinichnia*, tunnel systems produced by semi-sessile sediment-mining organisms; *Pascichnia*, complex meandering trails which systematically cover surfaces without crossing, and which record grazing and feeding activities; *Cubichnia*, generally shallow resting traces which correspond approximately to the form of the producer; and *Repichnia*, which are simple locomotion traces.

In addition to this behavioral grouping of trace fossils, recurrent associations of traces, often dominated by particular behavioral types, have been recognized. The composition of these associations (or trace-fossil facies) was controlled by environmental conditions. They are: terrestrial (non-marine) *Scoyenia* facies; *Skolithos* facies, which represent high energy littoral conditions of rapid sedimentation and transport; *Glossifungites* facies, associated with shallow-water submarine erosion surfaces; *Cruziana* facies, or shallow-water, but sub-littoral conditions; *Zoophycos* facies, from deeper (or quieter) waters transitional to the abyssal zones; and *Nereites* facies, which represent abyssal or deep basinal conditions, often associated with turbidites.

Trace fossils are of only limited stratigraphic value; and individual traces are often (in time) long-ranging, since they were produced by several members of a group or even by quite unrelated organisms carrying out the same type of activity. In a few cases, however, notably *trilobite tracks, there is close correlation between hard-part morphology and trace fossils.

Although at first sight an individual trace fossil tells us little, we can find from them much more about the history of life on Earth than from some of the perfectly preserved fossil animals of (comparatively) recent time.   WJK

Vertebrate Animals

Vertebrates are animals with backbones. They comprise five groups; fish, amphibians, reptiles, birds and mammals. Entries dealing with these groups are in evolutionary sequence; that is, the order in which they first appear in the *fossil record and in which they formed dominant elements of the faunas of the past – an order that is so impressive that the history of the Earth is commonly divided into the Age of Fishes, the Age of Amphibians, and so on.

Where more detailed entries, on the varied fish or reptilian types, are included, their sequence is more arbitrary but nevertheless corresponds roughly to the order of their appearance.   AI

Jawless Fishes

Small plates of bone-like material found in middle Ordovician rocks of the USA represent the earliest evidence of vertebrate life. Little is known about the animals that possessed these plates except that they were members of the class Agnatha, the jawless fishes. In addition to their lack of jaws, another primitive feature that they show is the absence of true paired fins, although in some of them fleshy flaps were developed. Both of these features must have imposed limitations on feeding and movement: it is unlikely that they could have chased and captured active, struggling prey.

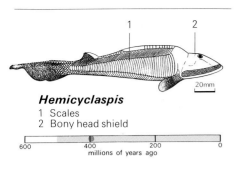

Hemicyclaspis
1 Scales
2 Bony head shield

600   400   200   0
millions of years ago

Evidence of agnathans is most abundant in *Silurian and *Devonian rocks, where they are represented by a great variety of forms commonly known as ostracoderms (shell-skinned). Ostracoderms were small creatures, rarely exceeding 18in (45cm) in length. *Cephalaspis*, a Devonian form, is a well known example. There was a small mouth on the underside of the head and this, together with the general shape of the body, suggests that ostracoderms lived on the sea bottom and fed on organic debris that accumulated on the surface of the mud. The probable method of feeding was to suck in or scoop up the surface mud and the organic debris together. The nutritional disadvantages are obvious.

The earliest ostracoderms lived in shallow marine waters, and this was to remain their chief environment until the end of the Silurian, when several groups adopted a life in the lower reaches of rivers and streams. By the middle Devonian they had added lakes to their range of habitats. Ostracoderms became extinct by the end of the Devonian, and today the lamprey and the hagfish are the only survivors of the ancient agnathan lineage. Both have lost the bony covering seen in their forerunners.

The lamprey is specialized, having adopted a semi-parasitic lifestyle: the mouth is surrounded by a suction disk which is used for attachment to other fish, and there is a rasping tongue to scrape away the host's flesh. Such a mode of feeding may well have developed from the habit that one or two ostracoderms seem to have had of scraping algae off rock. A larval lamprey, however, feeds as the majority of ostracoderms must have done, by sucking in mud.

Studies of ostracoderms have suggested that the original environment of the vertebrates was the sea, and that bone, such a typical vertebrate feature, was first formed in the skin.   PF

Jawed Fishes

The appearance of jaws and associated teeth was one of the most important steps in vertebrate history. Jaws allowed the vertebrates, at that time confined to the water, to capture active prey and so do away with the necessity of sucking in mud, which has generally only a low food-content.

Evidence from the studies of embryology and comparative anatomy suggests that jaws were developed from the front members of the gill-arch series, which lies beneath and behind the braincase. The gill-arches are skeletal structures which support the gills, and when seen from the side each is shaped like a "V" lying on its side, with the apex of the "V" directed backwards.

During the evolution of jaws the front gill-arch became enlarged and the two limbs of the "V" became joined at the apex. This enlarged gill-arch was attached to the braincase by ligaments and moveable joints. In most groups of fish the gill-arch next in line also became modified to provide further support for the jaws.

Together with the development of jaws came the development of two pairs of fins corresponding in position to our arms and legs. These paired fins, the pectorals just behind the head and the pelvics further along the body, helped to control and steer the fish through the water.

Many jawed fishes had thick, heavy scales—seen clearly in this specimen of *Dapedius* from the lower Jurassic beds of Dorset, England.

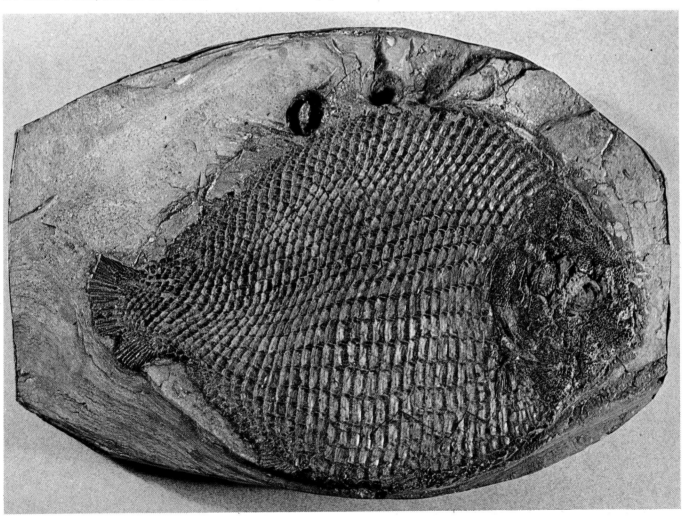

Placoderms

The placoderms or "armored fish" were an exclusively Devonian group of *jawed fishes. A thick armor made of tightly interlocking bony plates covered the head, and this shield was articulated by way of a neck joint with a similarly constructed shield that covered the front part of the trunk. The rest of the trunk and the tail were usually devoid of any bony covering.

There were several different kinds of placoderm. Arthrodires (meaning literally "jointed-neck") were of streamlined shape; and instead of true teeth had large bony shearing blades anchored to the jaws. These features suggest that the arthrodires were active predators – and some, up to 26ft (8m) long, must have been fearsome inhabitants of the late *Devonian seas. The majority were, however, of moderate size, rarely exceeding 3.25ft (1m) in length.

A somewhat curious order of placoderms were the antiarchs. As well as showing the typical placoderm armor, they had a pectoral fin that took the form of a bony appendage rather like a crab's leg. These "limbs" may have been used to raise the front part of the body off the muddy bottom.

The antiarchs were exclusively freshwater dwellers and their remains are found in upper Devonian deposits from all over the world: this distribution is an important addition to the circumstantial evidence suggesting that the land masses of the present world were once conjoined into larger units.

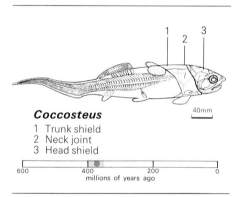

Coccosteus
1 Trunk shield
2 Neck joint
3 Head shield

600   400   200   0
millions of years ago

Cartilaginous Fishes

The cartilaginous fishes, the sharks, rays and the highly specialized ratfish, are first recorded from the middle *Devonian. The name of the group is derived from the fact that the internal skeleton is composed of cartilage, bone being totally absent. The surface of the body is covered with many tiny scales (denticles) instead of large bony plates.

From the beginning the cartilaginous fish were swift, agile predators. The jaws were equipped with many rows of teeth which if lost could be rapidly replaced so that, at any one time, there was always a complete set of razor-sharp teeth.

Most cartilaginous fish of the Paleozoic and early Mesozoic were superficially similar to modern sharks – except for one obvious feature: the base of the pectoral fin

of a Paleozoic shark was very wide, in contrast to the narrow-based fin of later types: the broad-based fin is relatively immobile while the narrow-based fin is more flexible and so allows more rapid turning and upward and downward movement.

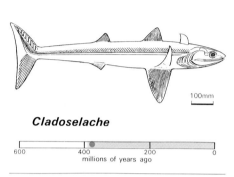

Cladoselache

600   400   200   0
millions of years ago

The first rays are found in the middle *Jurassic, and looked very similar to modern rays. It is probable that they evolved from a shark-like ancestor sometime in the early Mesozoic. The pectoral fins, which were used as the chief propulsive organ, are enormously expanded and merge with the body outline. The tail is reduced to a whip which, in forms such as the stingray, may bear a poisonous spine. Rays feed on hard-shelled invertebrates and for this purpose the jaws are equipped with low-crowned teeth used for crushing.

The cartilaginous fishes were and still are a predominantly marine group. Details of their fossil history are not well known since little of their skeleton is capable of being preserved, so that it is only in occasional circumstances that anything more than teeth and scales is found.

Spiny Sharks

During the Silurian a small group of fishes, the acanthodians or "spiny sharks", made their appearance. Most less than 12in (30cm) in length, they were streamlined and had a body covered with tiny scales which superficially resembled those of sharks: however, the microscopic structure of these scales is completely different, being more like that of *bony-fish scales. The fins comprised a leading spine followed by a thin web of skin. Some early spiny sharks had several small intermediate fins between the pectoral and pelvic fins. Sight must have been important in the life of a spiny shark since the eyes were large.

Spiny sharks lived in medium-depth and surface waters and, although they had large jaws, they frequently did not have any teeth. From this it seems possible that they were plankton feeders, straining food from the surface waters.

Bony Fishes

By far the most numerous and most diverse group of fishes are the bony fishes, the class Osteichthyes; familiar examples include the eel, herring, guppy, perch and cod. Less familiar are the lungfish, coelacanth and the extinct rhipidistians. These last are very

Bony fishes during and after the Cretaceous period underwent a phase of rapid evolution which produced a considerable diversity of body form. *Acanthonemus* has large dorsal and anal fins composed of a small number of fin rays, contrasting with the larger numbers found in more primitive bony fishes.

important as they were probably very similar to the ancestors of the *amphibians, the first vertebrates to conquer the land.

The name of the group is derived from the fact that in the adult the internal and external skeleton is made of bone. The external covering in early bony fishes consisted of thick, tightly fitting, rhomboid scales on the body, and bony plates over the head. Unlike the bony shield of the *placoderms, the head plates could move relative to one another, providing protection with the minimum sacrifice of flexibility. Internally, the early bony fishes had sac-like outgrowths of the esophagus which represent the first stages in the development of lungs.

By middle *Devonian times three major groups of bony fish had become differentiated; the *actinopterygians, the *dipnoans and the *crossopterygians.

Dipnoans

The dipnoans or lungfish are a small group of specialized *bony fish first recorded from the middle *Devonian: today the few surviving species are found in freshwater environments in South America, Africa and Australia. Devonian lungfish show several differences from their actinopterygian contemporaries. The paired fins are limb-like, with the internal skeleton and the muscles extending outside the body. The upper jaw is fused with the braincase, and instead of small teeth there are a few large tooth plates

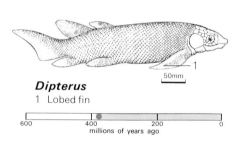

Dipterus
1 Lobed fin

600   400   200   0
millions of years ago

used to crush aquatic plants and hard-shelled invertebrates.

Modern forms have retained the original function of the lung and can breathe air when the pools they inhabit become stagnant. The South American and African lungfish breathe air exclusively for months when encased in cocoons following the seasonal drying-up of their native pools. Since the Devonian, lungfish have changed very little, the chief difference being that in the later forms much of the internal skeleton fails to ossify in the adult and is instead represented by cartilage.

At the turn of the century it was held that lungfish were involved with the ancestry of the *amphibians. This was founded on

superficial resemblances of lungfish fins to the amphibian limb and the common habit of air-breathing. However, more thorough studies have shown that the lungfish are not amphibian relatives but represent a highly specialized lineage of bony fish.

Crossopterygians

The crossopterygians or tassel-fin fishes include the coelacanths and the extinct rhipidistians. They have paired fins outwardly like those of *dipnoans, but lack the latters' skull specializations.

The coelacanths, like the lungfish, are a conservative group, the Devonian forms being little different from later types. The body is plump and the tail has equally developed upper and lower lobes with, between them, a small central lobe. Most of the Paleozoic coelacanths inhabited fresh water but during the Mesozoic many adopted a life in the sea.

It was long believed that the coelacanths had died out in the upper Cretaceous: however, in 1938, a fisherman off the coast of South Africa hauled in a strange-looking fish quickly recognized on reaching port as a coelacanth. Many more specimens of *Latimeria* have now been recovered. Great interest centers around "old fourlegs" since it is the nearest living fish relative of the land-dwelling vertebrates and the extinct rhipidistians.

The earliest rhipidistians are found in lower *Devonian rocks and the latest from the lower *Permian. Most lived in fresh water. Their most interesting feature is that they very probably share a common ancestor with the amphibians.

An example is *Eusthenopteron*, one of the best known fossil fishes. The plump body was about 1.6ft (0.5m) long, with the dorsal and anal fins far back near the tail. The head was large and the mouth particularly so. The overall picture suggests a lifestyle similar to that of the modern pike, lying quietly among the vegetation and darting out to snap at passing prey. Inside the mouth were batteries of small teeth as well as a few large tusks. If one of these tusks is cut across and examined under a microscope, it can be seen that the enamel coat is infolded into the dentine core in a labyrinth pattern. This is significantly similar to the kind of tooth found in labyrinthodont *amphibians.

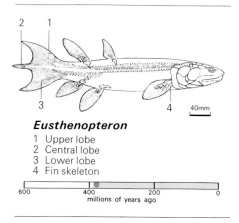

Eusthenopteron
1 Upper lobe
2 Central lobe
3 Lower lobe
4 Fin skeleton

600   400   200   0
millions of years ago

Another characteristic seen in both rhipidistians and land-dwelling vertebrates is the internal nostril, a feature associated with air-breathing; so it is generally assumed that rhipidistians used lungs much as do the modern amphibians and lungfish (although lungfish do not have true internal nostrils). The characteristic red color of many Devonian rocks is often taken to indicate that arid conditions were prevailing at that time, so that the presumed ability of rhipidistians to breathe air would have had definite survival value.

Behind the head, the spine was composed of bony vertebrae which were very similar in construction to those of the early amphibians. In the paired fins were bones perfectly comparable with the bones of the upper and lower segments of the amphibian fore and hind limb: however, fingers and toes were absent. Significantly, the shape of the limb bones indicates that the limb muscles of *Eusthenopteron* were capable of rotating the limb to a considerable degree (a feature actually observed in a modern coelacanth). This rotation is a prerequisite for walking on land. Indeed *Eusthenopteron* and its allies appear to have been capable of taking short excursions onto the land, and may well have done so to escape the stagnant pools in which they were living.

By the later Devonian the amphibian had appeared, and so the history of the land-dwelling vertebrates had begun. The history of the fishes saw a gradual replacement of primitive Devonian types by fishes superior in swimming and feeding abilities. The present fish fauna is dominated by the *actinopterygians and the *cartilaginous fishes.

Actinopterygians

The ray-finned fishes or actinopterygians are distinguished from other *bony fish by the structure of their paired fins: the muscles which move the fins are inside the body, so that the only parts of the fin visible from the outside are the slender rays which support the web of skin.

*Devonian actinopterygians were streamlined in shape with large eyes, indicating that sight rather than smell was important in the life of these predatory fishes. The jaws were long and had many pointed teeth. These early forms are called *chondrosteans* and were predominantly a Paleozoic group, though a few, such as the sturgeon, survive today. Though the sturgeon is a highly specialized form, it still has the long, upturned tail seen in extinct chondrosteans.

During the Mesozoic the actinopterygian lineage was represented by the holosteans and teleosts. Most holosteans still had the early type of scale forming a tough body covering, but other features indicate improvements in swimming and feeding ability. The lungs became modified to form a swim-bladder, lying above the center of gravity of the fish and functioning as a float chamber, so that the body of the fish approached neutral buoyancy, an energy-saving development since it eliminated the

need for constant swimming in order to stay at one level in the water. Concomitant with this development, the tail became shorter and less upturned and produced a more nearly horizontal thrust than did the chondrostean tail which tended to drive the head of the animal downwards, an obvious disadvantage.

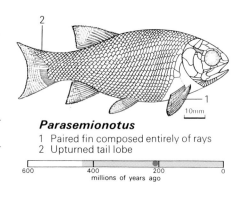

Parasemionotus
1 Paired fin composed entirely of rays
2 Upturned tail lobe

600   400   200   0
millions of years ago

Holosteans were a varied group. Some forms such as the *Jurassic *Dapedius* were deep-bodied with teeth adapted for crushing, while *Aspidorhynchus*, also a Jurassic type, was elongate with a long, bill-like nose. Most became extinct by the end of the Mesozoic, though two forms, the bowfin and the garpike, survive today in freshwater environments in North America.

By the end of the *Triassic early teleosts had appeared. The teleosts are the largest and most diverse group of actinopterygians, about 20,000 species being extant today.

The evolutionary trends seen in the teleost fishes parallel those in the holosteans, but went much further. The jaws became shorter and more mobile. The tail became outwardly symmetrical resulting in a perfectly horizontal thrust, and this, plus the fact that there was a well developed swimbladder, obviated the need for rigid pectoral fins to act as hydrofoils: indeed, in the great majority, the pectorals moved to lie high up on the side of the body so that they could be used as brakes for rapid stopping and to aid in quick turning. The scales became thin, circular and overlapping, protection thus being sacrificed for flexibility, in contrast to the holosteans and chondrosteans. Most of these trends resulted in unsurpassed ability to maneuver in the water.

Although the teleosts are known from the early Mesozoic, it is not until the lower *Cretaceous that their remains are abundant. By this time several surviving groups had arisen: the tarpons, the herrings, the osteoglossomorphs, and extinct relatives of the salmon and trout. Later in the Cretaceous there is evidence of primitive members of two important lineages. One, the spiny-rayed teleosts, comprising the largest and most diversified group of teleosts, is today exemplified by the perch, mackerel, plaice and angelfish: as the name suggests, these fishes have spines in the dorsal and anal fins. The other includes the cod, whiting and anglerfish. The Cenozoic saw the appearance of a very large group of freshwater fishes which includes the minnows, carps and catfish. Recent research suggests they had marine ancestors in the Cretaceous.   PF

Amphibians

It is in many ways unfortunate that the word "amphibian" is used to describe the early, Paleozoic vertebrates which first colonized the land. The word certainly describes their ability to live both on land and in the water. Like most modern amphibians, they also laid and fertilized their eggs in the water, and these eggs developed into aquatic larvae with gills, which only later emerged onto the land. But "amphibian" makes most people think of the little living forms, such as frogs, newts and salamanders, which are very different from their remote Paleozoic ancestors. The main difference lies in the fact that living amphibians respire not only through the lungs but also through the skin: the skin must therefore be kept moist, and amphibians consequently continuously lose water through it. This limits both their size and the range of habitats they can colonize; they are unable to survive for long in dry environments or in the sea.

Paleozoic amphibians cannot yet have developed this peculiar specialization, for many had a covering of scales or, more rarely, a dry leathery skin. They were therefore able to grow to a much greater size, and a few took to the seas.

Origin of the Amphibia. Amphibians evolved from the rhipidistian lobe-finned fishes (see *crossopterygians). These fish had not only lungs but also, as their name implies, rather stout, muscular fins which could have supported them on land. They probably first crawled ashore as juveniles, trying to escape the attacks of larger predatory fish. Able both to breathe and to move about on land, they would have found also a new and unexploited source of food in the insects and other invertebrates then beginning their own invasion of the land.

This situation provided the opportunity for the first step in the vertebrates' conquest of the land. The amphibian step was, however, a very hesitant one. It appears that the overwhelming majority of the Paleozoic amphibians spent all, or nearly all, of their lives in the water. This may be partly illusion: the majority of the deposits from which we know *Carboniferous amphibians were laid down in the coalswamps of the northern hemisphere, whose inhabitants would of necessity have been aquatic. Possibly other, more terrestrial amphibians lived on higher, drier ground. But *reptiles evolved from amphibians in the middle to late Carboniferous; so the reason that we know very few land-dwelling amphibians is probably that competition from the reptiles excluded them from a terrestrial way of life. This is also the reason for the gradual disappearance of nearly all the amphibians during the late Permian and the Triassic.

Paleozoic amphibians can be subdivided into two groups according to a difference in the structure of the vertebral column. In the first group, the lepospondyls, that part of each vertebra that lies below the spinal cord is made up of a single bone. In the other group, the apsidospondyls, this region is made up instead of several blocks of bone: they are often called labyrinthodonts because the enamel tooth surface is folded into the center of the tooth in labyrinthine fashion.

Labyrinthodonts. The earliest known amphibian is *Ichthyostega*, from the latest Devonian of Greenland. Its skull had no trace of the "operculum" which covers and protects the gills of fish, so it presumably did not have gills (at least during adulthood), and must have breathed through its lungs alone – its body was covered with fish-like scales so it cannot have respired through the skin. The fins of its fish ancestors had become stout limbs, the upper parts projecting sideways from the body, which was thus suspended between them rather than supported above them: this posture is found in most amphibians and reptiles.

Later labyrinthodonts are divided into two groups, the temnospondyls and the anthracosaurs, which differ in the details of construction of the vertebrae. The temnospondyls include the greater number and variety. Most were aquatic, with a rounded body and slightly elongated skull with many teeth: they probably fed on fish. The rather small size of their limbs shows that they would have found it difficult to move on land.

By the early Permian had appeared such semiaquatic crocodile-like types as *Eryops*, whose broad skulls suggest that they may have preyed on other amphibians or even lurked in the water for reptiles that came down to drink. Some little amphibians with gills, once placed in a separate group known as the branchiosaurs, were in fact the aquatic larvae of such forms as *Eryops*, showing that the life history of these Paleozoic forms was indeed the same as that of living amphibians. A few totally terrestrial types, the dissorophids such as little *Cacops*, are also known from the early Permian.

Other temnospondyls developed an extremely elongate, narrow many-toothed snout, like that of the modern fish-eating crocodile, the gavial. Some of these, the Permian archegosaurs, lived in fresh waters, but the Triassic trematosaurs took to the seas – the only marine amphibians known.

The Triassic temnospondyls were all semiaquatic, with wide, flattened skulls. In some, the capitosaurs and metoposaurs, the skulls were quite long; while in others, the plagiosaurs, it was very short: types such as *Gerrothorax* probably lay open-mouthed on the bottom, attracting fish by means of a

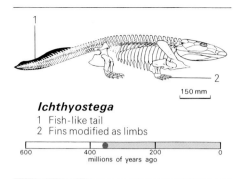

Ichthyostega
1 Fish-like tail
2 Fins modified as limbs

600   400   200   0
millions of years ago

colored fleshy lure.

The other major group of labyrinthodonts, the anthracosaurs, contains both aquatic and terrestrial forms: aquatic types are called embolomeres. Some were fisheaters, such as *Eogyrinus*, an elongate Carboniferous amphibian about 13ft (4m) long. Its relative, *Archeria*, of the early Permian, about 6.5ft (2m) long and with a fish-like fin on its long tail, had a number of small, peg-like teeth and may have fed on tiny animals which it strained out of the water.

The terrestrial anthracosaurs, known as seymouriamorphs, include the only large terrestrial amphibians known. *Seymouria* itself, from the early Permian of Texas, was 5ft (1.5m) long and seemed so completely adapted to a terrestrial way of life that it was classified as a reptile until it was discovered that its young lived in the water, showing that it was really an amphibian. Its relative *Diadectes* was even larger, some 10ft (3m) long: its bulky body and flattened grinding teeth suggest that it was a herbivore – if so, it is the only known herbivorous amphibian. Though reptiles are probably descended from the seymouriamorph anthracosaurs, they evolved from that group much earlier, during the Carboniferous.

Lepospondyls. Unlike the labyrinthodonts, the lepospondyls were all quite small – most were only 4–6in (10–15cm) long. The majority were completely aquatic and lived during the Carboniferous. Some, such as *Ophiderpeton* and *Phlegethontia*, were limbless and elongate, swimming by side-to-side undulations of the body, like water snakes today. Others, such as *Microbrachis*, retained their limbs and were more newt-like. Only a few early Permian relatives of *Microbrachis* had sturdier limbs and were, at least as adults, apparently wholly terrestrial.

Modern Amphibians. Modern forms are in three groups: the tailless frogs and toads; newts and salamanders; and the limbless, burrowing apodans. These groups represent the only ways of life to which amphibians have been able to cling in face of competition from the reptiles.

Though quite different from one another in appearance, they share a number of specializations, such as peculiar, hinged teeth and use of the skin for respiration, suggesting that they probably evolved from a single Paleozoic group by a single original line of descent, diverging later; but the identity of this group is still uncertain. Both

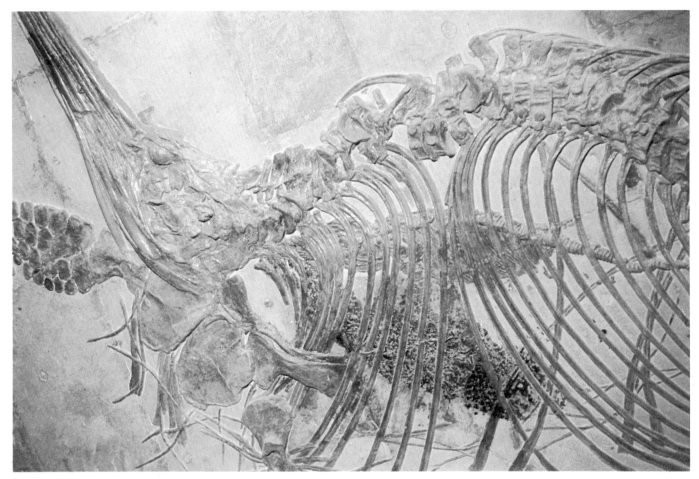

The vast majority of living reptiles lay eggs. Here we see evidence that marine reptiles of the Mesozoic, the ichthyosaurs, were able to bear live young. An immature *Ichthyosaurus* can be seen within the body cavity of its parent. Below this unborn young it is possible to see the remains of the adult's stomach contents.

the dissorophid temnospondyls and the *Cardiocephalus*-like lepospondyls have features that suggest that they may have been ancestors of the modern amphibians, but intermediate forms are unknown.

The earliest known frog is the Triassic *Triadobatrachus*, already showing the start of the great shortening of the body and enlargement of the hind limbs associated with the jumping habits of this group. Newts and salamanders did not appear until the late Cretaceous; and the apodans not until the Paleocene, but it is not surprising that few remains of these little, frail-boned creatures have been preserved. CBC

Reptiles

The hard or leathery egg-shell, protecting its contents from desiccation and small predators, is the characteristic feature of reptiles. They are classified primarily by the skull structure. In the most primitive, the *cotylosaurs, and their specialized descendants the *turtles, the skull roof is solid except for openings for the eyes and nostrils: this type of skull is known as *anapsid*.

In all other reptiles, openings appeared

behind the eyes to reduce the weight of the skull. The *synapsid* type is found in the *mammal-like reptiles, the *parapsid* type in the aquatic *placodonts, *plesiosaurs and nothosaurs.

The commonest skull type is *diapsid*, present not only in *lizards and *snakes but also in the great group of archosaurian reptiles – the *dinosaurs and their ancestors the *thecodonts, their relatives the *crocodiles and *pterosaurs, and their descendants, the *birds.

Reptiles evolved in the early *Carboniferous, and were the dominant land vertebrates from the early *Permian until the end of the *Mesozoic, when the mammals became dominant.

Cotylosaurs

This group of anapsid *reptiles includes three different types. The captorhinomorphs include the earliest known reptiles, from the early *Carboniferous. Similar to modern lizards in size and appearance, and probably also in diet, they survived until the late *Permian.

The second group were the pareiasaurs, which were up to 10ft (3m) long. The many teeth and clumsy, lumbering body suggest that they were herbivores: if so, they were the first successful reptilian herbivores; but their success was short-lived, for they are found only from the late *Permian. Their extinction may have been due to competition from the dicynodont *mammal-like reptiles.

The third type are the procolophonids,

20 inches (0.5m) long, with skulls often ornamented with protective spikes of bone. Probably omnivorous, procolophonids appeared in the late *Permian and survived until the end of the *Triassic. It is possible that they were the ancestors of the *turtles.

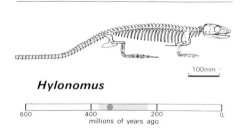

Hylonomus

600   400   200   0
millions of years ago

Turtles and Tortoises

Their unique bony shell, fused to the ribs and the outer surfaces of the vertebrae, is the most obvious characteristic of these animals, the order Chelonia. They are the only surviving anapsid *reptiles, and probably owe their survival to the protective shell. The first chelonian, *Proganochelys*, appeared in the late *Triassic. It was already completely tortoise-like except that it still had teeth. Many of the *Jurassic and some *Cretaceous chelonians, in which the specializations of the neck vertebrae found in later forms had not yet appeared, are placed in a suborder, Amphichelydia.

These specializations involve two different methods, both of which appeared in the early Cretaceous, of withdrawing the head into the shell. The neck is flexed sideways in the suborder Pleurodira, which is mainly confined to the southern hemisphere and includes only a few living forms; while in the suborder Cryptodira the neck is flexed vertically. This latter suborder includes most living chelonians, including terrestrial, freshwater and marine forms.

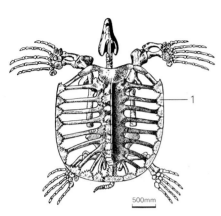

Archelon
1 Armor plates attached to ribs

600   400   200   0
millions of years ago

Ichthyosaurs

Just as seals and *whales evolved from land mammals, so some *reptiles found new opportunities in returning to the sea. One of these groups, the ichthyosaurs (the others were the *plesiosaurs and nothosaurs, and the *placodonts), developed a very porpoise-like appearance. They had fish-like propulsive tails, soft dorsal fins and streamlined bodies, which were leathery and had no scales. The limbs have become small, inflexible paddles which can have been used only for steering and certainly not for support on land, so it is not surprising to find some specimens containing the skeletons of young individuals, indicating that ichthyosaurs almost certainly bore living young, as do sea-snakes today.

Most ichthyosaurs were about 10ft (3m) long, but specimens 40ft (12m) long are known. They had a long, narrow snout with many short teeth, and must have fed on fish and ammonoids.

The first ichthyosaurs, known as mixosaurs, evolved in the middle *Triassic. At that time the tail was still low and elongate. An unusual Triassic group, the omphalosaurs, had a short, strongly-built skull and stout, blunt teeth, which they probably used for crushing mollusk shells.

Ichthyosaurs became common and diverse in the *Jurassic, and are found in marine deposits in most parts of the world. They are divided into "longipinnate" forms, in which the paddles contained only five elongated fingers, and "latipinnate" forms, in which the paddles were shorter but broader, containing up to four extra fingers. The latipinnate forms were the more successful: the longipinnates did not survive beyond the early Cretaceous.

Ichthyosaurs continued into the *Cretaceous, but were less common. Though they became extinct somewhat before the end of the Cretaceous, their disappearance is part of a general pattern of extinction at that time of so many creatures on land and in the sea and air.

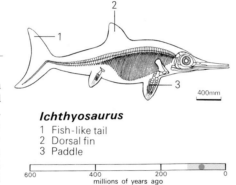

Ichthyosaurus
1 Fish-like tail
2 Dorsal fin
3 Paddle

600   400   200   0
millions of years ago

Plesiosaurs and Nothosaurs

Plesiosaurs and nothosaurs had the characteristic parapsid skull and a long series of pointed teeth. Like the *ichthyosaurs and *placodonts, they were reptiles which returned to the sea; but, unlike the ichthyosaurs, they retained their limbs as a method of propulsion instead of developing a fish-like tail. They had a rather inflexible spindle-shaped body, and their limbs became enlarged into powerful paddles. In life, the paddles were probably used rather

like those of turtles today, with a graceful up and down stroke rather like a bird's wing in slow motion. Most must have fed on fish.

The nothosaurs were the first to appear, in the middle *Triassic. Up to 3.25ft (1m) long, they seem to have lived mainly in the coastal waters of Tethys, the sea that covered parts of Europe and the Middle East at that time. But they have been found also in shore deposits, and so had not yet become as thoroughly adapted to marine life as did the plesiosaurs. This is also apparent from their limbs, for their hands and feet were merely webbed and slightly elongated, and did not develop into large paddles. Nothosaurs ranged from 1ft (30cm) to 20ft (6m) in length, and became extinct before the end of the Triassic, probably due to competition from the plesiosaurs.

These appeared in the late Triassic, probably from a nothosaur ancestor. They can be divided into two groups whose most obvious difference is in the length of neck. The Plesiosauroidea had a long neck, with up to 44 vertebrae, and a rather small head. They may have used the flexible neck in catching their maneuverable food, fish. The creatures themselves were from 10 to 42ft (3-13m) long. The Pliosauroidea, in contrast, had a large head on a shorter neck. They became common in the middle Jurassic. Some, like *Stretosaurus* and *Kronosaurus*, were 40ft (12m) long with a massive head. Just as sperm whales today feed on squid, these pliosaurs fed mainly on a type of cephalopod, the *ammonoids, whose remains have been found inside their skeletons.

All the plesiosaurs became extinct at the end of the *Cretaceous.

Placodonts

Like the *ichthyosaurs and *plesiosaurs, placodonts were reptiles which returned to the sea to live. But, unlike most other marine reptiles, they were specialized for a diet of *mollusks. To pull the mollusks from rocks, or to dig them up, the front end of the jaws bore forwardly directed teeth or horny beaks. The shells were then cracked between enormous flattened teeth, set into strongly built jaws.

Placodonts lived in the Tethys, and propelled themselves by their long tails and their flipper-like paddles, the body being short and inflexible. Later forms, such as

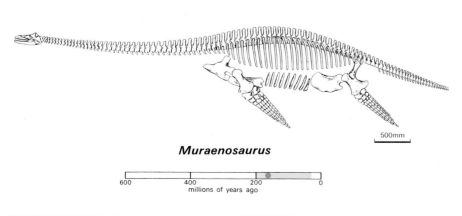

Muraenosaurus

600   400   200   0
millions of years ago

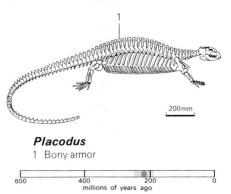

Placodus
1 Bony armor

600   400   200   0
millions of years ago

An almost perfectly preserved specimen of the Triassic nothosaur *Ceresiosaurus*. Unlike the related plesiosaurs, nothosaurs did not have paddles; their limbs were relatively unmodified although these reptiles were undoubtedly aquatic.

Placodus and *Henodus*, had a very turtle-like armor of bone, but differing from that of *turtles in being composed of a large number of bony plates, and in not being attached to the ribs and vertebrae. The ventral armor was also flexible, to allow the animal to breathe by expanding and contracting the volume of the body. *Henodus* also resembled turtles in having strong horny plates in place of teeth.

Placodonts ranged in size from 3.25 to 6.5ft (1–2m). They were a short-lived group, becoming extinct by the end of the Triassic.

Snakes

These reptiles, which originally had a diapsid skull, are descended from *lizards, in which the amount of bone in the skull is reduced. The process is taken even further in snakes, both pairs of holes in the skull losing their lower borders so that the skull becomes very flexible. Together with hinges in the lower jaw, whose right and left halves can also swing apart at the front end, these features make it possible for snakes to swallow in one piece prey that is larger than their own body diameter.

Apart from a short-lived middle *Cretaceous group, the earliest known snake is *Dinilysia* from the late Cretaceous. This appears to be related to snakes such as boas which kill their prey by constricting and so suffocating them. The smaller type of snake, known as colubroids, which includes 90% of living snakes, are not known until the *Eocene. However, their remains are more difficult to find than those of larger snakes, and the group almost certainly originated much earlier, probably in the Cretaceous.

Several types of colubroid snake de-

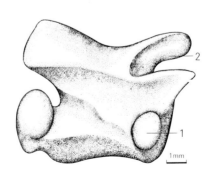

Coniophis

Snake vertebra
1 Articulation facet for rib
2 Articulation facet for adjoining vertebra

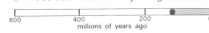

600   400   200   0
millions of years ago

veloped poison, which can be injected into their prey by means of enlarged fangs. The elapids, in which the fangs are fixed, and the viperids, with fangs which can be rotated back up into the roof of the mouth when not in use, are both first known from the *Miocene but probably evolved much earlier.

Lizards

These evolved from the later captorhinomorph *cotylosaurs. Their earliest known ancestors are the paliguanids from the late *Permian to early *Triassic: the skulls of these had already evolved from diapsid to distinctly lizard-like. An unchanged diapsid skull is found only in the rhynchocephalian line, which led to the peculiar herbivorous rhynchosaurs of the Triassic, and to the modern tuatara, *Sphenodon*.

The hallmark of true lizards was the rapid lightening of the skull by the loss of bone. Despite its lightness, the skull retains strength by becoming very flexible. The earliest known true lizards are the very specialized *Kuehneosaurus* and *Icarosaurus* from the late Triassic. Our knowledge of *Jurassic and *Cretaceous lizards is still very imperfect. At least six of the eleven or twelve modern superfamilies had appeared by the late Jurassic, and they must have increased in variety and abundance in the early Jurassic to achieve an importance similar to that which they show today. They also gave rise to a group of marine lizards, the early Cretaceous aigialosaurs, whose late Cretaceous descendants, the mosasaurs, were up to 20ft (6m) long and swam by means of a powerful tail. It was also from the lizards that *snakes evolved.

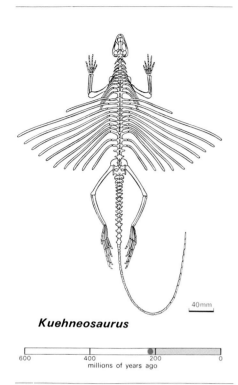

Kuehneosaurus

40mm

600 400 200 0
millions of years ago

Thecodonts

The thecodonts were the ancestral group of all the archosaurian reptiles, and therefore directly or indirectly the ancestors not only of the *dinosaurs and *pterosaurs, but also of the *crocodiles and *birds. They had strongly-built diapsid skulls, and diversified into a wide variety of Triassic reptiles whose interrelationships are still only imperfectly understood. However, three main types can be recognized: amphibious forms, bipedal terrestrial forms, and quadrupedal terrestrial forms. Though such a division may not accurately reflect their evolutionary relationships, the thecodonts as a whole are best understood by considering them in this way.

Surprisingly, the earliest known thecodonts, *Proterosuchus* (*Chasmatosaurus*) and its relatives, were already amphibious forms. 3.25 to 6.5ft (1–2m) long, these animals were crocodile-like in appearance, with powerful elongate jaws, though the front end of the upper jaw was turned down in a strange fashion. They are found only in the early *Triassic; but may have given rise to the two other semiaquatic types, the poorly-known proterochampsids of the middle and late Triassic, and the late-Triassic phytosaurs. The latter, too, looked very like crocodiles, but have an obvious distinguishing feature: their nostrils are positioned just in front of their eyes rather than at the end of the elongate snout. Phytosaurs are little known from the southern hemisphere.

Though it probably normally walked on

all fours, *Euparkeria* of the early Triassic could move on two legs when running fast. It may have been the ancestor of the later large bipedal carnivorous thecodonts, such as *Ornithosuchus*. Ten feet (3m) long, this late Triassic thecodont is barely distinguishable from a small dinosaur.

The quadrupedal thecodonts, too, appeared quite early – in the form of *Erythrosuchus*. Stockily-built and 11.5ft (3.5m) long, this early Triassic animal had a massive head and must have been a formidable carnivore, preying on *mammal-like reptiles. It was probably ancestral to the variety of quadrupedal thecodonts found later in the Triassic. Most of these were carnivorous, but they include also two late Triassic herbivorous groups – the aetosaurs, pig-like root-grubbers with bands of bony armor, and the stagonolepids.

Though the dinosaurs, crocodiles and probably pterosaurs descended from the thecodonts, the thecodont group from which each evolved is still uncertain. But the disappearance of the thecodonts at the end of the Triassic must have been due to competition from their descendants.

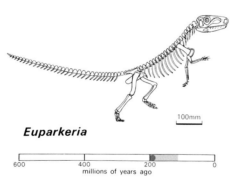

Euparkeria

100mm

600 400 200 0
millions of years ago

Pterosaurs

Though these flying reptiles, relatives of the dinosaurs, are often called pterodactyls, that name should really only be applied to the more advanced of the two suborders of pterosaur, the more primitive being known as the rhamphorhynchoids.

Though they had a leathery flight membrane like a bat's, that of pterosaurs was borne behind the elongated wrist and fourth finger, not spread across several fingers. The first three fingers are of normal size, and must have been used for grasping and for support when at rest. The flight membrane continued alongside the body to the hind limbs, which were small and weak.

Pterosaurs are usually found in marine deposits, and it seems likely that they were fish-eaters, flying out to sea in search of their prey. Their wings were large, and they must have mostly glided. They probably lived on sea cliffs, since on flat terrain they would have been vulnerable to predators and would have found it difficult to become airborne. They had diapsid skulls, and probably evolved from the *Triassic *thecodonts, but nothing is known of their ancestry.

The primitive rhamphorhynchoids appeared first at the end of the *Triassic and survived throughout the *Jurassic. They had long tails ending in a vertical rudder membrane, a relatively short wrist, and a wing-span of up to 3.25ft (1m).

They were replaced fairly suddenly in the late Jurassic by their descendants the pterodactyloids, in which the tail was reduced to a stump and the wrist bones were more elongate. In many pterodactyloids the teeth were reduced or lost and replaced by a horny beak.

They ranged from the sparrow-sized *Pterodactylus* to *Pteranodon*, with a wingspan of nearly 23ft (7m) and a large crest projecting from the back of its head. An unusual recent find was the partial skeleton of an enormous pterodactyloid, *Quetzalcoatlus*, whose wing-span may have been 40ft (12m): apart from its great size, it was exceptional in being found far inland.

The sparrow-sized pterodactyloids are found only in the late Jurassic, but the pteranodontids survived until the end of the *Cretaceous. Though the rise of the *birds from the late Jurassic onward may have contributed to their extinction, it is probably significant that their final disappearance at the end of the Cretaceous coincided with the extinction of so many other animals both on land and in the sea.

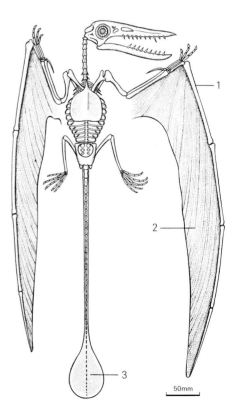

Rhamphorhynchus

1 Fourth finger
2 Flight membrane
3 Rudder membrane

50mm

600 400 200 0
millions of years ago

Some of the finest dinosaur fossils have been recovered from Dinosaur National Monument, Utah, USA. These bones are the remains of individuals drowned in a river and deposited on a sandbank where accumulation of sediment was extremely rapid.

Dinosaurs

No other time has such a romantic appeal as the period between 200 million and 65 million years ago, when the world was dominated by dinosaurs. Not only because of the great varieties of type, including some of immense size and others with a bizarre armor of plates and spikes of bone, but also because of their still unexplained sudden disappearance, dinosaurs fascinate our imaginations.

Dinosaurs were reptiles, and therefore laid eggs, some of which have been found in the sands of the Gobi Desert and elsewhere. But not all large reptiles are dinosaurs, and dinosaurs themselves can be divided into two great groups which may have evolved independently from ancestral *thecodonts. These two groups, the Saurischia and the Ornithischia, can be easily distinguished from one another by their pelvic girdles.

Both groups appeared first during the second half of the *Triassic and had evolved into a variety of different types by the end of that period. Because the Earth then contained only a single supercontinent, Pangaea, with few great mountain ranges, and because the climate was mild and uniform, these early dinosaurs soon spread throughout the world.

Saurischian Dinosaurs. These were the first dinosaurs to appear, in the middle Triassic. Though several different saurischians are known from the late Triassic, most of these were not ancestors of the later, Jurassic, dinosaurs, but were instead members of a separate group known as the prosauropods. They had a long neck and tail, and a fairly bulky body. Though some may have been flesh-eaters, most had smaller, serrated teeth better suited to a diet of plants. Like most herbivores, they had begun to increase in size. Some, such as *Thecodontosaurus* were only 6.5–10ft (2–3m) long and, though they normally walked on all four legs, probably reared onto their hind legs to feed on higher foliage or to run fast, their long tails helping to balance the rest of the body. Larger forms, such as *Messospondylous* and *Plateosaurus*, 20ft (6m) long, may have been able to rear up on two legs when feeding, but would not have been able to run in this fashion.

The prosauropods became extinct at the end of the Triassic: their successors probably evolved from early prosauropods. These successors, the sauropods, are the great quadrupedal herbivores which dominate the museums of the world today as they must have dominated Jurassic and Cretaceous landscapes. From the 91ft (28m) long *Diplodocus* to the 39ft (12m) high, 100 ton *Brachiosaurus*, these animals hold all the size and weight records for terrestrial animals.

With massive legs and long necks and tails, sauropods have often been portrayed as amphibious animals, living in lakes and streams. This has been based mainly on the belief that their limbs would have been unable to support the weight of their bodies. But it is difficult to see how these great animals would have been able to find enough plant food in such an environment. Also, their comparatively small feet would have sunk into the mud, fatally trapping them. It has similarly been suggested that the long neck of the sauropod evolved to enable it to move in deep water and still keep its head above water. But the body would then have been so far below the surface that water-pressure would have made it impossible for it to expand its chest to breathe air into its lungs. For these reasons, many paleontologists now believe that sauropods lived on land, where plant food is much more abundant, and used their long necks in giraffe-like fashion to feed on the foliage of tall trees.

Alongside these quadrupedal herbivores lived a variety of both large and small carnivorous saurischians, all bipedal. The smaller ones, called coelurosaurs, first appeared in the late Triassic. Such little, slenderly built forms as *Coelophysis* had long flexible necks and a long balancing tail. Even smaller coelurosaurs existed in the Jurassic, *Compsognathus* being only the size of a chicken.

The coelurosaurs had long hind legs and must have been fast-moving. They survived until the end of the Cretaceous, latterly giving rise to the ornithomimids, which looked rather like an ostrich with long arms. Nearly 10ft (3m) long, these very slender, long-legged dinosaurs clearly did not prey on other animals of similar size, for they had no claws or teeth, their rather weak jaws bearing a horny beak.

The existence of such massive herbivores provided the opportunity for the evolution of carnivores large enough to take advantage of this source of food. Like their great prey, the carnosaurs appeared at the start of the Jurassic, when such forms as *Megalosaurus* were already up to 30ft (9m) long. Carnosaurs had massive heads and hind limbs and short, heavy necks, but the forelimbs were comparatively small and bore three powerful clawed fingers.

Towards the end of the Cretaceous, the largest megalosaurids were replaced by their descendants, the tyrannosaurids, the largest and most formidable carnivores the world has ever known. This type of carnosaur is distinguished by having very tiny forelimbs, ending in two clawed fingers: the function of these little limbs is uncertain. The best known tyrannosaur is *Tyrannosaurus* itself, which was 50ft (15m) long and 16–20ft (5–6m) high.

Ornithischian Dinosaurs. The first of the ornithischians appeared in the late Triassic, with such little metre-long bipedal forms as *Fabrosaurus*. These not only had the characteristic pelvis of ornithischians, but also, like all members of that group, had a horny beak in place of front teeth. This

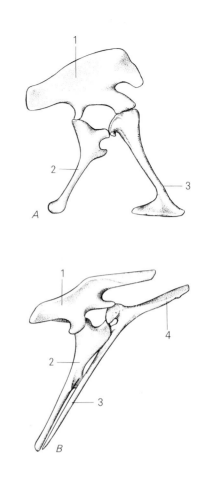

The two types of pelvic girdle found in dinosaurs. (A) The saurischian type and (B) the ornithischian type. Ilium (1), ischium (2), pubis (3) and front process of the pubis (4).

may have been one of the reasons why all the ornithischians seem to have been herbivores or omnivores. Their success as herbivores may also have been due to the fact that, like mammals but unlike most reptiles, they apparently had muscular cheeks which helped retain the food and force it into the battery of many leaf-like teeth. Most ornithischians probably stayed on all fours when at rest or moving slowly, but could rise up onto their hind legs for fast movement, the body being balanced by a rather stiff, inflexible tail.

Few early Jurassic forms are known. Larger ornithischians, known as ornithopods, had appeared in the middle Jurassic, but the best-known is even later, *Hypsilophodon* from the early Cretaceous. Very like *Fabrosaurus* in general proportions, it was about 5ft (1.5m) long. Though at one time it was thought that it was semi-arboreal, it has now been recognized as a normal terrestrial dinosaur.

Larger ornithopods evolved from the hypsilophodonts during the Jurassic and Cretaceous. The most conservative were the iguanodonts, which were little more than enlarged versions of *Hypsilophodon*. *Iguanodon* itself was about 16ft (5m) high

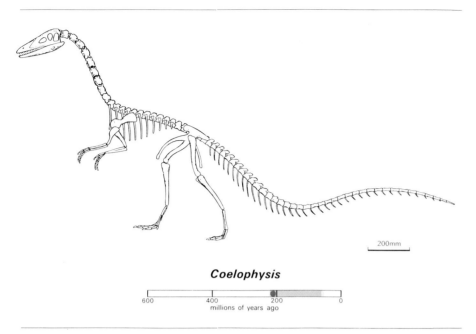

200mm

Coelophysis

600   400   200   0
millions of years ago

and 36ft (11m) long, and weighed about 4.5 tons. Its forelimbs were quite large, and the thumb had become modified into a spike-like structure whose function is still uncertain.

From the iguanodonts in turn came the bizarre hadrosaurs, which first appeared in the early Cretaceous. 30ft (9m) long and weighing about 3 tons, they are sometimes called the duck-billed dinosaurs because of the flattened shape of their horny beaks, behind which was an even more extensive battery of teeth than that found in other ornithischians. But the most remarkable feature of most of them was the extension of the bones of the forehead into a variety of weird crests and horns, through which ran the nasal passages. The most likely explanation of these structures is that they served a social function in these herbivores, which probably lived in herds, much as antlers affect the social structure of modern herds of deer. Moreover, the crest's hollow cavities would have magnified the bellows and cries of the animals. Some scientists have suggested that hadrosaurs

were semi-aquatic, but the facts that their fingers and toes bore hooves, and that the fossilized stomach contents of one hadrosaur contains the remains of land plants and conifer needles, indicate otherwise.

A rather similar function has been suggested for the greatly thickened skull roofs that give the name "dome-heads" to another group of ornithopods, the pachycephalosaurs. Otherwise rather like *Hypsilophodon*, these animals had skull roofs 2in (5cm) thick, and it is thought that these were used in mating battles, the males charging each other head on, as rams do today, until the lighter male submitted to his more powerful adversary.

The remaining ornithischians were all completely quadrupedal descendants of the ornithopods, having developed defensive plates and spikes of bone. The earliest, the 13ft (4m) long stegosaurs of the middle and late Jurassic, had a line of projecting triangular plates or spikes protecting their backs. This group was replaced in the early Cretaceous by the ankylosaurs, whose backs were covered by bony plates, knobs

or spikes, forming a close protective carapace. Up to 16ft (5m) in length and 5 tons in weight, they must have been cumbersome and slow-moving.

The ceratopians, which appeared in the late Cretaceous, were better equipped to defend themselves, for the head of most was armed with rhinoceros-like horns. They originally owed their success to their very large heads, with powerful jaws whose muscles were attached to a bony frill which projected backwards over the creature's neck. The earliest, 6.5ft (2m) long *Protoceratops*, was hornless, but later forms had a nasal horn and usually also a pair of horns above the eyes. The largest, *Triceratops*, was 36ft (11m) long, and must have weighed about 8.5 tons.

The Distribution of Dinosaurs in Space and Time. Most of the major types of dinosaur seem to have appeared in the late Triassic or early Jurassic. Apart from the extinction of the prosauropods at the end of the Triassic, and the replacement of the Jurassic stegosaurs by the Cretaceous ankylosaurs, all the dinosaurs survived until the late Cretaceous. At that time, the world's climate and vegetation underwent profound changes.

The floral change was the replacement of the gymnosperms, such as pines, ginkgos, araucarians and cycads, by the *angiosperms, or flowering plants. This commenced during the early Cretaceous, and became complete during the late Cretaceous. It seems likely that the herbivorous dinosaurs which appeared during this time, such as hadrosaurs and ceratopians, did so as a response to the availability of the new type of food. The carnivorous tyrannosaurids and omnivorous ornithomimids also appeared during the late Cretaceous.

But all these new forms were appearing in a world geographically very different from that in which the first dinosaurs had evolved. *Continental drift, together with the spread of seas across the continents themselves, resulted in the appearance of a number of different land areas in the late Cretaceous. For some reason, all the new types evolved in Asiamerica. Though some may have reached South America at the end of the Cretaceous, none are known to have reached other parts of the world.

The End of the Dinosaur World. The fact that dinosaurs were still actively evolving new types, both herbivores and carnivores, in the late Cretaceous makes it all the more difficult to understand why, only a few million years later, they had all disappeared. Clearly it was not because they could not cope with the vegetational changes of the late Cretaceous, and this would seem to indicate the improbability of any mysterious "racial senescence" that would make them incapable of responding to change in the biological world around them having played a part. Equally, their disappearance cannot be blamed on the little *mammals that were to replace them: the mammals had evolved at the same time as the dinosaurs themselves, in the late Tri-

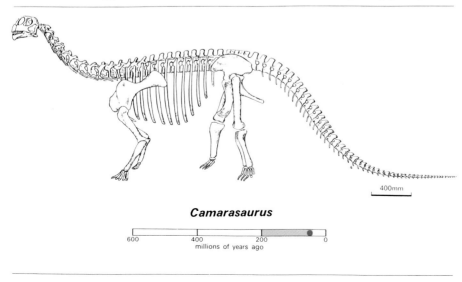

400mm

Camarasaurus

600   400   200   0
millions of years ago

assic, and the two groups had been coexisting without any signs of incompatibility for some 135 million years.

It is logical, therefore, to seek the explanation in the physical world. And here a possible explanation of the dinosaurs' extinction can be found in current interpretations of their probable physiology. Dinosaurs were clearly active creatures, like birds and mammals today. Like them, they were probably "warm-blooded" – that is to say, could maintain a constant, warm body temperature. But, unlike birds and mammals, they had no warm, insulatory covering of feathers or hair. Instead they probably relied on their great bulk, which contained such an enormous reservoir of warmth that day-to-day heat losses were comparatively insignificant – as long as they were not too great and did not continue for too long.

But there is evidence, from floral changes in the late Cretaceous, that climates became cooler at that time. This may have caused temperatures to fluctuate outside the limits of control of the rather crude temperature-regulation of the dinosaurs, and so caused their sudden disappearance. But this conclusion is based on a tenuous series of hypotheses, and we should be unwise to conclude that the certain key to this 65-million-year-old mystery has been found.

Crocodiles

Most crocodiles are amphibious reptiles, feeding in fresh waters or (more rarely) the sea, swimming by means of the powerful tail, but resting and laying their eggs on land. They are, however, archosaurian diapsids which, like the dinosaurs, evolved from terrestrial *thecodonts. The earliest crocodiles may even have been quite fast-moving land animals, for the bones of their ankles are elongated in a fashion normally found only in animals with this way of life. Like thecodonts, crocodiles have an armor of bone under the skin of the back and sometimes also on the belly.

The earliest known crocodile is the late *Triassic *Protosuchus*, which is very close to its thecodont ancestors in structure. Together with a few other late Triassic relatives, it is placed in a separate crocodilian suborder, the Protosuchia.

It is not until the *Jurassic that typical crocodiles appear, with an elongate, flattened skull and the beginnings of a "secondary palate" – a partition of bone separating the mouth from the air passage that leads from the nostrils to the back of the throat. This secondary palate is still short in the suborder Mesosuchia, first known from the early Jurassic. Several Jurassic and *Cretaceous mesosuchians took up a marine existence, feeding on fish, and developed a narrow, many-toothed snout like that of living gavials. Some marine forms, such as the teleosaurs, looked otherwise like normal crocodiles; but the thalattosuchians of the late Jurassic and early Cretaceous developed a vertical tail-fin like that of an *ichthyosaur.

Though some marine forms survived until the early *Cenozoic, most mesosuchians were replaced during the Cretaceous by their descendants the eusuchians, in which the secondary palate isolates the air passage all the way to the rear end of the skull. This final suborder is known first from the early Cretaceous, and includes the lines leading to the living carnivorous crocodiles, alligators and caimans, which appeared in the late Cretaceous, and also to the fish-eating gavials, which are unknown before the *Pliocene.

During the milder *Mesozoic climates, crocodilians extended much further north than their modern relatives, which are almost unknown outside the tropics. The late-Cretaceous eusuchians also included the giant form *Deinosuchus*, some 50ft (15m) long, which must have preyed on dinosaurs.

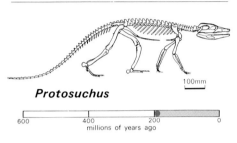

Protosuchus

600   400   200   0
millions of years ago

Mammal-Like Reptiles

Though less glamorous than the *dinosaurs, the mammal-like reptiles were in many ways the more important group of the two. They proliferated from the late Paleozoic, earlier than did the dinosaurs, and they were the first to establish a complex terrestrial ecosystem including herbivores, carnivores, insectivores and omnivores. Furthermore, they were in a way more successful than the dinosaurs: they were the ancestors of the mammals, which fill the modern world, while the dinosaurs came to an abrupt end some 65 million years ago.

Mammal-like reptiles form a completely independent line of reptile evolution which can be traced back to the late *Carboniferous. They are distinguished by their synapsid skull, and the group is known as the subclass Synapsida. Another notable feature is that, while many dinosaurs moved on two legs, this is unknown for any synapsid.

Synapsida is divided into two orders: the Pelycosauria, which include the earlier and more primitive forms, with a sprawling posture; and the Therapsida, their descendants, in which the limbs have become somewhat more erect and more efficient in support and locomotion.

Pelycosaurs.

Three different types of pelycosaur are known from the early Permian but, though representatives of all are known also from the late Carboniferous, their interrelationships are still uncertain. Most primitive appear to be the ophiacodonts, little elongate forms 3.25–6.5ft (1–2m) long, whose long, low skulls bore many teeth: they may have been semi-aquatic fish-eaters. Their larger and more strongly-built relatives, the sphenacodonts, were up to 10ft (3m) long. Such sphenacodonts as *Dimetrodon* had powerful teeth and were the dominant carnivores of the early Permian community. Their herbivorous prey included the edaphosaurs, up to 10ft (3m) long, whose mouths contained many blunt chewing teeth, and such giant pelycosaurs as *Cotylorhynchus*, of similar length but very much greater mass, weighing nearly 775lb (350kg).

A remarkable feature of *Dimetrodon* and many edaphosaurs is the extension of the vertebrae into a row of spines interconnected by a sail-like membrane. This was probably for temperature regulation, the animal standing broadside to the Sun when cold, the heat being absorbed and circulated by blood vessels in the "sail": some modern animals employ a similar system.

Therapsids.

The pelycosaurs died out at the end of the early *Permian. Intermediates between them and the therapsids are known from the middle Permian: some features suggest that therapsids evolved from the sphenacodontid pelycosaurs. The therapsid radiation otherwise appears suddenly in the late Permian Karroo Beds of southern Africa, rapidly spreading throughout the world.

Like their ancestors, the therapsids included both herbivores and carnivores. The most successful herbivores were the dicynodonts, 4in–6.5ft (10cm–2m) long, with teeth partially or wholly replaced by a turtle-like horny beak. Their only therapsid competitors were some members of the group known as dinocephalians, which had a bulky body, blunt herbivorous teeth and a thickened skull which may have been used for butting with the head during mating combats. Not all dinocephalians were herbivores, for genera such as *Titanophoneus* had a carnivore-type dentition.

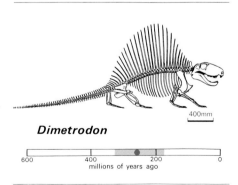

Dimetrodon

600   400   200   0
millions of years ago

The therapsids also included more exclusively carnivorous groups, such as the gorgonopsids. Like saber-toothed tigers, these animals had enlarged, stabbing canine teeth, the teeth further back in the mouth being reduced in size. The gorgonopsids were about 3.25ft (1m) long. Less specialized carnivores included the therocephalians and their descendants the bauriamorphs. These were of similar size but had a normal reptilian dentition.

Apart from some large dicynodonts

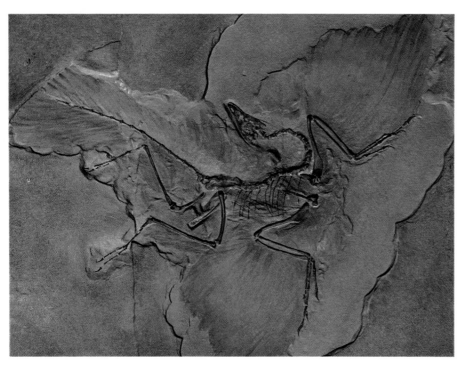

One of the few known specimens of the early bird *Archaeopteryx*. Preservation is so complete that impressions of the feathers of the wings and tail are clearly seen.

which persisted into the late Triassic, and some early-Triassic bauriamorphs, the only synapsids that survived the end of the Permian were members of the only remaining group, the cynodonts. These began in the late Permian as small insectivores and carnivores, about 1.6ft (0.5m) long. Some large Triassic cynodonts developed wide, peg-like cheek teeth and must have been omnivores or even herbivores. Rather rodent-like descendants of these animals, known as tritylodonts, survived until as late as the middle Jurassic.

Yet other Triassic cynodonts became active little insectivores with sharp, many-cusped cheek teeth, and it is from these that, in the late Triassic, the mammals evolved. Like *mammals, they had a bony partition or "secondary palate" separating the mouth cavity from the air passage leading from the nostrils to the throat. Unlike the cold-blooded reptiles, mammals cannot stop breathing for long, and so need a secondary palate in order to continue to breathe while chewing. Its presence in the Triassic cynodonts (and in the bauriamorphs) suggests that these ancient reptiles were becoming mammal-like in physiology as well as in anatomy.   CBC

Birds

Compared with other groups, birds appear rather late in the *fossil record. However, since their first representative, *Archaeopteryx* from the upper *Jurassic, is partly reptilian, partly avian, it would appear that what we have here is indeed the first true ancestor of the birds – or, if not, then at least we can be fairly confident it is a close relative of the as yet unknown ancestor of birds.

Archaeopteryx is linked by only a few scattered bone fragments to the main avian sequence of fossil remains that extends onward from the middle Cretaceous. Birds suffer paleontologically from having small, fragile and fragmentary remains that can often be overlooked and which are, in any case, difficult to identify; and from the very fact that the kind of strata in which fossils are likely to occur favors the larger water birds at the expense of other forms.

Evolution. From the fossil record we can deduce three stages in bird *evolution – although we lack evidence of any species that might link them together. These three stages are usually treated, taxonomically, as subclasses of Aves, the class of birds. The first subclass, Sauriurae or lizard-like birds, contains only *Archaeopteryx*. This creature, known from six specimens from Bavaria, shows the intermediate stage between reptile and bird – not with each characteristic intermediate but with the overall structure made up of a mosaic of bird and lizard characteristics. The toothed jaws are relatively short and stout, the limbs bird-like, though the digital bones of wings and legs are not fused as in modern birds. The bony tail is long and slender, and there is no evidence of a bird-like keeled breastbone for the attachment of flight muscles. The wings are composed of long flight feathers exactly like those of later birds, and the presence of a row of similar feathers along either side of the tail shows that these had a support function in movement even if, as some people suggest, *Archaeopteryx* was incapable of true flight.

The second subclass, the Odontoholcae or toothed birds, is known from the North American middle to late Cretaceous, al-

though a recently described incomplete humerus from the lower Cretaceous of the English Weald may also be referred to this group. Like *Archaeopteryx* they differ from all other birds in possessing true teeth in the jaws.

All the known forms are seabirds. The remains of the seven species in the genera *Ichthyornis* and *Apatornis* are very like those of other birds, but with a few osteological peculiarities. In the remaining genera, *Hesperornis* and *Coniornis*, are three species of diving birds, with legs set far back on the body and tiny, vestigial wings: evolutionary diversification had clearly already progressed a long way.

All other known species are contained in the third subclass, Ornithurae or typical birds. We have at present no knowledge of the forms that might link them, in terms of evolution, with the toothed birds because the fossil record is so incomplete.

A wide range of fragmentary remains from the lower *Eocene indicates that most modern orders had evolved by then: in view of the incompleteness of the remains and the number of species that are still being discovered, we cannot assume that the apparent absence of any particular group is good evidence that it had not yet evolved. The evidence we have suggests that the divergent evolution that was to produce the diversity we know today occurred mainly during the Cretaceous, so that by the early Tertiary a typical range of avian forms was already in existence.

The Tertiary. The Passeriformes and the mainly arboreal Coraciiformes and Piciformes are very poorly represented in the early Tertiary: their main radiation may have occurred much later, or their absence may merely reflect that most of the bird remains we have are from sea or coastal deposits. In other groups, early Tertiary bones are very similar to those of modern birds of the same orders, but may be a little less specialized in structure or, as in the Pelecaniformes, lack the air-spaces of later bird bones. There is evidence to suggest a rather wider range of forms, resulting in a more even gradation between different kinds of birds, and that loss of many of these forms has produced the "gaps" now apparent between discrete modern orders of birds.

In general, however, the picture is one of early diversification with repeated extinction and adaptive radiation. And there is a tendency for certain types of specialization to recur several times in different groups of birds. For example, after the toothed birds had disappeared there emerged a group with bony tooth-like projections along the jaws, the Odontopterygiformes. These were giant seabirds found from all over the world from the lower Eocene to the upper Miocene or possibly even the Pliocene. It is of interest to note that, among modern birds, ducks of the genus *Mergus* have small tooth-like processes in the bill. These are formed from the bill sheath.

Greater aquatic adaptation, with increase

in leg size and reduction of wings, recurs repeatedly through the evolutionary history. Apparent from early times in penguins, and briefly apparent in Eocene divers and Miocene gannets, it produced the flightless auks of the genus *Mancalla* in the Pliocene – long before the famous, recently extinct, Great Auk.

Another recurrent feature is the appearance of huge, flightless running birds. The ostrich is an example of a group persisting from early Tertiary times to the present, while a jaw of what is possibly a giant running bird is known from the North American upper Cretaceous. The Diatrymidae occur from the Eocene of both Europe and North America. Most are presumed to be grazers, but the Phororuscids of the South and Central American Oligocene and Miocene, with huge heads and eagle-like bills, seem to have been scavengers or raptors (snatching at passing prey) that proliferated in the absence of predatory *mammals. Later grazers were the Holocene elephantbirds of Madagascar, the Aepyornithiformes; and the Moas, Emeidae and Diornithidae from the Pliocene to Holocene of New Zealand.

Today. With this constant adaptive fluctuation it is incautious to suggest a time of maximum diversity, but overall there is a suggestion of increase from the late Cretaceous to a possible maximum in the early Pleistocene, although by then some of the groups we have mentioned had become extinct. Subsequently there is evidence of the disappearance of many larger forms – possibly related to Man's hunting of them. Since many modern species are of late Pleistocene origin and show external differences which are small and may not be reflected in the skeleton (and hence the fossil), strict comparisons between the number of species extant today and the number present in past geological periods are not possible.   CH

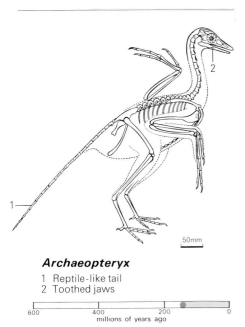

Archaeopteryx

1 Reptile-like tail
2 Toothed jaws

600   400   200   0
millions of years ago

Mammals

The mammals are treated here in more detail than the rest of the Animal Kingdom, and the entries that follow correspond to orders. The reasons for doing so are twofold: mammals comprise most of the best known animal groups living today and, secondly, they are of particular interest because they include in their number Man himself.   AI

Primitive Mammals

In the late *Triassic, 200 million years ago, the first mammals appeared. From Wales, South Africa and China come remains of these small shrew-like beasts. They evolved from small *mammal-like reptiles, and the transition is so gradual that the point at which a reptile became a mammal is often difficult to fix. Most methods of differentiating living reptiles from mammals depend on soft anatomy; but, in fossils, bone and tooth characteristics must be used. Mammals have three small middle ear bones; their lower jaw is a single bone; and their teeth are differentiated into incisors, canines, premolars and molars, and there are usually two sets during the lifespan, a milk dentition followed by the permanent set.

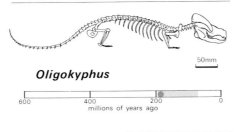

Oligokyphus

50mm

600   400   200   0
millions of years ago

During the *Mesozoic, six major mammalian stocks evolved, some "dead ends" and some giving rise to later mammals. The dead ends include triconodonts, with teeth in which three cusps were arranged lengthwise on each tooth; and multituberculates, which grew as large as beavers and were adapted like *rodents to gnawing with chisel-shaped incisors and multicusped cheek teeth. The most important Mesozoic stock were the pantotheres, with a complex tooth pattern not unlike that of a shrew; from these, in the *Cretaceous, evolved the three groups of living mammals, the *monotremes, the *marsupials and the placentals, or "modern" mammals.   RJGS

Monotremes

Monotremes, the egg-laying mammals, are represented by the Spiny anteaters and the Duck-billed platypus of Australia. They are considered to be mammals because they possess hair and the females secrete milk with which to feed the young. Many of their anatomical features are, however, reptilian in character. The earliest fossil monotreme is from Miocene deposits, but it is likely the group has a longer history which extends back to, perhaps, the late Mesozoic. AI

Marsupials

Marsupials, the pouched mammals, include

opossums, koalas, wombats and kangaroos. They are an ancient group extending back to the *Cretaceous when they evolved from pantothere ancestors (see *primitive mammals): they live today in Australia and the Americas. Their young are born very prematurely and continue development in the mother's pouch, and this distinguishes them from the placental *mammals.

There are differences in the skeleton and dentition (teeth) which enable us to differentiate fossilized marsupials and placentals. Marsupials do not have a set of milk teeth later replaced by a set of permanent teeth: there is only one set, though sometimes a single tooth may be replaced. In general, also, marsupials have more incisor and molar teeth than do placental mammals.

In *Tertiary times, marsupials radiated to fill a wide range of ecological niches in South America and Australia, and insectivorous, carnivorous and herbivorous stocks developed. They also lived in North America and Western Europe, but no remains have been found in either Asia or Africa.

The South American fossil record displays a vast array of species, some of which range back as far as the Cretaceous. Early marsupials were insectivore-like and it was only later that from these all the more specialized kinds evolved.

During much of Tertiary time the marsupials evolved species that paralleled placental types on other continents. Among these was *Borhyaena*, which was hyena-like; *Thylacosmilus*, with a great sabertooth, paralleling the saber-tooth cats of North America and Europe; and *Lycopsis*, a marsupial version of the dog. Among the largely extinct suborder Caenolestoidea were many rodent-like creatures, including bipedal species rather like the modern jerboa.

In Australia, the fossil marsupial record is rich in the late Pliocene and *Pleistocene, but poor in earlier times: the earliest known are a few *Oligocene specimens, including a primitive kangaroo. Most fossils fit into or close to, living Australian families, so we are still in ignorance of the earlier differentiation of marsupials here.

There are eight families of Australian marsupials of which two are extinct, namely the thylacoleonids and the diprotodontids, fossils of both dating from the Pliocene and Pleistocene. *Thylacoleo* was a large lion-like beast, with very large tusk-like incisor teeth and enormous shearing cheek teeth; it is thought to have been a carnivore. *Diprotodon* was bigger than a rhinoceros and again had tusked incisors, but its cheek teeth were suited for grinding vegetation. Other fossils include gigantic kangaroos 10ft (3m) high.

Of great interest to zoogeographers is the peculiar distribution in time and space of marsupials. Probably marsupials originated in South America in Cretaceous times and soon radiated into North America. During the *Eocene, some migrated from there *via* a land bridge across the Arctic circle into western Europe. By the end of the *Miocene they were extinct in both North America and Europe. In South America, where they faced less competition from placentals, they were more successful; and from here they migrated *via* Antarctica to Australia, possibly in *Paleocene or Eocene times. RJGS

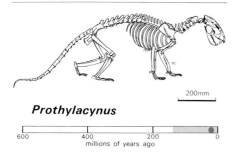

Prothylacynus

600   400   200   0
millions of years ago

Insectivores

Insectivores are the most primitive living placental *mammals: they include hedgehogs, moles and shrews. They have an ancient origin and a good fossil record from the *Cretaceous onward. They are all small, and sometimes have a poison gland. They feed on a wide variety of items, including insects as well as other small invertebrates, small vertebrates and even fruit. Their classification is exceptionally complex and they are more a ragbag collection of small insectivorous mammals than a true natural order of mammals. We can group them into three divisions: Deltatheridioids, extinct shrew-like mammals known mainly from North America and Asia from the Cretaceous to the *Oligocene, and including the ancestors of carnivores and ungulates, and hence most other modern placental mammals; Proteutheres, seven families of extinct insectivores, ranging from the Cretaceous to the Oligocene; and the Lipotyphlans, comprising about seven families of living insectivores with a fossil record dating back to the *Eocene. RJGS

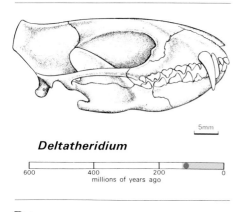

Deltatheridium

5mm

600   400   200   0
millions of years ago

Bats

Bats are essentially flying *insectivores with front legs modified for flight by elongation of four of the fingers, between which is the leathery membrane. They have a poor fossil record, though occasionally almost com-

plete specimens are preserved, like *Icaronycteris* from the *Eocene of the USA. We know nothing of the evolution of flight among the insectivores before this.

There are two groups: microchiropterans ("small bats"), including a wide variety of carnivorous, bloodsucking and insectivorous bats; and the larger megachiropterans ("big bats"), mainly fruit eaters, which evolved from them. RJGS

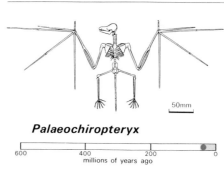

Palaeochiropteryx

600   400   200   0
millions of years ago

Carnivores

The lion is the king of beasts, but 25 million years ago there was a beast that would have made a lion look like a toy dog – *Megistotherium*, a gigantic hyena-like mammal, the largest land carnivore that has ever lived.

Carnivores, the meat-eating placental *mammals, classified in the order Carnivora, come in many sizes and shapes; there are running, climbing, burrowing and swimming kinds. Some are exclusively flesheaters while others are more catholic in their tastes: a few are secondarily vegetarian. The feet usually retain four toes which carry prominent claws; the eye or "canine" tooth is often a large stabbing tooth; and in the cheek area some teeth are usually modified for slicing meat. The earliest occur in *Paleocene sediments, and they have been fairly abundant ever since in North America, Eurasia and Africa. Until relatively recently their place was taken in South America and Australia by carnivorous *marsupials.

There are two groups of living carnivores, fissipeds and pinnipeds, and one extinct group, the creodonts.

Fissipeds. In this group are placed dogs, bears, raccoons, weasels, mongooses, cats and hyenas. Most of the families can be traced back to the *Miocene and some, like dogs and mongooses, to the *Eocene: bears and raccoons evolved from dog-like relatives, while cats and hyenas evolved from mongoose relatives. Among the extinct kinds the most spectacular are the sabertooth cats which prowled America, Eurasia and Africa from the Miocene to *Pleistocene.

Bears tend to be large, heavy, slow and omnivorous beasts. Raccoons and pandas are mainly arboreal and often vegetarian. Mongooses and civets are small and feed on small lizards, snakes, birds and mammals. The weasel family is very varied, with

swimming otters, arboreal martens, burrowing badgers, skunks and ratels. Hyenas have specialized in bone crushing; and cats can be regarded as the ultimate in carnivore evolution.

Pinnipeds. These aquatic carnivores – the seals, sea-lions and walruses – are not a natural group, since seals evolved from otter-like ancestors and sea-lions evolved separately from dog-like ancestors, with walruses as a sideline. Seals and sea-lions have numerous simple peg-like teeth, feed mainly on fish, and swim with flippers which are modified hind feet. Walruses break off mollusks from the sea floor with their huge tusks and crush them with their cheek teeth. All are relatively rare fossils though their ancestry can be traced back to the Miocene.

Creodonts. These prowled around the world early in the *Tertiary, and in Miocene times almost all had become extinct, having been replaced everywhere by the more intelligent fissipeds. Creodonts had a separate ancestry from other carnivores, and indeed they evolved animals which paralleled dogs, weasels, bears, cats and hyenas – including the gigantic *Megistotherium*. They are distinguished from fissipeds in having small brains, a different type of slicing dentition. RJGS

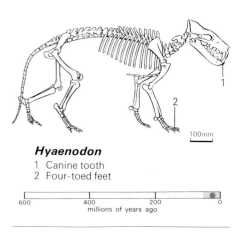

Hyaenodon
1 Canine tooth
2 Four-toed feet

600   400   200   0
millions of years ago

Subungulates

Grouped together as subungulates are no less than 16 orders, of which 11 are extinct: the survivors are aardvarks, pangolins, hyraces, seacows and elephants, of which elephants are the most important. All are basically hooved animals feeding on a variety of plants and adapted to many ecologies in different parts of the world.

In the late *Cretaceous animals with preferences for plant food and having broad flattish teeth evolved from insectivorous stock – they also developed a digestive system to cope with the cellulose in their diet. These, the condylarths, looked much like small piglets. By *Paleocene times they had reached all continents except Australia and Antarctica. They evolved into all the later hooved or ungulate animals.

Condylarths reached South America

The skull and part of the body of a mammoth preserved in Russia on the banks of the Berezovka river and excavated during a thaw in 1902.

before it was cut off from North America in the *Eocene and evolved there in isolation from most other placental *mammals for much of the *Tertiary. They developed a vast array of bizarre and now extinct stocks. Most successful were the notoungulates: some, such as *Toxodon*, were large rhinoceros-like animals, and others, such as *Typotherium*, small rodent-like kinds. One stock migrated into North America and across into China.

Hyraces and elephants had their early evolutionary centers in Africa. By the *Oligocene hyraces were the dominant herbivores, but never achieved this position again, giving way first to giraffes and rhinoceroses and then to bovids.

The story of elephant evolution is well-preserved in their fossil bones and teeth. It is one of increase in size – the bigger they became the less able were predators to attack them. The earliest elephant was *Moeritherium* from the Eocene, about the size of a pig and weighing 4cwt (200kg). As elephants grew bigger, so the legs lengthened or the animals would have been immobilized. At the same time they were developing tusks, imposing a considerable extra weight on the skull, which had thus to be held close to the body since the strain of carrying 200lb (90kg) of tusk at the end of a long neck would have been intolerable. With long legs and a short neck the animals

would not normally be able to drink without kneeling, thus putting themselves in mortal danger from carnivores; and so a trunk developed for both drinking and food gathering. Increased size made more food necessary, and the teeth adapted to this by becoming much bigger and emerging cyclically: only one tooth is present in each half of the jaw at any one time but, as it wears out, another moves up from behind to replace it.

Until the *Miocene Africa was the center of elephant evolution, and then they migrated into Europe and Asia and, later, North America. By the *Pliocene they had developed teeth that could cope with tough siliceous grasses, and all later kinds were primarily grazers. *Pleistocene mammoths were a very widespread and successful stock. In the Arctic, some fell down crev-

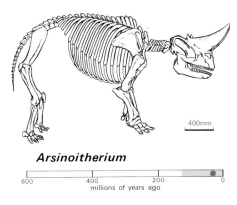

Arsinoitherium

600   400   200   0
millions of years ago

asses and were "deep frozen", remaining intact for thousands of years. So well preserved are some that even their last meal is still present in the stomach.

Among the minor subungulate stocks are the seacows (manatees and dugongs); aardvarks, pig-sized burrowing anteaters of Africa; scaly pangolins; and the extinct embrithopods. RJGS

Perissodactyls

Horses, rhinoceroses and tapirs, together with the extinct brontotheres and chalicotheres, make up this large order of herbivorous *mammals. They are odd-toed (as opposed to the even-toed *artiodactyls): the toes on either side of the hoof are reduced, and weight is taken mainly on the third or middle toe, sometimes with support from the second and fourth toe. They arose from condylarth ancestors (see *subungulates) in the *Paleocene and reached their peak in the *Eocene; since then they have dwindled in diversity, except for the horse family, which has continued to expand.

Tapirs are today restricted to two species in central America and southeast Asia; they are the most primitive members of the order and have never been spectacularly successful. Rhinoceroses, on the other hand, roamed America, Eurasia and Africa and adopted many forms; some with horns, some without, some with tusks, some without, some large, some small, some semiaquatic, some running types. *Baluchitherium*, an extinct hornless rhinoceros from the Oligocene of central Asia, was the largest land mammal that has ever lived; it stood about 18ft (5.5m) high at the shoulder and must have weighed about 16 tons.

The extinct brontotheres or titanotheres of the Oligocene deposits were also huge rhinoceros-like animals reaching 8ft (2.4m) at the shoulder: they had a pair of bony horns.

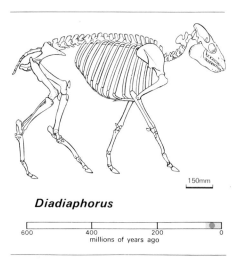

Diadiaphorus

600	400	200	0
	millions of years ago		

Chalicotheres are rare but curious fossils. Related most closely to horses, they have big, wide feet with claws rather than hooves. They occur occasionally in Eurasia, while in Africa the last record is in the Pleistocene. Some reports appear to suggest the chalicotheres may not be extinct but are still living in the African forests.

The horse family is certainly the most important perissodactyl stock. Horses are known in detail from their origin in the Eocene through to today. The main center of evolution was North America, from where they migrated at various times: Australia and Antarctica are the only continents they did not inhabit during the course of the Cenozoic.

The story of the horse is like that of an Olympic runner; faster and faster, each time improving technique and performance. Early Eocene horses were about the size of a terrier. Longer legs developed for faster running: as these were used solely in running and were not required for grasping, the ability to twist was lost, so reducing the chances of sprained ankles – this was achieved by fusing the two bones in the lower limb. The smaller an animal's feet the better it can run: the horse lost the toes at the side of the feet, leaving the third or middle toe to bear all the weight; they had achieved a fully functional one-toed condition by the late Miocene. Then again, an animal should not grow too heavy or, like elephants, it will be able only to amble. The optimum size/speed ratio is achieved in the modern racehorse.

Another important evolutionary aspect is feeding adaptation. Early horses were browsers on shrub vegetation, but as they grew bigger they needed more food, and so the teeth had to change to grind more efficiently the tough fibers. In the early Miocene grasses appeared and horses quick-

ly took to feeding on these, and so living on plains where they could make maximum use of their speed.

From *Eohippus* 60 million years ago to *Equus* today the horses have become one of the most successful and most intelligent of mammals.   RJGS

Artiodactyls

The artiodactyls, the even-toed or cleft-hoof ungulates, include pigs and cattle. They have four or more usually two toes on each foot, each toe carrying a horny hoof. They first appeared in the *Eocene and rapidly expanded at the expense of the *perissodactyls, which declined in numbers: they had an explosive radiation in the *Miocene when grasses appeared and the bovids adapted to grazing them. Sizes ranged from tiny hare-like antelopes to gigantic pigs, giraffes and cattle.

The stomach has usually several compartments so that the maximum value is extracted from the food by ruminating – food that has already been chewed once is passed back to the mouth from the stomach, *via* a compartment called the rumen, to be rechewed before digestion. On the skull often develop outgrowths of bone (giraffe), antler (deer) or horn (antelope).

There are over 500 genera of which about 400 are extinct. The 25 families can be considered in 3 groups.

Suina. Pigs, peccaries and hippopotamuses are the living families in this group, anthracotheres and entelodonts the extinct ones. All are essentially stocky, short-legged animals, usually with four toes on each foot; some are semiaquatic. They are ground browsers and rooters, with low-crowned teeth.

Suids, or pigs, have a fairly good *fossil record and are stratigraphically valuable. Entelodonts were gigantic pig-like animals found mainly in the *Oligocene of North America and Eurasia. Anthracotheres, also pig-like, are known from Eocene to *Pleistocene times. Hippos may have originated in the African Miocene, and are found fossilized in the Pleistocene from England to Jawa.

Tylopods. Camels and two related extinct families make up this group. Members have either four or two toes on each foot, the canine tooth is vestigial, and the stomach has three compartments. Cheek teeth have crescentic cusp patterns and the animals usually browse on shrub vegetation. Wild camels occur today only in central Asia. In South America live their cousins, llamas and vicunas.

Camels have a good fossil record, and their many kinds include *Stenomylus*, a slender gazelle-like animal, and *Oxydactylus*, a long-legged, long-necked species. The extinct cainotheres of the European Oligocene and Miocene were much like hares; and the extinct Oligocene oreodonts were abundant browsing antelope-like animals.

Pecora. This, the largest, most advanced group, includes bovids, chevrotains, giraffes, deer and antelopes. All are two-

toed with a fully ruminating four-compartment stomach. Skull outgrowths are common.

The chevrotains are small, primitive, tropical gazelle-like animals: some North American fossil cousins had bizarre bony nasal outgrowths. The Giant Irish Deer, *Megaloceros*, of the Pleistocene is the largest of the deer family, with branching antlers which often spanned 13ft (4m); borne only by the males, these were shed annually. Some fossil giraffes also had great bony outgrowths from the skull, but these were present on both sexes and not shed.

The bovids are the largest family of pecorans, containing muskox, bison, cattle, sheep, goats, antelopes and gazelles.   RJGS

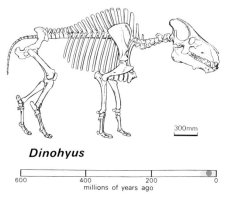

Dinohyus

600	400	200	0
	millions of years ago		

Edentates

The name Edentate implies "toothless" mammals, but this is true only of some varieties of this exotic order of herbivorous and insectivorous American mammals. Included in the order today are giant anteaters, armadillos and tree sloths. The extinct members include ground sloths and glyptodons, known from the *Eocene to the *Pleistocene.

Megatherium, a giant ground sloth from the *Pliocene and Pleistocene, reached over 23ft (7m) in length, bigger than an elephant. It had large claws on front and hind feet, probably used for digging. *Glyptodon*, a mammalian version of the turtle, was equipped with a truncheon-like tail to fight off predators.   RJGS

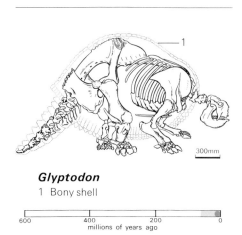

Glyptodon
1 Bony shell

600	400	200	0
	millions of years ago		

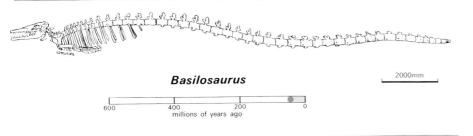

Basilosaurus

2000mm

600   400   200   0
millions of years ago

natural abundance at any time in the past. The present widespread distribution of the rabbit is due to Man rather than to its celebrated breeding habits.   RJGS

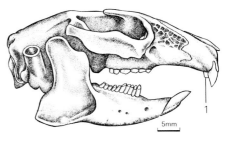

5mm

Palaeolagus

1 Second pair of incisor teeth

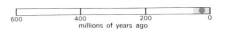

600   400   200   0
millions of years ago

Whales

The Blue whale is the largest animal that has ever lived; it reaches lengths of up to 100ft (30m) and weighs around 100 tons. There are, however, many small whales, such as dolphins and porpoises. Most live in the oceans, but some small dolphins inhabit rivers. All are totally aquatic, never coming ashore – they give birth in the water. Next to primates they are the most intelligent *mammals.

The earliest fossils, the archaeocetes, occur in *Eocene and *Oligocene sediments. Some were over 50ft (15m) long and their jaws bore saw-edged teeth. They are so like the modern whale that the ancestry of the group is difficult to establish: possibly they evolved from a group of *carnivores during the Paleocene.

From archaeocetes evolved the two living groups, odontocetes and mysticetes. Odontocetes or toothed whales also appear in the Eocene and are characterized by having many peg-like teeth in the jaws. The mysticetes or baleen whales appeared in the Oligocene and grew to enormous size (they include the Blue whale). Rather than teeth they have plates of chitinous baleen, or "whalebone", which trap the minute plankton on which they feed. Since baleen does not fossilize, fossil jaws of these whales look toothless.   RJGS

Rodents

Of the 5000 living species of mammals, half are rodents; and there are over 400 extinct rodent genera. They are the most successful *mammals, adapting to the widest range of climates, altitudes and ecological niches. Their striking characteristic is their adaptation to gnaw, using a single pair of incisors in each jaw to chisel off nuts, bark and bone. Enamel is restricted to the front side of the teeth and, as the softer dentine behind wears more rapidly, a chisel edge is produced. The incisors continually grow replacement tissue to counter the rapid wear. Most rodents, but far from all, are small scampering animals.

The harvest mice are among the smallest of all mammals with a head and body only 2in (50mm) long: the largest living rodent is the capybara from South America, about 4ft (1.3m) long. Some of its fossil cousins were twice as large.

The 45 families can be considered in 4 groups.

Sciuromorphs. These include the most primitive rodents, the extinct Paleocene paramyids, which were already distinctly rodent-like, and the squirrels.

Myomorphs. This, the largest group, contains rats, mice, voles, lemmings, jerboas, mole rats and many other small animals. They are most useful in stratigraphy from the *Eocene onward. Their geographic spread has been so rapid that they give a finer indication of the age of a sediment than do any other mammalian fossils.

Caviomorphs. This group includes chinchillas, coypus, agoutis, guinea pigs and the capybara. Fossil members include gigantic forms like *Artigasia* and *Eumegamys* with skulls over 20in (50cm) long. Members of this group evolved in South America from the Oligocene onward.

Other families. Grouped together under this ragbag heading are fossil and living families such as the Eocene and Oligocene theridomyids; the Oligocene phiomyids; beavers, known from the Oligocene onward; and porcupines.   RJGS

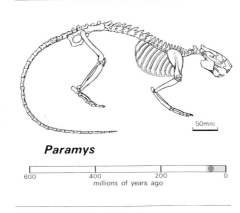

Paramys

50mm

600   400   200   0
millions of years ago

Lagomorphs

Pikas, hares and rabbits are members of the small order Lagomorpha. While superficially like rodents, they are not closely related: lagomorphs have two pairs of incisor teeth in each jaw and the enamel forms a continuous band around the tooth, rather than the single pair, with enamel only at the front, characteristic of *rodents.

The earliest known lagomorphs are from the *Paleocene: from this stock evolved two families, the leporids (hares and rabbits) and the ochotonids (pikas). In *Eocene times they spread into North America, in *Oligocene times into Europe, in *Miocene times into Africa and in *Pleistocene times into South America. Early kinds were small scampering animals from which later evolved running and leaping varieties. Though lagomorphs are never plentiful in the fossil record, this may not truly reflect their

Primates

Man, apes, lemurs and monkeys are all members of the order Primates, one of the oldest mammalian stocks, going back some 70 million years to a time when *dinosaurs were still plodding the Earth.

The characteristics distinguishing primates from other mammals are mostly primitive unspecialized features – if you like, their lack of specialization. In many ways they resemble primitive Eocene mammals in their retention of digits and a fairly complete and unspecialized dentition. Features which mark them out are the opposable thumb, the flattened nails, stereoscopic vision and the large brain.

There are two major groups of primates, prosimians and anthropoids. Prosimians are the more primitive, and living kinds include lemurs, lorises and the tarsier. The anthropoids comprise monkeys, apes and Man.

Early Evolution. Primates probably originated directly from an insectivore stock or indirectly *via* primitive condylarths, a now extinct group transitional between *insectivores and herbivorous *mammals. The earliest known primate is *Purgatorius* from the late *Cretaceous, known only from some isolated teeth that show a few primate characteristics. In the early *Paleocene are four families of primates, three of which appear to be dead ends: carpolestids were very peculiar primates with some resemblances to multituberculates; picrodontids were a fruit-eating stock; and plesiadapids were essentially squirrel-like with claws and laterally placed eyes. The paromomyids constitute the fourth family, and includes *Purgatorius*: they are probably close to the stem of the later primates. All were small generalized feeders and nothing is known of their skeletal anatomy.

In the *Eocene, primates faced increasing competition from *rodents and the two stocks diverged – primates tending to become more arboreal while rodents remained ground-dwelling. There is a persistence of some Paleocene stocks – paromomyids and plesiadapids – and the appearance of two new groups, lemuroids and tarsioids. The lemuroids survive today only on Madagascar and we have nothing in the fossil record to link them with the Eocene forms. Eocene lemuroids were all lemur-like animals with opposed first digit, stereoscopic vision and fairly large brain. From the Isle of Wight come remains of a small tarsier-like primate, *Microchoerus*, but again there is a gap in our knowledge of the group from the Eocene until the present.

The Oligocene. After the Eocene, the new- and old-world primates evolved separately: the opening of the north Atlantic made migrations impossible between Canada and western Europe. While all our knowledge to the end of the Eocene is derived from North America, Europe or Asia, in the succeeding *Oligocene virtually all our information comes from Africa, a continent from this time on of great importance in primate evolution.

At Fayum Oasis, 60mi (100km) southwest of Cairo, is a succession of lake and river sediments that has yielded all we know of primate life in the Oligocene. Dense tropical forests existed around the Fayum in Oligocene times, 30 million years ago. In the forests lived a vast array of mammals, including many kinds of primate.

Most of the primate fossils belong to two families, each represented by two genera. In the parapithecids there are *Apidium* and *Parapithecus*, and in the pongids are *Aegyptopithecus* and *Propliopithecus*.

Parapithecids have three premolar teeth, and molar teeth that are constricted across the middle – characteristics unique among old-world anthropoids. In *Apidium* the face was short, smell poorly developed, and the eyes placed close together giving stereoscopic vision. It had a leaping gait like living lemurs.

Among the pongids, *Aegyptopithecus* is known from a nearly complete skull: the snout is long, the eyes placed well forward, the canine teeth large and the sense of smell weak; the molar teeth are larger toward the back of the mouth. It was probably rather like living lorises in appearance. The other genus, *Propliopithecus*, is rather different: the face is short and the canine teeth small; in addition the molar teeth do not become larger towards the back of the mouth. *Propliopithecus* could well be an ancestor of the *hominids.

Among the other primates is *Oligopithecus*, which may be close to the ancestry of cercopithecids or old-world monkeys.

The Miocene. The next phase of primate evolution of which we have evidence is from the early *Miocene of East Africa. Sediments around Lake Victoria have yielded a rich fauna, due to the untiring efforts of *Leakey and his colleagues. These fossils are about ten million years younger than those of the Fayum, but we know nothing of intermediate primates.

Proconsul, an animal about the size of a

small baboon, is known from a good skull, jaws and some limb bones: the teeth are in some ways similar to those of chimpanzees. It may well stand in line of ancestry to the great apes, and was probably mainly a ground-dweller, like baboons, living on forested volcanic slopes. Also from Kenya comes *Limnopithecus*, a gibbon-like animal and possibly an ancestor of the gibbons, the smallest living apes.

During the Miocene in both Europe and Asia there were other baboon-like primates referred to collectively as *Dryopithecus*. They were essentially similar to *Proconsul*. One of the Indian types may be ancestral to the orang-utan.

Later Evolution. The last five million years have seen the gradual evolution of present-day species and some extinct sidelines: there are ceboid monkeys from Columbia, cercopithecoid monkeys from Kenya, a giant lemur, *Megaladapis*, from Madagascar, and from China a gigantic gorilla, *Gigantopithecus*.

So, in the fossil record, we can trace the history of the four living types of ape back 20 million years, and recognize even from 30 million years ago animals that could be hominid ancestors.   RJGS

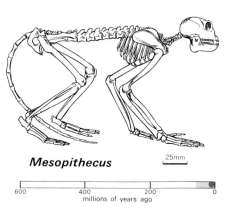

Mesopithecus   25mm

600   400   200   0
millions of years ago

Hominids

Hominid fossils discovered near Olduvai Gorge in Tanzania during 1975 by Dr Mary Leakey have been dated at around 3.5 million years old, and thus are certainly the earliest reliably dated hominid fossils known. But what do we mean by hominid? The hominids are a family containing Man and his close relatives, distinct from the family of apes, the pongids.

Man and the Apes. Man shares many characteristics with the other *primates, and some which clearly distinguish him from all others. Only bones and teeth fossilize, so difference in soft tissues cannot be checked out in extinct animals and need not concern us here (see *fossil record). The major skeletal differences between Man and the apes relate to locomotion and to feeding. Man stands upright and walks on two legs: all apes walk on four legs, though they can if need be walk short distances on their hind

legs. Man's bipedalism has influenced the shape of his hip bones, thigh bones and foot bones, and given him a characteristic S-curved backbone. Further, the skull is carried on top of the backbone rather than being hooked on the end as in apes.

In Man the skull roof is domed over the very large brain, while in apes, which have smaller brains, there is often along the skull roof a prominent ridge, to which are attached strong chewing muscles. The short human face contrasts with the projecting face and jaws of apes, and these differences mirror dental characteristics. Human teeth are arranged in a continuous arcade, all being on the same level, and the canine is not enlarged. Apes have two parallel rows of cheek teeth, terminating in large projecting canines, with a gap before the transverse incisors – this gap is necessary to accommodate the tips of the lower canine teeth when the jaws are closed.

Early Hominids. These differences enable us to easily distinguish the skeletons of present-day Man and present-day apes. But both shared a common ancestry, perhaps 30 million years ago, differences being only gradually acquired. So when we examine any monkey-like fossil we are looking for evidence of specialized hominid characteristics.

One member of the large fauna of anthropoids from the *Oligocene of the Fayum, *Propliopithecus*, might be considered a hominid ancestor; but we must beware of reading too much into a few broken jaw bones from 30 million years ago. For the next evidence of hominids we have to travel some 15 million years or more to the middle *Miocene of Kenya, where *Kenyapithecus* was found. From sediments of similar age in northern India comes another animal named *Ramapithecus*, so like *Kenyapithecus* that they probably belong to the same genus. They have flat, broad, squarish cheek teeth, molars that are all of the same pattern, and small canines; and the dentition appears to have been arranged in an arcade: these are all hominid characteristics not seen in apes. They lived in forests but we cannot tell whether they were arboreal or ground dwellers. It was, however, a time when the pongids were well established and these fossils are quite different from them, so there are good grounds for placing them in the family of Man.

Following the mid-Miocene fossils, there is again a long gap in the record. There are a couple of isolated teeth from the Lake Baringo area of Kenya which can be aged at 10 and 6 million years and which show hominid features, but isolated teeth are not enough to enable us to say that there were hominids there.

The Pliocene and Pleistocene. From cave sites in the Transvaal have come hundreds of hominid fossils of the genus *Australopithecus*. At least two kinds existed, a gracile form named *A. africanus* and a robust form named *A. robustus*. The cave *breccias are impossible to age precisely

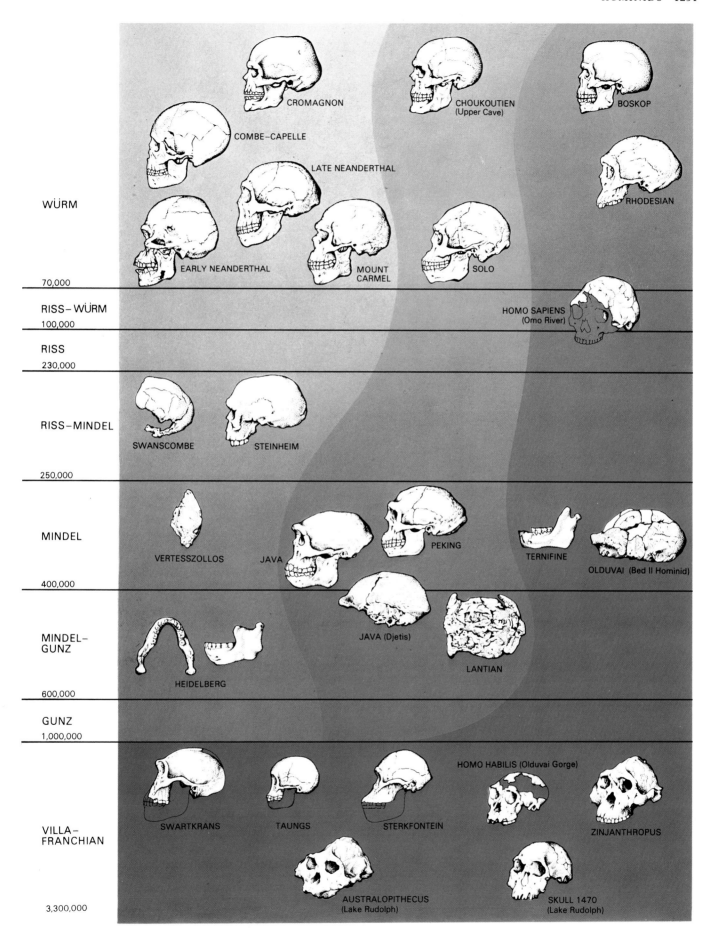

The chronological position of the later hominids in relation to the glacial and interglacial periods of Europe.
Colored bands show, from left to right, Europe, Asia and Africa.

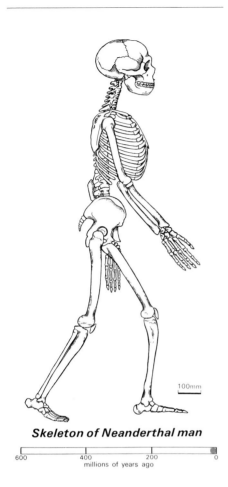

Skeleton of Neanderthal man

600   400   200   0
millions of years ago

with radiometric methods, but on other grounds we believe the fauna to be between 1 and 2 million years old.

With such large quantities of material – one site alone has yielded over two hundred individuals – we can learn a great deal about these primates. They were short, averaging 4.5ft (1.4m) in height and weighing around 70lb (32kg). Their brains range in size from 16.6 to 44.5in^3 (280–750cm^3) with an average of 28.5in^3 (480cm^3). For comparison, the gorilla's brain is around 29.7in^3 (500cm^3) and modern Man has a range of 59.3–118.6in^3 (1000 to 2000cm^3) with an average of 80.1in^3 (1350cm^3). So the largest *Australopithecus* brain was only a little smaller than the smallest human brain.

The robust species had heavy crests along the skull roof similar to those found in apes and indicating strong chewing muscles. The teeth were similar to those of modern Man, but much bigger, suggesting a heavy grinding dentition. They probably had a life expectancy of only 18 years.

In addition to these is a jaw which represents another line, closer to modern Man. It has been named *Telanthropus* and may be comparable with some specimens from East Africa.

By far the richest discoveries of early Man have been made by members of the *Leakey family at Olduvai Gorge in Tanzania and in the East Rudolf area of northern Kenya. The Olduvai Gorge sites give

an almost continuous succession over the past two million years. Well dated by radiometric methods, they have yielded a prodigious number of implements, a wealth of information on the mammals that lived around the early hominids, and a dazzling array of hominids themselves.

From the early beds (between 1 and 2 million years old) are recognized two kinds of hominids. One is *A. boisei* (sometimes called *Zinjanthropus*), which has strong similarities with *A. robustus* from South Africa: its brain capacity of 31.4in^3 (530cm^3) is within the range of the Transvaal specimens. The second kind is *Homo habilis*, a smaller, much more human-like species, only about 4ft (1.23m) high but with a brain capacity of around 38.6in^3 (650cm^3): *Telanthropus* could also belong to this stock.

Associated with these are vast quantities of tools belonging to the Oldowan culture. They are the most primitive known tools, stones flaked to give a cutting edge sharp enough to cut through a mammalian hide.

Further north along the shores of Lake Rudolf (now Lake Turkana) have been found rich collections of hominid fossils. There appear to be three kinds: a robust australopithecine like the Olduvai *A. boisei* and the South African *A. robustus*; a gracile australopithecine like *A. africanus* from South Africa; and a third kind with resemblances to *H. habilis* from Olduvai. These fossils are similar to those from the early beds at Olduvai, though some may be rather older.

Other but less extensive australopithecine discoveries have come from west of Lake Rudolf; from the Omo valley north of Lake Rudolf; and from the Lake Chad area. Some hominid fossils from northern Israel may be australopithecine and if so they are the only known occurrence of the stock outside Africa.

Recent emphasis has been placed on earlier sediments, and there have been two notable successes: from the Afar region of Ethiopia has been reported a fairly complete skeleton of a hominid which is provisionally dated as over 3 million years old; and from Laetolil near Olduvai in Tanzania Dr Mary Leakey has reported finding partial dentitions of eleven individuals confidently dated at around 3.5 million years. It is too early yet to pronounce judgment on the relationships of these specimens to other hominids, but it can be said that they carry the history of Man's ancestry back a further million years.

Outside Africa there is almost no evidence of hominids until middle Pleistocene times, with then the rich faunas of *H. erectus* from Jawa and China. During the 1930s, scientists in Jawa discovered skulls often referred to as Jawa apeman, *Pithecanthropus erectus* or *H. erectus*: the beds in which they were found are between 0.5 and 0.75 million years old. Similar hominids have been found in the Choukoutien caves south of Pekin in China, where there are tools and evidence of the use of fire. Fossils of the

same species have been identified in the higher levels of Olduvai Gorge, and elsewhere. *H. erectus* was much more advanced than *Australopithecus*: he had a brain capacity of 44.5–59.3in^3 (750–1000cm^3), the top of which range is close to that of modern Man; but he may represent a dead end rather than an ancestral link with ourselves.

Homo Sapiens. The final phase of human evolution took place in the late Pleistocene. Many fossils are known from Europe, Asia and Africa, but as yet none until rather later in the Americas or Australasia. The earliest claims to the name *Homo sapiens* are the partial skull from the Thames estuary at Swanscombe, England, and a skull from Steinheim in West Germany. Both are almost indistinguishable from modern Man and are probably about 250,000 years old.

One of the most numerous kinds was Neanderthal Man – his remains have been found all round the Mediterranean, and specimens from as far afield as Jawa and Rhodesia may also belong to this stock. Neanderthal Man is sometimes regarded as a separate species of *Homo* and at other times as only a subspecies. His average height was only around 5ft (1.5m) but he had a brain capacity of around 95in^3 (1600cm^3). His heavy eyebrow ridges and sloping forehead give him a rather ape-like appearance. Although the average brain capacity was higher than in modern Man the brain itself seems to have been less complex and so he was probably not so intelligent.

Another paleolithic culture was that of Cro-Magnon Man, physically indistinguishable from modern Man, and responsible for the famous cave paintings of northern Spain and southern France. There are many African late Paleolithic sites which have yielded remains of *H. sapiens* – for example, the youngest beds at Olduvai.

The lineages leading to modern Man are not clear. It is not known whether Neanderthal Man was a direct ancestor of some or all modern men. At Mount Carmel in Israel, in deposits about 40,000 years old, there is a population with characteristics intermediate between Neanderthal and Cro-Magnon Man, and these could be interpreted as representing a transitional link between the two kinds or the product of interbreeding between them. It seems possible that the Rhodesian neanderthaloid man might be an ancestor of the bushman and perhaps also of the negroid types. However, the differences between present-day human "races" are scarcely more than skin-deep; using only bones and teeth and allowing for the wide range of variation in populations, there is so much overlap that racial differences are virtually undetectable.

We can now trace the major developments in human evolution over the course of millions of years. By the middle Miocene we see evidence of a stock differentiated from the apes in being less fully vegetarian; that possibly lived on the edge of the forests,

View across the Serengeti Plain, Tanzania. Olduvai Gorge is in the middle of the plain.

kept mainly to the ground and hunted small mammals to supplement its diet.

By about 2 or 3 million years ago we see three kinds of hominid. Each has a number of human characteristics – upright gait, teeth very like those of modern Man, and brain capacities greater than those of the apes but still, generally, less than that of modern Man. The presence of tools in association with these fossils clearly defines a cultural level distinctly human.

In the later stages we see a complex of types, some of which could have contributed to present-day stocks and others of which may have been dead ends. In spite of exciting finds over the past decades, there is still much we have to discover about our ancestry.   RJGS

The Making of Geology

Man and the Earth

From earliest times, Man has tried to understand, and by understanding to control, the planet of his destiny, the environment which he inhabits, the ground which he treads: the Earth. And investigation of the Earth has figured large in the development of many basic sciences, sciences of the universe in general, such as cosmology, cosmogony and general natural philosophy; sciences of elements, such as alchemy and chemistry; sciences of structures, such as mineralogy, gemmology and cystallography; sciences of the environ-

ment, such as meteorology, physical geography, topography and oceanography; and the sciences of the living creatures and plants which inhabit the Earth, natural history, biology and ecology.

But most of these sciences treat the Earth as only a fraction of their subject-matter – or they focus upon only a few of its features and materials. By contrast, distinct and special investigation of the Earth itself, as the object of an autonomous science – geology – is a quite recent development. The same is true for the subdivisions of geology, such as geomorphology, paleontology and petrology. The currency of the very word "geology" (literally "Earth-

knowledge") does not date back more than two hundred years. For practical and philosophical reasons, both the study of the planets – and indeed of the universe in general – and the minute analysis of individual fossils and rare minerals advanced earlier, faster and with greater confidence than the science of planet Earth. Not until quite recently have men wanted, or been able, to create a science which takes pre-

A 17th-century illustration of the geocentric universe, the sphere of the fixed stars being outermost, then Saturn, Jupiter, Mars, Sun, Venus, Mercury and Moon.

Thales' view of the flat Earth floating on water (air and fire above complete the four elements).

cisely the Earth as its object, and which poses the questions of geology familiar to us today.

From Early Times to the Renaissance. Like so much of European culture, the modern sciences of the Earth are indebted to traditions of thought which crystallized in the Near and Middle East and the Mediterranean societies in the first two millennia BC. These traditions differed between civilizations, but embodied common outlooks which were suggested by common patterns of life. All civilizations, from the Assyrian through to Medieval Latin Christendom, were fundamentally dependent on the land, whether agrarian or pastoral. Man was close to the soil, in daily contact with the face of the Earth, aware of being part of an economy of Nature which nourished his body – a body which, from dust, in due course would to dust return.

On the one hand, this situation bred an insistent sense of the precariousness of the human condition in the face of the Earth's features and forces. Men recognized the curse of ceaseless toil, the need to bow to the course of the seasons and to the unarguable brute facts of volcanoes and earthquakes, droughts and floods, barren deserts and mountains. Yet, at the same time, men of the Mesopotamian twin rivers, of the Nile Valley and of the Mediterranean coastline could also experience Nature at her most benign, an Earth which provided a bountiful and comfortable habitat, a landscape long-settled by Man, redolent with human associations, tamed and assimilated by generations of agriculture.

Above all, these civilizations experienced the Earth only on a minute – and homely – scale. Beyond adjacent parts of the Eurasian and North African landmass, the globe was *terra incognita*. And, in the absence of concrete experience, mythological alternative worlds were conjured up – of burning tropics, lost continents and exotic monsters. There was little perspective on the Earth's past, nor solid knowledge of the depths of the crust. The known Earth was the here-and-now Earth. The starry firmament was a far more visible training-ground for the infant natural sciences.

Not surprisingly, such civilizations realized the Earth in their sciences very differently from subsequent interpreters. Above all, up to the Renaissance practically all schools of philosophy took a unified and highly integrated view of the whole cosmos. The Earth could be understood only in terms of its place and function within all the bodies which made up the universe. In fact, the Earth was most commonly seen as being at the *center* of them: the science of the Earth was part of cosmology and cosmogony, because the cosmos was thought to be geocentric. The Earth was influenced by planets and stars – for example, through astrological powers, and through the control which supralunary bodies exercised

over the growth of minerals and plants on Earth, and over the life of Man. Metals, for instance, had their controlling planets: iron was the metal of Mars, lead of Saturn, gold of the Sun. Gems reflected cosmic light.

Similarly, the Earth was also seen not just as a planet but also as an element which pervaded all matter within the corruptible regions of the cosmos. In turn, the planet Earth was composed not solely of its own element, but also of three other elements – water, air and fire. Ancient science stressed the unity and relatedness of all parts of the environment: the atmosphere, crust, oceans and "bowels" of the Earth. Thus Lucretius saw clouds as the caverns of the skies, the lairs of the winds; and *Aristotle thought earthquakes and volcanoes the terrestrial forms of thunder and lightning: significantly, the great Greek scientist set down most of his ideas about the Earth in a work entitled *Meteorology*.

Early science thus saw the Earth as a central, integrated part of the entire cosmos. Similarly, it also regarded the nature, operations and destiny of the Earth as inseparable from those of Man. The cosmos was more than geocentric, it was

anthropocentric. The Earth had clearly been designed as a habitat for Man, the rational and superior creature who tilled its soil, dug its mineral resources, explored and conquered it, mapped it and enjoyed it. Within the Christian account of the Creation, for example, God had created the Earth – indeed, Paradise – specifically for Man's needs, immediately before creating Man himself: once God had created Man, creation ceased. God willed that Man should go forth and multiply, and have dominion "over all the Earth and over every creeping thing that creepeth upon the Earth".

Furthermore, in their operations, Man and the Earth had the same nature, and reflected and responded to each other. For example, within Classical Greek medicine, Man's humors, his disease symptoms, his temper and disposition were seen as the equivalents in the microcosmic human body of the combinations of dryness and wetness, cold and heat, of the macrocosmic elements of earth, water, air and fire which made up the body of the Earth. The Hippocratic medical tradition saw many diseases as occasioned by climatic and en-

An early 16th-century view of Man, the microcosm, in relation to the universe, the macrocosm.

be at the center of the Earth.

Thus, the Earth was as nothing compared with the Deity who had created it, and who would terminate its existence in the fulness of time. Nevertheless, it bore evident marks of divine intervention and purposes. Practically all cultures saw volcanoes and earthquakes, floods, droughts and storms either as gods themselves or as the work of gods. Special mountains, islands, wells and springs were set aside as holy places. The Earth was enchanted and populated by good and evil spirits. In a Christian formulation, the Earth was the Book of God's Works, which the intelligent could read and find full of emblems and tokens of God's purposes.

Such was the general framework for understanding the Earth which arose from the geographically confined and technically quite simple societies which sprang up in the Mediterranean and Middle Eastern regions a few thousand years ago; an outlook which carried over into European civilization. Within this general philosophy, certain more specific investigations were carried out and observations made on particular terrestrial phenomena. Practical mining experience, and the notion that the Earth was a living organism, posed the question whether metals and minerals were generated and continually grew – and if so, how? Seeing all things beneath the Moon as compounded of the four elements created interest in the relations of the Earth's core, surface and atmosphere. For example, volcanoes suggested that the core was full of fire, trapped, trying to escape: on the other hand, the fact that rivers originated from springs which welled out of the Earth suggested to others that there must be great internal reservoirs connecting the ocean beds to the sources of rivers in a continuously flowing system. The Roman philosopher Seneca, among many others, was fascinated by the parallels between atmospheric explosions – thunder – and earthquakes and volcanoes.

Similarly, viewing the Earth as a theater of ceaseless elemental imbalance focused interest upon change: the continual ebbings and flowings of the tides; the changing courses of rivers, estuaries and deltas, such as the Nile; the creation and destruction of land. Pythagorean and Stoical philosophy, as expressed by naturalists like Strabo and Pliny, and by poets such as Ovid, suggested that continents and oceans, mountains and valleys, were in constant revolution. Such a viewpoint looked favorably upon interpreting the appearance of bones and shells embedded in solid rock as genuine organic remains which had been petrified in a former state of the world, perhaps when such strata had been the seabed. Debates as to whether fossils were organic remains or were, like minerals and crystals, forms produced in her own womb by great creating Nature, continued throughout the Mid-

vironmental imbalances – effluvia given off by the Earth, dampness caused by rivers or marshy areas, or poisonous airs around mines. Catastrophes in the natural world – such as comets, storms, and earthquakes – presaged human disasters.

In turn, the Earth was explained as an organic, living replica of the human body, and of other living things. Its round shape suggested an egg, with a hard, thin shell and – it was supposed – successive layers of different fluids beneath the shell. Chains of mountains were frequently called its bones, lowlands its flesh, rivers its veins and arteries, the tides the coursing of the blood caused by the pulse of its "heart" somewhere at the "core" of the Earth, and vegetation its hair. Hills were sometimes seen as warts on the face of the Earth.

Belief in the harmonious integration of Man, Earth and cosmos could offer a pastoral vision. Classical and Christian culture both had their rosy myths of Man in harmony with the Earth: Paradise, the Garden of Eden, the state of nature, the Golden Age, where Nature spontaneously yielded her bounty for Man, who knew no shortage, no toil, no disease, no old age. But

not wholly so. For Nature was also thought, like Man, to have cycles of old age and decay, when the Earth became barren and enfeebled, grew cold or feverish or decomposed. Natural disasters could be interpreted as the wrath of the gods directed against wayward Man. Within the Christian myth, Man had been expelled from Paradise at the Fall and condemned to work a refractory Earth by the sweat of his brow.

Thus early science saw the Earth wholly in relation to the cosmos and to Man. But it also saw it in a larger, transcendental vision, a divine framework. Before and after, above and beyond the Earth and the cosmos, was some overriding Deity – or deities. By contrast with things divine, which were eternal, changeless, spiritual, perfect and heavenly, the Earth was a theater of change, decay, transience, imperfection. Plato saw the Earth as "unreal", a mere reflection of Ideal truth. St Augustine contrasted the mundane vale of tears of the *civitas terrena* (the Earthly city) with the heavenly bliss of the *civitas Dei* (the city of God). Early Christians urged contempt for the world. Within much popular Medieval Catholicism, the location of Hell was believed to

The dominant medieval schools of thought accepted that space was finite. Here a man looks through the boundary to God's realm beyond.

dle Ages and the Renaissance in the work of naturalists such as *Leonardo and *Gesner.

Ancient and Medieval science did not produce distinguished investigation of the relief of the Earth, its deep structure, its processes or its historical alterations over time comparable in quantity and quality to contemporary work in astronomy or medicine (for example). Too little of the Earth's surface was known, too little of the Earth's depths was accessible. Understanding advanced on two other levels.

Firstly, the period down to and including the Renaissance achieved a steadily accumulating body of knowledge on particular products of the Earth – minerals, gems, fossils, metals, crystals, useful chemicals and medicaments. This was originally set out in encyclopedic natural histories such as those of Pliny (23–79) and Isidore of Seville (560–636). It was later embellished, reorganized and sometimes corrupted by later Arabic commentators such as Avicenna (980–1037) and Averroës (1126–98), and by Medieval scholastics such as *Albertus Magnus (1193–1280) and Thomas Aquinas (1225–74). Natural-history accounts of particular objects described and defined them, investigated their chemical and medical properties, and listed their locations, as well as being fascinated with their etymologies and with marvellous anecdotes associated with them.

Secondly, comprehensive philosophies of the Earth were being established. The one which was to have most influence upon later Western science was the Christian revelation of Creation as set out in the first chapter of Genesis; and the Christian view of the subsequent development, purposes and destiny of the Earth which could be digested from many parts of the Bible, perhaps above all from the Psalms and the Book of Revelation.

It saw the Earth – and indeed, the cosmos – as the product of a single, purposeful act of Creation, answering to God's ends for Man. Whether or not the Biblical chronology of the "days" of Creation, and the continuous descent from the first man, Adam, through to contemporary times was taken precisely literally, this Christian view saw the Earth as recent – perhaps no more than 6000 years old – in contradistinction to the apparent belief of Aristotle and other pagan philosophers that the Earth was eternal. It thought of the Earth and Man as practically coterminous. It envisaged time as directional, not cyclical. God had made the Earth perfect but, in response to sin, had sent Noah's Flood to punish and reform Man by setting him in a newly harsh environment, one of decay, struggle and the niggardliness of Nature. Such decay would continue until God had completed His purposes with Man, when God would

either destroy or transform the Earth, probably by fire, in the consummation of all things.

From the Renaissance to the End of the 18th Century. From the time of the Italian Renaissance of the 15th and 16th centuries onward, scientific study of the Earth gradually but steadily developed a new impulse, and interpretation of the Earth began to be transformed. This was, of course, part of a very general intellectual and scientific revolution stimulated by the recovery of writings from classical Greece and Rome, the invention of printing, the vast increase in education, literacy and communication, and growing faith in the goodness, dignity and progress of Man. But it was also quite specifically a product of European society's changing relations with,

and experience of, the globe.

For, within Europe, the surface of the Earth was being increasingly altered by agricultural advance and urban development. The depths of the crust were ransacked for useful metals and coal. Travel and exploration blossomed. As human technical powers over Nature grew, attitudes towards the Earth itself changed in their wake. The environment was tamed, civilized, brought within human experience. Mountains, once thought desolate, threatening and ugly, were transformed by a mental revolution into objects of awe and beauty – and sport for the climber.

At the same time, Europe spread out by voyages and conquest to become by the 18th century the first civilization bounded only by the limits of the globe. The de-

Travelers brought back tall tales of their encounters: these dog-headed and long-eared individuals were said to have been seen in India.

John Woodward's theory of the internal structure of the Earth, with regular strata throughout. Water from depth rises to the surface to provide the sources for rivers.

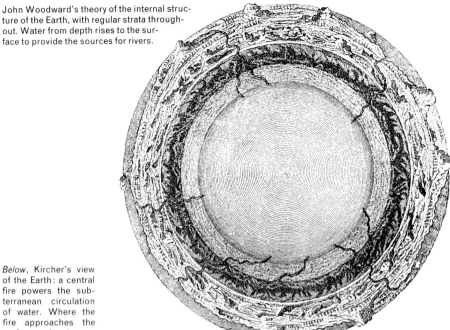

Below, Kircher's view of the Earth: a central fire powers the subterranean circulation of water. Where the fire approaches the surface, volcanism results.

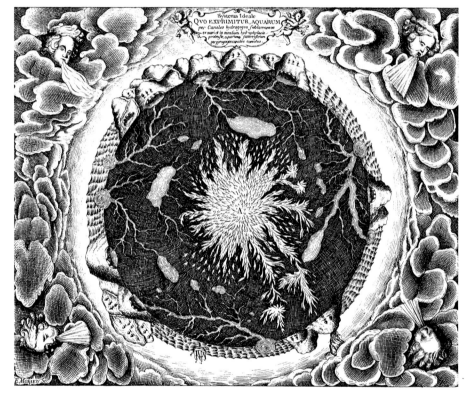

traditional macrocosm-microcosm analogies and the animistic belief that the Earth was "alive". The four Aristotelian elements were abandoned. All these increasingly led to the separation of the scientific study of the Earth from that of the cosmos at large. Thus, when late in the 17th century scientists like *Steno, *Hooke and *Woodward developed "theories of the Earth", they focused attention on the issues of the origin and destiny of the Earth, independently of the larger canvas of the universe in general. The Earth was increasingly conceived as having its own internal laws and economy. The geocosm gave way to the planet, Earth.

Furthermore, between the 15th-century Renaissance and the 18th-century Enlightenment, Christians gradually came to take up more liberal and rational stances on the relations between Scripture and scientific truth. Many European scientists abandoned Christianity for less dogmatically specific forms of theism and deism. In such a climate, the broad Christian pattern of Earth history, moving from original divine Creation through to final destruction, was usually maintained. Nevertheless, taboos against believing that the Earth was extremely old, and that it might have an indefinitely long future, began to be broken down in the work of scientists such as Hooke, *Buffon, *Hutton and *Lamarck.

In the 18th century it became generally accepted for the first time that the Earth had long predated the creation of Man. Furthermore, the Scriptural vision of a personal God of love and wrath yielded to the Supreme Architect Deity of the Enlightenment, a God of order, reason, and benevolence. By reflection, this meant that the Earth itself could be envisaged as possessing order and permanence in its fundamental laws and economy; as being a stable and functional system of processes deploying materials in good mechanical order. Divine interventions receded. Anthropocentrism was watered down.

Impressed with the power and success of the great 17th-century synthesizers – Galileo, Descartes, Newton and Leibniz – to give comprehensive rational order to the celestial world, scientists now looked for a Newton of the terrestrial globe. Hence the ambition was developed to grasp the Earth's economy in terms of a minimum of powerful natural laws applicable to all periods of the Earth's history, uniting past and present, and also to all parts of the globe, without the need for extraordinary or miraculous events beyond the normal course of nature. Originating in the 17th-century theories of the Earth, this movement culminated in the work of Buffon, Hutton and Lamarck.

Empirical examination of the Earth was now being pursued with ever greater energy and thoroughness. In part, this was founded upon the analysis of specimens in pursuit of the traditional disciplines of natural history, and spurred on by ever grander collections and museums. This in turn provoked the urgent need to introduce

signedly close fit between inhabitant and habitat, which had characterized the anthropocentric Christian view, was thrown off balance by new accounts of greater extremes of relief and climate than previously experienced. Areas of the globe such as much of North America were found scarcely inhabited – and sometimes almost uninhabitable. Entirely new fauna and flora were discovered. The globe began to appear a much more complicated planet. The stable world of Mediterranean Europe was dwarfed. Furthermore, old myths were dissolved, such as that the tropics were an impassable region of fire, or that there could

be no Antipodes. In the wake of circumnavigations, the globe had increasingly to be seen as an integrated Earth system; and new problems, such as that of the appearance and disappearance of whole continents, loomed larger.

In this situation, the science of the Earth was reconceived. The development of Copernican astronomy denied that the Earth was at the center of the planetary system. Belief grew – aided by the telescope – that the universe was indefinitely – or even infinitely – large, and that the Earth and the Solar System occupied no special place in it. The new mechanical philosophy rejected comprehensive systems of classification into the diversity of minerals, rocks and fossils. Once agreement was reached – by the late 17th century – that fossils were indeed organic remains, meticulous examination of fossils by naturalists such as *Hooke and *Steno established that many were the remains of creatures and plants lacking extant analogues, and hence there emerged Hooke's notion of a succession of former faunas and floras now extinct.

A series of great 18th-century mineralogists, including *Lehmann and *Werner, established the principle of a correlation between particular "mineral" and lithological characters and location of that specimen within the horizontal sequence of the strata. Furthermore, the vertical order of the strata themselves was increasingly acknowledged to be an index of temporal succession. For rock-forms were now being categorized according to their composition, origin and location into an ordering principle – such as Werner's Primary, Transitional, Secondary, Recent and Volcanic.

Primary rocks were broadly identified as being massive, frequently crystalline, non-fossiliferous, non-stratified and found at the base of rock-formations, often at steep angles to the horizon. They had supposedly been deposited out of a universal ocean by chemical means. They commonly made up rugged uplands and mountainous areas. Secondary rocks were believed mechanical in their deposition; were stratified and were thought to have been consolidated on former seabeds out of the detritus of earlier Primary formations. They were commonly fossiliferous, and frequently bedded more nearly parallel to the horizon. Transitional rocks shared some of the characteristics of both. Recent rock formations were less consolidated, and were to be found adjacent to the surface. For Werner, few other rocks than true lavas were volcanic or igneous. These were essentially extraneous to the above-mentioned succession, localized, and exceptional.

Of course, there were many rival classifications of rocks, and all were highly controversial. In particular, battle raged in the late 18th century over the nature of *basalt, and by extension over a range of other massive rocks which revealed vitreous and/or crystalline structure. Were they of aqueous or igneous origin? Not only was the classification of a number of rocks at stake, but so also were comprehensive rival conceptions of Earth history. One, the Wernerian, saw the Earth's crust uniquely and successively precipitated out of aqueous solution. The other, culminating in the work of *Hutton, asserted the continual formation of all rock types proceeding from the power of the Earth's supposed central heat over an indefinite timespan.

At the same time as collection, analysis and classification of specimens were bounding in popularity, meticulous examination of the Earth *in situ* by scientific traveler-naturalists also enormously expanded. It led to the detailed investigation for the first

A mid-19th-century illustration of a coral reef. Charles Darwin's explanation of their origin was a major contribution to physical geology.

A mid-18th-century diagram showing the formation of surface features through the buckling of rock strata.

time of European landscape and crustal features; but it also stimulated exploration of global phenomena not encountered in Europe, such as the volcanic islands and the coral atolls of the Pacific. In the 18th century, the work in particular of Lehmann, Pallas, Arduino, Sir William Hamilton, de Saussure, de Luc, Dolomieu and Hutton built up a tradition of *fieldwork*. Their attention shifted away from planet Earth in its entirety, focusing specifically on its crust.

Such fieldwork could take many forms. In some cases it simply recorded the terrestrial phenomena visible along the length of travels and traverses. In a more systematic way, fieldworkers began exhaustively to comb the topography of entire regions. They thus began to trace the distribution and continuities of strata, fossils, landscape features and structural faults across a terrain. Furthermore, fieldworkers increasingly saw the importance of probing perpendicularly down through the Earth's crust, making use of exposures at cliffs, mountainsides, mines, canal diggings, quarries and the like. When incorporated into a regional survey, such sections added a grasp of the composition of the crust. This in turn was ever more successfully visualized through the development of maps, sections, panoramas and block diagrams.

Above all, the growth of fieldwork focused attention for the first time on a hitherto

The Flood, by Francis Danby (1793–1861). The Flood was long regarded as an established event in Earth history.

little-investigated feature of the crust: the strata themselves. From the mid-18th century the strata became perhaps the chief focus of Earth science. Some geologists like *Lehmann studied them mainly to establish their general vertical order of succession; others organized their fieldwork around pinpointing the distribution of their outcrops throughout a region.

Furthermore, investigation of strata in the field increasingly provided an interpretative framework for grasping other crustal features. This was especially so because it came to be recognized that the vertical succession of the strata piled on top of each other represented, in general, the temporal sequence of their formation or deposition. Hence strata provided an index of the history of the Earth. Thus, by the end of the 18th century, consensus had been achieved among geologists that there was a correlation between the incidence of particular fossils and particular strata (or, in William *Smith's terms, that strata could be identified by organized fossils). Similarly, strata, landforms, and processes at work on the face of and beneath the surface of the globe were recognized as being interconnected, and their relations were explored. For, as *Hutton and his followers *Playfair and *Hall insisted, forces of denudation were destroying all existing rock formations. Yet, out of this detritus of denuded continents, the strata of future landmasses would be consolidated.

The Golden Age. Thus, by the turn of the 19th century, powerful traditions of examining the Earth's crust, both in the field and as specimens, had grown up. Attention was being focused on the strata, for strata gave meaning to other features of the Earth, and were the index of the history of the globe. By now, it was agreed the Earth had had an extremely long history, characterized by ceaseless change and profound revolutions. In short, an organized, integrated science of the Earth had developed, which contemporaries were, for the first time, beginning to call "geology". From the early 19th century there is a reasonably smooth development of Earth science up to the present.

The 19th century was the golden age of geology. It was taught at major institutions such as *Werner's Mining Academy at Freiberg, Saxony, and at the School of Mines in Paris. In England, the Geological Society of London (founded 1807) orchestrated pursuit of the science. In all major nations, state-financed Geological Surveys were set up. These were led by, and employed, first-rate geologists such as *De la Beche, *Murchison and *Geikie in Britain; *Élie de Beaumont in France; *Logan in Canada; and *Hall, *Powell and *Gilbert in the USA. Such surveys conducted the task of mapping the stratigraphy of their appointed regions. But they also in turn pioneered conceptual advance, as, for example, *Lapworth's work on the Silurian and Ordovician systems. Publicly-funded

oceanic voyages also enabled scientists like *Dana, *Darwin (Charles), *Huxley and *Murray to make substantial contributions to understanding oceans, islands and marine life, and the general balance of Nature.

Moreover, geology became a science deeply attractive to the amateur. For several generations, gentlemen amateur geologists such as *Scrope, *Lyell, *Murchison, von *Buch and von *Humboldt held the field, giving way only gradually to the professional and the academic. And, of course, throughout the century geology was to the fore in public controversy, especially in the religious debates which raged over the historicity of the Biblical Deluge, the contesting realities of miracles and the uniformity of Nature, the theory of *evolution by natural selection, and the question of the antiquity of Man. Industrial and economic applications of geology were also increasingly capitalized upon, at first for the discovery of coalfields to feed the hungry steam engines of the Industrial Revolution and then, later, ever more in the search for *petroleum and metals, particularly in imperial territories overseas.

Geology advanced in many important fields in the first half of the 19th century. The detailed order of the strata was explored for particular regions. Georges *Cuvier and Alexandre Brongniart undertook classic work unravelling the Cretaceous succession of the Paris Basin. In England, William *Smith's pioneering labors established the sequence of outcrops

A minor eruption at Krakatoa about six months before the disastrous explosion of August 1883.

of Secondary strata from the coal measures (i.e., *Carboniferous) up to the Chalk (i.e., *Cretaceous). *Sedgwick and *Murchison went to work on the complex formations of the western parts of Britain, hitherto confusingly known as Transition Grauwacke, and proposed – with much conflict – a division into *Cambrian, *Silurian and *Devonian systems. *Lyell established in all essentials the modern concept, and divisions, of the *Tertiary: in Lyell's classifications, *Smith's principle of identifying strata by their type fossils was used – but extended. For Lyell, the divisions of the Tertiary hinged upon their relative balance of extinct and currently existing fossils. The principle of (relatively) dating strata by type fossils rather than by lithology was triumphantly employed by Albert Oppel in his classic comparative studies of the Jurassic in France, Switzerland, Germany and Britain.

Perhaps more trail-blazing was the growing success in using fossil evidence to reconstruct a history of life. 18th-century naturalists had gained a general awareness that the Earth had formerly been populated by creatures now extinct, ranging from enormous vertebrates of elephant-like form (mastodons) down to huge shells, such as ammonites. But this was given new precision and perspective, above all by the work of *Cuvier. Using the rich collections of fossil bones available to him in the Paris Museum of Natural History, he applied the principle of the correlation of function and structure within the method of comparative anatomy to reconstruct hitherto unimagined extinct vertebrates – saurians, birds and mammals.

Furthermore, Cuvier was concerned to integrate zoology and geology by reconstructing the *total* physical environment of each epoch of such extinct creatures, viewed as particular stages in the development of life on Earth; each with its own distinct climate, terrestrial conditions, fauna and flora. In Cuvier's work, and that of those who followed in his footsteps, entire populations of extinct crustaceans and saurians, birds and mammals, were reconstructed. As the paleontological record was pieced together, rising upward through the strata, it suggested that such populations had existed in a temporal succession which led from Azoic times to invertebrates, and then on to vertebrates; from fish to reptiles to mammals; from simple to complex; from extinct to living. Early generalizations, such as that warm-blooded creatures had not existed in the Secondary epoch, or that pre-Silurian rocks were azoic (without life), were shaken, of course, by subsequent research: nevertheless, through the first half of the century the *fossil record seemed to yield ever more solid evidence of a progressive succession of forms of life, culminating in Man, each population apparently separated by periods

of "revolution".

Hotly debated, however, were questions as to the precise method of geological inquiry. These in turn were deeply connected with the fundamental problem of constructing a theoretical interpretation of the Earth. The challenging difficulty of geological inquiry was to reconstruct past stages of the Earth which had never been directly observed by Man. As a guide, geologists had relics of this past, in the form of rocks, fossils, and relief features such as rivers, valleys, and erratic boulders, from which deductions could be made. They also had the analogy of the present processes and economy of the Earth.

One school of geological thought, the "Uniformitarian" school, developed by *Hutton and, later, *Playfair and *Hall – and taken up by *Lyell – declared that the only properly scientific method of inquiry was to explain the Earth's past in terms of causes of the same kind and intensity as those currently active: to go beyond was to enter the realm of mere speculation and

religious miracles. "The present was the key to the past."

Moreover, claimed the Uniformitarians, *given enough time* the Earth's past could actually be explained in terms of the cumulative effects of gradual causes. In time, rivers would excavate their own valleys; in time, the sequence of earthquakes would build whole continents out of the sea, or raise mountain-ranges; in time, ecological pressures would gradually cause the extinction or migration of entire biological populations.

Other geologists, including *Cuvier, *Buckland and *Sedgwick, denied that it was unscientific to postulate that sudden, catastrophic events had occurred far back in geological times, events for which we had no current analogy. In fact, they claimed, evidence *demanded* such interpretations. The magnitude of the disruptions of strata throughout mountainous areas of the globe testified to sudden, catastrophic dislocations. Dry valleys equally seemed to prove that the theory of gradual fluvial

A mid-19th-century illustration of an Alpine glacier. Investigation of glaciers prompted glacial theory.

*erosion was false. The sheer extent of alluvial materials and erratic blocks scattered across northwest Europe could not be explained by any known cause.

This debate, however, was not confined to issues of method in geology, for it also embodied rival conceptions of the very patterns and direction of Earth history. *Hutton and *Lyell were postulating a steadystate Earth – ceaseless piecemeal local change was occurring. But the consequence of such change was to maintain from the indefinite past to the indefinite future an overall, constant equilibrium in the terrestrial economy. Lyell, for example, believed that even though particular species had come into being or become extinct, there was no general direction or development in the history of life – Man alone excepted.

Geologists such as Cuvier, Élie de Beaumont, Buckland, Sedgwick, De la Beche and Murchison, however, were putting forward a completely different, "directional" picture of Earth history. In this, time was not a cycle but an arrow: they postulated a gradually cooling Earth, a solidifying crust, an irreversible and unrepeatable succession of strata, a diminution of energy located within the globe. They believed that the Earth had supported successive, discrete populations of flora and fauna, usually regarded as specially created by God.

In fact, both points of view made their mark upon the approaches of most geologists. The justice of Lyell's claim that most "catastrophist" explanations reflected ignorance and explained nothing was increasingly admitted. On the other hand, paleontology seemed to provide mounting evidence for a profound historical sequence of lifeforms. Very few geologists were prepared to accept Lyell's claim that this was a gigantic illusion created by the random and misleading accident of the survival of fossil evidence: once the "catastrophist" case had been freed from the taint that it was "unscientific" in introducing miracles and in seeking to confirm Scripture, most geologists were prepared to admit a genuine succession of the stages of life. A typical compromise was that of *Scrope, who demanded that geology proceed by actual causes, but conceded that these had diminished in intensity in the course of Earth history.

The geology of the second half of the 19th century was to solve many of these dilemmas by putting them in new perspective. The principle of evolutionary organic transformation was almost universally adopted in the years following the publication of *Darwin's *Origin of Species* (1859). This helped to confirm the claim of the "directionalists" that life had proceeded through a significant succession of levels, while bearing out Lyell's emphasis on the gradualness of change. The

band of great palaeontologists – *Huxley, *Marsh, *Cope and *Osborn – employed fossil evidence to chart the branching directions and the pulse of evolutionary progress, now that enough "missing links" had come to light to trace a solidly connected progression of forms.

Secondly, the great surge of interest in geophysics in the second half of the 19th century imposed powerful pressure from outside upon geologists searching for the correct pattern of Earth history. Above all, Thomson (later, Lord *Kelvin) applied the Second Law of Thermodynamics and the developing concept of entropy to the cooling of the Earth. Such work not only gave strong support to a "directionalist" view of the Earth but pointed to an Earth markedly less old than the Uniformitarians, or than Darwinian evolutionists, demanded. For Kelvin, thermodynamics applied within geophysics showed – contrary to the Uniformitarians – that the Earth had had a beginning, and would certainly, as a habitable planet, have an end. Hence, it gave some renewed credit to "catastrophic"

Earth and life histories.

Fierce debate ensued over the applicability of Kelvin's methods of physics and mathematics to "geological" problems. Many geologists claimed that the Earth had its own laws which were not reducible to the laws of general physics. And the discovery of radioactivity early in the 20th century reassuringly indicated that the Earth was cooling – if at all – at a far slower rate than Kelvin had believed, and so restored to the geologists their vast timescale. But the intervention of Kelvin was important in breaking down the dogmatically stubborn Uniformitarian preference for time-over-violence in Earth history, and in bringing narrowly geological speculations (such as Darwin's suggestion of 300 million years for the denudation of the English Weald – i.e., for Tertiary time alone) before the bar of other sciences.

In the second half of the 19th century, in a different area of geology, another theory, which transcended the polarity between the earlier "steady state" and "directional" theories of the Earth, gained importance.

This was the elaboration of glacial theory. In its original form, most famously advanced by *Agassiz, the theory postulated a former, more extensive distribution of ice across Northern Europe to account for effects such as erratic boulders, striated mountainsides and alluvium. In its later, more thoroughly developed shape, glacial theory began to suggest a whole succession of Ice Ages, in which a substantial portion of the European continent had been covered with glaciers. (See *glaciation.)

Many hypothetical causes were offered. Some were purely terrestrial, hinging upon the suggestion that the changing distribution of land and sea could have a major effect in transforming climate. Some, like *Penck, suggested external causes such as fluctuations in the Sun's heat.

The importance of glacial theory was that it demanded a more sophisticated conception of the pattern of Earth history than either "Uniformitarians" or "Directionalists" had originally offered. For Ice Ages were in a sense catastrophes – yet they were, at the same time, evidence that the path of Earth history was subject to major oscillations rather than being uniformly progressive.

Indeed, the most important and exciting development in theoretical geology in the period leading up to WWI was precisely the growing awareness that the real complexity of the present crust of the Earth and its history could not be explained by a rigid insistence upon uniformity of causation and an overall "steady state"; nor by a simple view of progress, with its neatly-tailored succession of stages leading up to the present. The great interest newly taken in geophysics was highly influential in this respect, for it demanded that geologists should envisage the forms and materials of the crust in terms which went beyond merely identifying strata and projecting surface causes back into the past. Thus the question of the deeper physical energies governing the rhythm and balance of continents and oceans became increasingly raised – i.e., the question of "isostasy". Kelvin's arguments as to the *age of the Earth revived physical controversy over the original nature of the Earth. Had the Earth once been incandescent? or had it taken its origin from the adherence of cool particles? Was the great mass of the Earth beneath the solid crust to be inferred as being solid? or as a fluid, magmatic core?

Similarly, in the work of *Dana and *Murray, theories were constructed of large-scale, counterbalancing raising and subsidence of the ocean bed in the Pacific. *Davis advanced comprehensive physical theories of continental denudation, and so attempted to put geomorphology upon a basis of general laws of landscape. Scientific sedimentology was systematized by the work of *Murray, *Grabau and *Barrell. The physical bases of lithogeny and orogeny were investigated.

Furthermore, stratigraphical observation in the field was growingly confirming this perception of the extremely complex rhythm of geological causation. Sophisticated investigation of type fossils, as, for example, by *Lapworth in his work on graptolites in the Southern Uplands of Scotland, was revealing evidence of hitherto unsuspected unconformities, reversed faults, thrust planes, and lateral displacements of formations on a scale previously hardly contemplated. The work of *Argand and *Haug revealed the nappe structure of the Alps. Peach and Horne showed the gigantic thrust planes and faults of the northwestern Highlands of Scotland, the products of forces contemporaneous with and subsequent to the laying-down of the strata. Such new perspectives indicated how incomplete was the former stratigraphical stress upon simply tabulating the *order* of the strata: more attention needed to be paid to the *deformations* of the rocks. In other words, the modern emphasis on tectonics was emerging.

The new focus on tectonics was closely associated with a growing analysis, in the field and in the laboratory, on metamorphic rocks; and, in its turn, such work on internal dynamics hinged upon the emergence in the second half of the century of petrology, the science of the physical and chemical understanding of rock materials. *Cloos initiated the study of flow textures of solidifying magma. And the rise of petrology was aided by the development of microscopic analysis of thin slices as pioneered by *Sorby.

The 20th Century. Thus, in some ways, geology marched into the 20th century having achieved a solid foundation of basic conceptions and empirical knowledge. Important progress had been made in charting the order of the strata and the succession of fossils. Such work was to continue through the present century. National surveys were mapping the face of the Earth. Related and subordinate sciences, like seismology and physical geography, were expanding. The study of human prehistory developed. Yet in other respects, and above all when faced with the problem of grasping the patterns and causes of the physical forces which governed the globe's dynamic tectonics, geologists were still groping in the dark.

Geology was to be transformed after WWI by the formulation of the theory of *continental drift, above all by *Wegener. This theory was, however, hardly commonly accepted until its incorporation within a comprehensive vision of *plate tectonics after WWII. In many ways, however, the rise of petrology, and the development of new interest in geophysics in the late 19th century had provided the basis for such a geological revolution.   RP

Great Geologists

Here follow, in alphabetical order, biographical notices of those scientists and philosophers who have made considerable contributions to our modern understanding of the Earth sciences.

Agassiz, Jean Louis Rodolphe (1807–1873)
Agassiz received his scientific training at Zurich, Heidelberg, Munich and Paris, where he was deeply influenced by *Cuvier. He became professor at Harvard in 1847, where he founded the Museum of Comparative Zoology. His fundamental *Researches on Fossil Fish* (1833–44) used Cuvierian comparative anatomy to describe and classify over 1700 species.

In his *Studies on Glaciers* (1840) he pioneered the concept of the Ice Age, which he saw as an agent of extinction separating past from present flora and fauna.

The later years of his life were spent on *Contributions to the Natural History of the United States* (1857–62), an exhaustive study of the American natural environment. He also became one of the most powerful opponents of *Darwin's theory of *evolution on religious, philosophical and paleontological grounds.   RP

Albertus Magnus (c. 1200–1280)
Born of good family in Bavaria, Albertus was educated in the liberal arts at Padua, and joined the Dominican Order. His life was divided between intellectual studies and administration within the Church. His importance to science lay in commenting on and popularizing the philosophy of *Aristotle. He accepted the general Aristotelian doctrine of the four elements; and seems to have believed that Democritus' doctrine of atoms might be incorporated. He was interested in alchemical experiments and in the possible transmutation of metals.

Aristotle wrote no work of mineralogy, but Albertus' *Book of Minerals* (c. 1261) took over many Aristotelian ideas. He accepted, for example, that there were subterranean exhalations: a dry one which produced earths and stones, and a moist one which produced metals. He also explored the relations between the Earth and the heavens, and was interested in climate. Most important, he listed about 100 minerals, describing them, citing classical authorities on them, and sometimes adding his own observations. Almost all subsequent mineralogies and lapidaries stemmed from Albertus.   RP

Argand, Émile (1879–1940)
Born in Geneva, Argand devoted himself to understanding the tectonics of Alpine regions, whose structure is complex through intense folding and metamorphism and difficult to unravel because of stratigraphical ambiguity and the relative absence of fossil markers. He carried his researches to the interior of the Alps; and developed techniques of geometrical projection to explain missing structures. He opened up as a major tool of structural analysis the dynamic direction and axes of tectonic organization and movement. Among his highest achievements lay his pioneering, theoretically sophisticated, block diagrams.

In later years, he developed a greater concern with the time-dimension of tectonics, especially with orogeny, and made

A 16th-century illustration of Albertus Magnus, who made a major contribution to the dissemination of the thought of Aristotle in medieval Europe.

use of *Wegener's continental-drift hypothesis as a framework for his ideas of Eurasian structural development.   RP

Aristotle (384–322BC)

Born in Chalcidice, Aristotle studied in Athens under Plato and became tutor to Alexander the Great. He founded the Lyceum as a center of teaching and research. His influence on the study of the Earth lasted until the 18th century, his influence on cosmology until Copernicus.

He thought the Earth, composed of four elements (earth, water, air and fire), was a sphere at the center of the universe. He was particularly interested in comparing earthquake and volcanic phenomena to climatic events like storms, explaining them as the produce of conmingling of dampness from rain with underground winds.

He believed that earthly objects were also due to exhalations from the Earth, fossils and minerals being produced by a dry exhalation, metals by a moist one. He seems to have attributed organic fossil forms to some kind of plastic force in the Earth, which imitated the workings of nature on the surface.

Aristotle was concerned also with the origins of springs and rivers, seeming to have accepted that rainwater was not the sole source of springs, and holding that the Earth itself intrinsically produced water as a result of its coldness.   RP

Arrhenius, Svante August (1859–1927)

Arrhenius' importance to geology rests on three works. His 1896 paper, "On the influence of carbonic acid in the air upon the temperature of the ground", postulated that the variable capacity of carbon dioxide to absorb infrared radiation from the Earth's surface might explain fundamental climatic changes in the Earth's history (e.g., Ice Ages). The paper was largely ignored.

His "Towards a physics of volcanism" (1901) sought to explain volcanic eruptions: at very high temperatures, he claimed, water forced its way into the magma, causing massive expansion and penetration into volcanic fissures. As this magma cooled, water was liberated, causing explosions.

In his *Textbook of Cosmic Physics* (1903) he turned to the problem of the *origins of life on Earth, developing the theory that seeds had been transported here from other cosmic systems by light-pressure.   RP

Bailey, Sir Edward Battersby (1881–1965)

Bailey served in the Geological Survey of Great Britain until 1929, when he became professor at Glasgow, only to return to the Survey as its Director in 1937.

His chief contributions were in the fields of tectonics, metamorphism and igneous geology. His most important metamorphic studies were of northwest Scotland, where he produced major reinterpretations of late Precambrian schists. In igneous geology, he helped to formulate the theory of the "cauldron subsidence" of Glen Coe, Scotland, and investigated the intrusion tectonics of Arran granite and the volcanic complex of Rhum.

He was a distinguished writer on the history of his science, publishing biographies of *Hutton and *Lyell and an account of the Geological Survey of Great Britain.   RP

Barrell, Joseph (1869–1919)

Born at New Providence, New Jersey, Barrell had a thorough general education in the natural sciences before specializing in geology. This may explain the two most marked features of his approach: he was always primarily concerned with the broad problem of the effects of the totality of physical agents upon the evolution of the Earth; and he was a philosophical geologist, more interested in a conceptual grasp of the problems of the Earth than in pioneering new fieldwork. Much of his work was concerned with the relations between volcanic phenomena, magma and metamorphism. His main interpretation of these forces lies in *Geology of the Maryville Mining District, Montana* (1907).

He was influential as a theorist of sedimentology. The traditional assumption was that almost all sedimentary rocks were of marine origin: Barrell put forward the view that a substantial proportion are in fact continental, fluvial or aeolian in origin.   RP

Barrois, Charles Eugène (1851–1939)

Born in Lille, France, Barrois spent his working life attached to the Lille Faculty of Sciences. He excelled in all aspects of field geology and paleontology.

His chief love became Primary geology (see *Werner). In the late 1870s he undertook minute research on the Primary formations of northern Spain, and later the Sierra Nevada. And, throughout his career, he occupied himself with mapping and interpreting the formations of Brittany, a task made especially difficult by metamorphism and the absence of fossils.

Though a distinguished descriptive paleontologist, he made little use of fossils to unravel the history of life, avoiding entanglement in evolutionary controversy because of religious commitments.   RP

Bowen, Norman Levi (1887–1956)

Norman Bowen was born and educated in Kingston, Ontario. As a graduate student, he worked at the Geophysical Laboratory in Washington, then recently founded, and in 1912 published his first results on the experimental melting of silicates and their crystallization behavior. He remained at the Geophysical Laboratory for most of his life, and over a period of more than forty years reported on and interpreted results from innumerable more extensive experiments.

During this period Bowen and his associates, notably O. F. Tuttle and J. F.

William Buckland outfitted to explore a glacier. His contributions to glacial theory arose from his preoccupations with catastrophism.

Schairer, established the physico-chemical principles relevant to the fractional crystallization of magmas and the formation of magmas by partial melting. They transformed igneous petrology from the descriptive science created by Zirkel and Rosenbusch into its current state, in which the origins of rock types and the evolution of magma are of prime interest.   KGC

Buch, Christian Leopold von (1774–1853)
Born at Stolpe, near Berlin, Buch passed his life as one of Europe's eminent amateur traveler-geologists. He studied mineralogy and chemistry at Berlin, and then under the great *Werner at Freiberg: though modifying and extending Werner's work in many respects, Buch remained a lifelong admirer. His great strength lay in his ability as an observer: his findings were published in a number of volumes of travels (1802, 1808, 1810, 1825).

In 1802 he developed his theory of elevation craters to explain volcano-like phenomena, maintaining that Auvergne *basalts had once been lava. He continued, however, to accept Werner's teaching that Saxon basalts were of aqueous origin, finding no volcanic phenomena associated with them.
                                                RP

Buckland, William (1784–1896)
Born at Axminster, England, Buckland attended Oxford University. Elected Reader in Mineralogy in 1813, he became Reader in Geology in 1818, and subsequently Dean of Westminster in 1845. His geological work has three main foci.

Firstly, he made important contributions to the descriptive stratigraphy of the British Isles, inferring from the strata a stage-by-stage history of the surface of the globe. Secondly, he became a distinguished paleontologist. He used the methods of Cuvierian comparative anatomy to reconstruct *Megalosaurus* and the history of the hyena cave den, Kirkdale Cavern, in his *Relics of the Deluge* (1823).

But his greatest concern lay in exploring evidence for catastrophic transformations of the Earth's surface in the geologically recent past, as indicated by features of relief, fossil bones, erratics and gravel displacement. In his *Geology Vindicated* (1819) he confidently attributed these to the Flood – an assertion he later withdrew. His concern for such phenomena helped him to become, however, a leading British exponent of glacial theory.   RP

Buffon, Georges Louis LeClerc, Comte de (1707–1788)
Though educated for the law, Buffon turned towards a scientific career, becoming a member of the Royal Academy of Sciences, Paris, in 1734. He contributed to many areas of science, but his major work was the *Natural History,* in 36 volumes, published from 1749. In the first volume he set out a theory of the Earth, stressing the gradual and ceaseless change of the Earth's crust

produced by natural causes; that new land was continually forming, and continents being destroyed by the sea. In his *Epochs of Nature* (1779) he somewhat modified this theory, now emphasizing that the Earth had been a fragment thrown off by the Sun, and had cooled gradually in seven stages, so accounting for the existence of primitive vitreous rocks, subsequent volcanic action, and more recent aqueous formations. The cooling Earth also explained the successive appearance of different forms of life, beginning with gigantic forms, now extinct, and

ending with Man.

He was one of the first to put an age to the Earth on the basis of experiments conducted with cooling iron balls, suggesting 75,000 years in public but as much as 3 million years in his private manuscripts. RP

Chamberlin, Thomas Chrowder (1843–1928)
Chamberlin's most important contribution to geological thinking lay in his attack on Lord *Kelvin. Kelvin had postulated that the Earth was rather young (less than 100 million years), basing his views on the

A reconstruction according to Cuvier of *Megatherium*, the largest of the extinct group of edentate mammals known as ground sloths.

assumption, derived from the nebular hypothesis, that the Earth had steadily cooled from a molten mass.

Chamberlin rebuked Kelvin for the dogmatic confidence he placed in extrapolations from a single hypothesis, and stressed that geological reasoning must follow from a plurality of working hypotheses. He also believed geological evidence anyway suggested the Earth to be older than Kelvin had estimated, backing his case against the nebular hypothesis by developing with the celestial physicist, F. R. Moulton, the planetesimal hypothesis. This postulated a gradual origin, by accretion of particles, for the Earth and other planetary bodies, an origin which was therefore cool and solid.   RP

Cloos, Hans (1885–1951)
Cloos made tectonics his lifetime's study. His pioneering work on the tectonics of Silesian granite revealed that, far from being structureless as commonly thought, it bore marks of features acquired soon after its intrusion: he opened up the study of the flow textures of solidifying magma. He later extended his tectonic studies to the jointing and cleavage features of the deformation of solid rocks. He was also one of the pioneers of the reproduction of tectonic processes in the laboratory.   RP

Cope, Edward Drinker (1840–1897)
Born in Philadelphia, Cope, as editor of *The American Naturalist*, was to the fore in airing and popularizing evolutionary views in the USA.

His chief work was as a student of the fauna – and above all, the fossil fauna – of the little-explored American Midwest, particularly in regard to fishes, amphibia, reptiles and mammals, pursuing the techniques of comparative anatomy, classification and systematics as laid down by *Cuvier, *Owen and *Huxley. He made pioneering studies of the dinosaurs of the *Cretaceous of New Jersey and the plesiosaurs of the Kansas Cretaceous.

A convinced evolutionist, he championed

Lamarckism; and argued for the creative role of consciousness in organic development, believing that favored variations were shaped by will. He wrote widely in his mature years on religion, psychology and general philosophy, interpreting the significance of evolution.   RP

Cuvier, Georges (1769–1832)
Born at Montbêliard in the principality of Württemberg, Cuvier received his training in natural history at Stuttgart, spent six years as a private tutor in Normandy, and came to Paris in 1795.

His great contribution was to systematize the principles of comparative anatomy to apply them to fossil vertebrates, thus effectively founding modern paleontology. In his *Researches on the Fossil Bones of Quadrupeds* (1812) and his *Animal Kingdom* (1817) he reconstructed extinct fossil quadrupeds such as the mastodon and the paleotherium.

His stratigraphical work in the Paris Basin demonstrated that fossil flora and fauna were specific to particular strata. Cuvier interpreted this as implying that the history of the Earth involved a series of revolutions ("catastrophes") which periodically swept away whole living populations, their place being taken either by migration or by the creation of new species. This theory, set out in his *Preliminary Discourse* (1812), expressly countered the evolutionary views of *Lamarck and the paleontologist Geoffroy Saint-Hilaire (1772–1844).   RP

Daly, Reginald Aldworth (1871–1957)
Born at Napanee, Ontario, and educated at Harvard, Daly became a widely experienced field geologist and one of the great synthesizers of geological fact in the early part of the 20th century.

He once remarked that geology was "drowning in facts" and urged more concern about the theoretical framework behind Earth processes. His principal field of study was *igneous rocks and he developed many of the ideas which are still

current on such subjects as the mechanics of magmatic intrusion; he added greatly to our knowledge of basalts and the ocean basins with his studies of oceanic islands such as St. Helena. Daly was among the first to look upon continental ice sheets as a means of testing the reaction of the crust to loading, and hence deducing information about the physical properties of the crust and upper mantle. In addition, it was Daly who suggested that submarine canyons might have been eroded by the action of turbidity currents. He also developed a hypothesis of the glacial control of sea level.   KGC

Dana, James Dwight (1813–1895)
The formative period in Dana's career came with his service with the Wilkes expedition of 1838–42, a natural history survey of Polynesia financed by the US government. He spent much of the 1840s writing reports of this expedition (*Geology*, 1849; *Crustacea*, 1852).

This experience led to a lifelong interest in coral and volcanic phenomena – his identification and classifications of Pacific corals have survived remarkably well. He was also preoccupied with the problem of the diversity of coral formations: why were there atolls, barrier reefs and fringe reefs? He became a firm supporter of *Darwin's theory that atolls were the result of subsidence, and confirmed it independently. From this he deduced the likely enormous extent of downward movements of the crust in the tropical Pacific.   RP

Dart, Raymond Arthur (1893–   )
Born in Toowong, Brisbane, Dart studied medicine at the University of Queensland, held teaching posts in anatomy in England just after WWI, and became Professor of Anatomy at Witwatersrand from 1923 to 1958.

His major work lay in the investigation of African fossil *hominids. In 1924 he discovered at Taung, South Africa, the skull of a man-ape child which he recognized represented an extinct ape group, called by him *Australopithecus africanus*. Subsequently more specimens were uncovered.

Later work by *Leakey and others has confirmed Dart's identification of the "missing link" and that the African continent seems to have housed the earliest specimens of Man.   RP

Darwin, Charles (1809–1882)
Up to the publication of his *Origin of Species* (1859), Darwin was best known as a geologist. Born in Shrewsbury, he was educated at Edinburgh and Cambridge Universities, before serving from 1831 on the famous five-year voyage of the *Beagle*. At Cambridge, under *Sedgwick, he had developed an interest in geology. His own extensive observations on the voyage, however, won him over to Uniformitarianism, as expressed in *Lyell's *Principles of Geology*. In particular, his South American experiences of the interconnectedness of volcanoes, igneous rocks, raised beaches and land uplift convinced him of both the paramountcy and the adequacy of the slow action of present-day causes.

This led to Darwin's major contribution to geology, his theory of coral reefs. Darwin saw that the perfect condition for the formation of coral atolls was the slow subsidence of former islands; whereas fringing reefs were the product of uplift of similar land areas. He showed how the Pacific could be divided between zones of fringing reefs and active volcanoes on the one hand and areas of atolls with extinct volcanoes on the other.

Darwin's theory of *evolution by natural selection was utterly dependent upon the indefinitely long and gradual Earth history postulated by Uniformitarian geology. Darwin himself believed that the *fossil record was not sufficiently full to adjudicate between rival theories of the succession of forms of life.   RP

Darwin, George Howard (1845–1912)

The fifth child of Charles *Darwin, George Darwin was essentially a mathematical cosmogonist, concerned with the application of detailed quantified analysis to cosmological and geological problems. His first major contribution was his 1876 paper "On the influence of geological changes in the Earth's axis of rotation". He then carried out celebrated work on the origins of the Moon, believing it to be the product of the fission of the parent Earth as a result of instability produced by solar tides. He dated the event as at least 50 million years old, seeing this as compatible with his friend *Kelvin's relatively low estimate of the antiquity of the Earth. However, by the early 20th century, Darwin was one of the first to recognize how the discovery of radioactivity overthrew Kelvin's estimates.   RP

Davis, William Morris (1850–1934)

In his day, Davis was the leading American scientist of the physical environment. He made contributions to three fields of science, meteorology, geology and above all geomorphology. He developed the organizing conception of the regular cycle of *erosion, a concept that was to influence the discipline for fifty years. He assumed a standard life-cycle for a *river valley, marked by youth (steep-sided valleys), maturity (flood-plain floors), and old age as the river valley was worn lower and lower into a "peneplain". Such cycles could be interrupted by uplift, which would rejuvenate the river and impose fresh cycles.

The Davisian cycle presupposed a strongly uniformitarian view of Earth history in which the present was key to the past, and gradual causes were paramount.   RP

De Geer, Gerard Jacob, Baron (1858–1943)

De Geer is remembered in science as the founder of geochronology, the dating of past events in the geological record.

In 1882 he conceived the idea that the finely banded deposits known as varved clays might hold within them a seasonal record of glacial melting during the retreat of the great Scandinavian ice sheets at the end of the glacial period. According to this hypothesis, each sandy layer represents

rapid sedimentation in a water body at the front of the glacier, while the clay layers represent the slow settling of fine particles after the sediment supply has stopped during winter. By painstaking measurement and comparison from one small exposure to another, De Geer and his colleagues were over a number of years able to build up a chronology of the glacial period which extended back for some 15,000 years. By 1920 he had extended his studies to North America and was able to correlate deposits there with those in Europe.   KGC

De la Beche, Henry Thomas (1796–1855)

Born in London, De la Beche became a gentleman amateur geologist, traveling extensively during the 1820s through Great Britain and Europe and publishing widely in descriptive stratigraphy. He became a scrupulous fieldworker, stressing the primacy of facts and distrusting theories, as can be seen from his *Sections and Views Illustrative of Geological Phenomena* (1830) and *How to Observe* (1835).

In the 1830s he conceived the idea of government-sponsored geological investigations of areas of Britain. He personally undertook a survey of Devon, for which he was paid £500, and then persuaded the government to formalize this arrangement. In 1835 the Geological Survey was founded, with De la Beche as director.

The Survey flourished and expanded. De la Beche's career reached its peak with the establishment of a Mines Record Office and then the opening in 1851, under the aegis of the Geological Survey, of the Museum of Practical Geology and the School of Mines in London.   RP

du Toit, Alexander Logie (1878–1948)

du Toit was the greatest of South African geologists. Born near Cape Town, he studied at Cape Town, Glasgow and the Royal College of Science, London. He spent the 17 most creative years of his career from 1903 mapping for the Geological Commission of the Cape of Good Hope.

At the height of his career, and following a visit to South America, he began to take seriously *Wegener's theory of continental drift. In his *A Geological Comparison of South America with South Africa* (1927) he systematically set out the numerous similarities in the geologies of the two continents, suggesting an original contiguity. These ideas were most fully and popularly stated in his important book, *Our Wandering Continents* (1937), in which he suggested that the southern continents had at one time formed the supercontinent of Gondwanaland, which was distinct from the northern supercontinent of Laurasia. This notion, though originally discounted, has grown in acceptance since.   RP

Élie de Beaumont, Leonce (1798–1874)

Élie de Beaumont studied mathematics and physics at the École Polytechnique in Paris before entering the School of Mines in 1819. His greatest work for the School was to take charge of drawing up the eastern division of the official geological map of

MONKEYANA.

Punch's contribution to the debate over Darwin's *Origin of Species*.

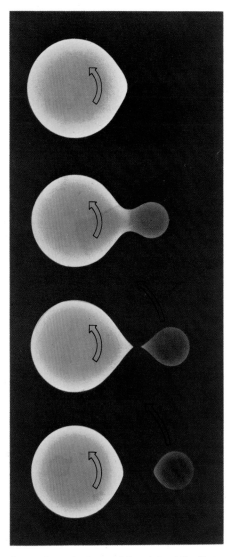

George Darwin's theory of the origin of the Moon. The length of the month compared with that of the day was explained by conservation of angular momentum.

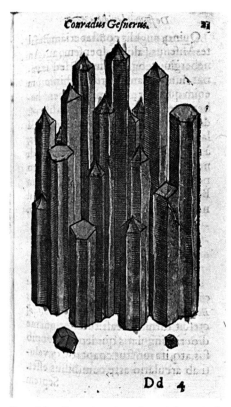

One of the illustrations from Conrad Gesner's *On Fossil Objects, Chiefly Stones, and Gems, Their Shapes and Appearances* (1565).

France, completed in 1831 on six sheets to a scale of 1:500,000.

Élie de Beaumont's main contribution to geological thought was set out in his *Researches on Some of the Revolutions of the Globe* (1829–30). He tried to show how the mountain ranges of the globe were of different epochs and sudden elevation. The shock of elevation had had global consequences which were probably the cause of the revolutions of flora and fauna (including extinctions) which *Cuvier's paleontology demonstrated. The theory attracted contemporary support, since it plausibly linked the history of the globe with that of life. RP

Eskola, Pentti Eelis (1883–1964)

Born in Lellainen, Finland, Eskola was educated as a chemist at Helsinki. He was a life-long student of metamorphic rocks with particular reference to the *Precambrian of Finland. He was one of the first to apply physico-chemical principles extensively to the study of metamorphism, and laid the foundations of most subsequent studies in metamorphic petrology. The main feature of his work was that it began to define the varying pressure and temperature regimes under which *metamorphic rocks are formed, and so enabled rocks of widely differing compositions to be compared in terms of their pressure and temperature of origin. KGC

Geikie, Archibald (1835–1924)

Geikie first became interested in geology as a hobby. In 1855 he managed to secure a post on the Geological Survey, and by 1867 had become head of its Scottish branch. In 1881 he was promoted to become its Director General, and in 1908 he became the first

– and so far only – geologist ever to be President of the Royal Society.

He contributed to many areas of geology. His fundamental work was on ancient volcanic phenomena in Great Britain, set out most fully in *The Ancient Volcanoes of Great Britain* (1897). Not least among his achievements were many works on the history of geology, including his popular *Founders of Geology* (1905), and a series of distinguished textbooks. RP

Gesner, Conrad (1516–1565)

Born in Zurich, Gesner was perhaps the greatest of the encyclopedic naturalists of the 16th century.

His interest in the Earth issued in *On Fossil Objects, Chiefly Stones, and Gems, Their Shapes and Appearances* (1565): by "fossils", Gesner meant any objects of special interest dug up from the Earth, not merely organic remains, though he did compare many of his fossils to living specimens. He was less interested in questions of the origins of fossils than in describing them – and their powers (e.g., medicinal virtues). His work was a milestone in the enumeration, identification and description of mineral objects, not least because of the many accurate woodcuts which accompanied his text. RP

Gilbert, Grove Karl (1843–1918)

Born in Rochester, New York, Gilbert joined the Geological Survey of Ohio and subsequently worked with *Powell's Rocky Mountain expedition, the beginning of a long and fruitful association with Powell. He rose to become the chief geologist of the US Geological Survey.

His main work was on subaerial *erosion, especially on the problem of fluvial erosion in valleys, where his work to some extent paralleled, and to some extent influenced, that of *Davis. His theories on river valleys are most fully set out in his *Report on the Geology of the Henry Mountains* (1877). In the early 20th century he pioneered laboratory experiments replicating and simulating erosive situations. RP

Goldschmidt, Victor Moritz (1888–1947)

Born at Zurich, Switzerland, Goldschmidt is regarded as the father of *geochemistry.

Working in Oslo from 1920 to 1928, and in Göttingen from 1929 to 1935, Goldschmidt and his colleagues set about a massive analytical program directed at all types of geological materials. As a result of their labors, the distribution of most elements in most rocks and minerals became well known; and Goldschmidt proposed rules governing the distribution of trace elements in minerals which did much to set geochemistry on a firm theoretical basis. KGC

Grabau, Amadeus William (1870–1946)

Born at Cedarburg, Wisconsin, Grabau studied at MIT and Harvard. He became one of the great pioneers of *paleoecology. He stressed the importance of the environment of deposition in determining the characters of rocks and their fossil assemblages. He also devoted much work to a petrological classification of *sedimentary rocks, placing particular emphasis on the need to arrange them according to origin as well as to composition and texture.

Grabau was concerned to explain the development of the distribution of land and sea throughout the globe, and devised an early theory of *continental drift. In his *Rhythm of the Ages* (1940) he developed a "pulsation theory" which saw the distribution of land masses as the product of major rhythmic marine advances and recessions. To a large extent his theory has been superseded by modern ideas. RP

Guettard, Jean-Étienne (1715–1786)

Born at Étampes, Guettard showed deep interest in botany and medicine, but his chief scientific pursuits were geological. He was the first to recognize the volcanic nature of the Auvergne district of Central France, and his discovery led to the enormous geological interest subsequently shown in the area.

Secondly, he played an important part in originating the debate on the origin of *basalt, at first asserting that columnar basalt was not volcanic in origin: however, after visits to Italy in the 1770s, he began to doubt his earlier views.

Thirdly, he pioneered geological cartography. In 1746 he presented his first mineralogical map of France to the Academy; and in 1766 he and Lavoisier were commissioned to prepare a geological survey of France, of which they completed about an eighth. RP

Gutenberg, Beno (1889–1960)

Together with Charles F. Richter (with whom he collaborated), Gutenberg stands as the leading seismologist of the 20th century. Much of his work centered on the problem of making inferences about the various layers of the Earth's mantle and core from the study of seismic waves, their patterns and velocities. He deduced the existence of a low-velocity layer at a depth of some 1800mi (2900km), computed from the travel-time of waves. This provided an important hinge for theories of crustal movements. RP

Hall, Sir James (1761–1832)

The son and heir of Sir John Hall of Dunglass, Berwickshire, Hall spent much of the 1780s traveling in Europe, becoming a convert to the new chemistry of Lavoisier and undertaking lengthy geological observation in the Alps and in Italy and Sicily.

He was a friend of *Hutton and an early defender of his theories. Hall's geological work centered upon finding experimental proofs for Hutton's speculations. In a series of furnace experiments, he showed with some success that Hutton was correct to claim that *igneous rocks could assume crystalline structures if cooled very slowly; that there was a degree of interconvertibility between basaltine and granitic rocks; and that limestone subjected to enormous heat would not decompose if maintained under sufficient pressure. RP

Hall, James (1811–1898)

Born in Hingham, Massachusetts, Hall was

employed from 1836 on the newly founded Geological Survey of New York State. Five years' work for this led to a stratigraphical outline and an unrivalled collection of invertebrate fossils. The fruit was Hall's massive 13-volume *Paleontology of New York (1874–94)*.

In 1843 he was appointed State Paleontologist, holding the post until his death. Partly under his prompting a state museum was established, of which he was made curator in 1864 and first director in 1871. Hall was also active in the establishment of other state geological surveys.

In 1857 he outlined the important idea of crustal downfolds at the edges of continents. He believed that these filled with sediments and in course of time could become mountain ranges (such as the Appalachians). *Dana was one who took up this notion. RP

Haug, Gustave Emile (1861–1927)

Born at Drusenheim, Alsace, Haug in 1887 migrated to Paris, holding a succession of posts at the Sorbonne, and becoming full professor in 1911. His research integrated many fields of geology, and the monument of his vision was his massive *Treatise of Geology* (1907–11). He made specific contributions to many fields. Among his lasting contributions to geological thought is his work on *geosynclines, including the formulation of Haug's rule, that subsidence in a geosyncline results in the regression of the sea over the adjacent epicontinental areas, and that folding in a geosyncline gives rise to marine encroachment. RP

Haüy, René-Just (1743–1822)

Born at St Just-en-Chaussée, Oise, Haüy entered the priesthood before becoming interested in mineralogy and crystallography. His two major works are the *Treatise of Mineralogy* (1801) and the *Treatise of Crystallography* (1822).

The regular forms of *crystals had drawn throughout the 17th and 18th centuries a plethora of causal explanations, in terms of shaping forces – some chemical, some physical, some atomistic – but none satisfactory. Haüy's approach was not to explain the causes of the regularly varied forms of crystals, but to try to classify those forms in terms of geometry – and above all, he hoped, through the geometry of simple relationships between integers.

He saw crystals as structured assemblages of secondary bodies (integrant molecules) that grouped themselves according to regular geometric laws. He proposed six types of primary forms: parallelepiped, rhombic dodecahedron, hexagonal dipyramid, right hexagonal prism, octahedron, and tetrahedron, and spent much of his career elaborating on this typology of forms. RP

Hess, Harry Hammond (1906–1969)

Harry Hess was a mineralogist, geologist, geophysicist and oceanographer. Born in New York, he received his geological education at Yale and Princeton after first studying electrical engineering. Hess was one of those rare scientists who achieved distinc-

tion in several fields.

He first began to study the oceans and geophysics in 1931, when he accompanied F. A. Vening Meinesz in an expedition by submarine to take soundings and measure gravity in the West Indies. During WWII he continued his oceanographic investigations while captain of the assault transport U.S.S. *Cape Johnson*; and it was at this time that he discovered the flat-topped sea mounts known as guyots. After the war he was an active sponsor of the Mohole project, in which an attempt was made to drill through the Earth's crust to reach the upper mantle.

His long interest in the oceans led in 1960 to the idea that convection within the Earth might lead to the generation of new ocean floor at mid-ocean ridges, the hypothesis known as sea-floor spreading. The interpretation of the magnetic anomalies of the sea floor by F. J. Vine and D. H. Matthews in 1963 provided the confirmation needed, and by 1968 *plate tectonics had become a reality.

The credit for this, the so-called "revolution in the earth sciences", representing the largest single advance in the earth sciences in the last sixty years, belongs largely to Hess. KGC

Holmes, Arthur (1890–1965)

Born at Hebburn, Newcastle-upon-Tyne, Holmes received his scientific education at Imperial College, London, first in physics and mathematics, then in geology.

He was distinguished in many branches of geology but is best remembered for his studies of geochronology, giving the first modern estimates of the *age of the Earth. Radioactivity had been recognized as promising a method by which the actual ages of minerals could be determined. In 1911 the first tentative mineral ages had been determined from uranium-lead ratios by Boltwood; and R. J. Strutt (later Lord Rayleigh) had discovered that the abundance of radioactive minerals in the Earth's crust was sufficient to provide a significant heat source, and thus that the assumptions used by *Kelvin in his estimate of the *age of the Earth were ill-founded.

Holmes began work on the uranium-lead method and in 1913 published *The Age of the Earth*, in which existing data were summarized and the first proper time scale for the Phanerozoic was presented. He continued work on the Phanerozoic time scale until 1959 but his original estimates did not require any fundamental changes.

Holmes' other important contributions included a notable text-book, *Principles of Physical Geology* (1st edn., 1944). KGC

Hooke, Robert (1635–1703)

Educated at Westminster and Christ Church, Oxford, Hooke showed genius in a wide range of sciences, falling short of Newton only in respect of his mathematical deficiencies. In geology his importance is twofold.

He was among the leading champions in his age of the belief that fossils were genuine organic remains. He was well aware that

many fossils were probably the remains of species which had become extinct.

Secondly, he advanced a theory of the Earth which stressed the power of natural causes to create, destroy and hold the Earth in equilibrium. He accepted the reality of denudation, while believing that volcanoes and earthquakes were creative processes in the reconstruction of the Earth. RP

Horne, John (1848–1928)

Horne entered the Geological Survey at the age of 19. He received his geological training from his superior, *Peach, and this initiated a lifetime's distinguished collaboration. Peach was the more imaginative and speculative member of the partnership, Horne the more judicious geologist, and the more articulate and lucid in print.

Their great work was on the northwest Highlands of Scotland. The orthodox view, established by *Murchison, was that the underlying fossiliferous Durness limestone passed up conformably into the eastern metamorphic schists, though voices had been raised against this. It took the deep researches of Horne and Peach to demonstrate conclusively the profound structural break separating the two orders of rock. RP

Humboldt, Friedrich Heinrich Alexander, Baron von (1769–1859)

Humboldt has exercised an enormous influence on the study of the globe, as an explorer, as a theorist, and as one who set out to chart the history of Man's interrelations with his planet Earth. In 1799 he set out on a pioneering and immensely productive expedition across Latin America, studying physical geography above all, but also collecting great quantities of geological, botanical and zoological material. The next 20 years were occupied in writing up his results in his *Narrative of Travels* (1818–19).

His ambition was to construct a new science, a "physics of the globe" which would demonstrate the deep interconnectedness of all terrestrial phenomena. He sought ultimately to understand relief in terms of Earth history, and geological phenomena in terms of more basic physical causes (e.g., the Earth's magnetism or rotation). He patiently collected evidence of similar geological phenomena from each continent.

His most popular work, *Cosmos*, begun 1845, is a profound and moving statement of Man's relationship with the Earth. RP

Hutton, James (1726–1797)

Son of an Edinburgh merchant, Hutton studied at Edinburgh University, Paris and Leiden, taking his doctorate in medicine in 1749. He spent the next two decades traveling and in farming. During this time he developed his taste in geology. About 1768 he moved back to Edinburgh and became a leading member of the scientific and literary establishment, playing a large role in the early history of the Royal Society of Edinburgh.

Hutton wrote widely on many fields of natural science, but he is best known for his

Baron von Humboldt (foreground), whose monumental *Narrative of Travels* (1818–19) contributed enormously to studies of botany, zoology and geology.

geology, set out in his *Theory of the Earth*, of which a short version appeared in 1788, followed by the definitive statement in 1795.

Hutton attempted to demonstrate a steady-state Earth, in which causes had always been of the same kind as at present, acting with the same intensity (Uniformitarianism). In the Earth's economy there was no vestige of a beginning, no prospect of an end. All continents were being gradually eroded by rivers and weather. Denuded debris accumulated on the sea bed, to be consolidated into strata and subsequently thrust upwards to form new continents by the Earth's central heat. Non-stratified rocks such as granite were of igneous origin. All the Earth's processes were very gradual. The Earth was incalculably old. The catch-phrase was: "The past is the key to the present."

Much attacked in its own day, Hutton's theory found more favor when popularized by ⋆Playfair and ⋆Lyell, and still forms the basis for much geological reasoning.　RP

Huxley, Thomas Henry (1825–1895)

Huxley trained for medicine and obtained a succession of teaching and honorific posts within the London scientific establishment. His most important role was as ⋆Darwin's bulldog in defence of *Origin of Species* (1859). In his early vindications, Huxley emphasized in an orthodox Darwinian way that the ⋆fossil record could not present positive evidence for evolutionary modifications of organic forms. By the 1870s, however, Huxley believed that the newly discovered extensive series of North American extinct horses, dating back to the upper Eocene, could now offer fossil proof that the gradual modifications demanded by Darwin's theory had actually occurred. RP

Kelvin, Lord (1824–1907)

Lord Kelvin, born William Thomson, was the son of a successful professor of mathematics and showed early mathematical aptitude. Throughout a long career he made enormous contributions to the development of modern physics. His one brief but notable foray into the Earth sciences had

profound consequences.

In the mid-19th century the doctrine of Uniformitarianism (see ⋆Hutton) was widespread among geologists, one of the accepted tenets being that the range of past time available for the explanation of geological phenomena was unlimited. Kelvin questioned this, and maintained that the Earth had a finite age. This he calculated as between 20 and 40 million years by considering the time required for a body like the Earth to cool from a molten state.

Kelvin underestimated the ⋆age of the Earth by a factor of more than 100, because he was unaware that an important extra heat source existed within the Earth – that is to say, its content of radioactive elements, notably uranium, thorium and potassium. Even in error Lord Kelvin performed a notable service for the developing Earth sciences, for he focused attention onto one of its most fundamental problems.　KGC

Lamarck, Jean Baptiste Pierre Antoine De Monet De (1744–1829)

Of impoverished noble stock from Picardy, Lamarck saw himself as a general natural philosopher, aiming to grasp the deep emergent unity of nature. He pursued studies in botany, zoology, paleontology, meteorology and chemistry, as well as developing the evolutionary theory for which he is most remembered, that acquired characteristics could be inherited.

He set out his geological views in his *Hydrogeology* (1802). The Earth was indefinitely old, and was being continually changed within a balance of gradual organic, climatic, and marine forces. Tidal forces were gradually eroding old continents and building up new ones. The sea and land masses were slowly progressing around the Earth. The sedimentary matter out of which rocks were built was essentially organic detritus (e.g., limestone from shells).

Lamarck seems to have believed that this geological theory obviated the need for extinction (the reality of which he fiercely denied) but produced those environmental pressures which explained complex diversities in the direction of organic ⋆evolution.
RP

Lapworth, Charles (1842–1920)

Lapworth's early work was on the Southern Uplands of Scotland. The shale-band outcrops had been thought to represent successive horizons in a very thick ascending series of strata. But, employing exact mapping and using the ⋆graptolites as an index, Lapworth was able to show how in reality the outcrops were repetitions of comparatively few bands, constituting a series of overfolds which had become parallel as a result of compaction. By examining graptolite evidence from many parts of the world, he showed his method of identification to be generally applicable.

We owe the conception of the ⋆Ordovician, filling the gray area between the Cambrian and the Silurian so much disputed by ⋆Murchison and ⋆Sedgwick, to Lapworth's suggestion.　RP

Leakey, Louis Seymour Bazett (1903-1972)

Son of a Kenya missionary, Leakey studied at St John's College, Cambridge. Working with his wife on the Miocene deposits of western Kenya, he discovered the skull of *Proconsul africanus*. His archaeological investigations lighted upon the Acheulian site of Olduvai, in the Rift Valley, where the skull of *Australopithecus boisei* and the first remains of *Homo habilis*, a *hominid dated at some 1.7 million years, were found.

Other skulls of the founders of the Acheulian culture at Olduvai, dubbed *Homo erectus*, have since been discovered. Leakey's son Richard (1944–) now appears to have discovered hominid remains dating back perhaps 4 million years.   RP

Le Gros Clark, Sir Wilfrid Edward (1895-1971)

Le Gros Clark excelled in two main fields of science, the comparative anatomy and physiology of the *primates, and questions of early Man and his antecedents. He was initially skeptical of the claims of *Dart and others for the hominid affinities of *Australopithecus*. Having visited South African sites for himself, however, he confirmed Dart's conviction that *Australopithecus* was close to the main line of *hominid evolution and separate from that of anthropoid apes. He also played a large part in exposing the Piltdown Man forgery.   RP

Lehmann, Johann Gottlob (1719-1767)

Lehmann has a strong claim to be called one of the founding fathers of stratigraphy. In his *Attempt at a History of Sedimentary Rock-Forms* (1756), he set out his view that there were fundamental distinctions between Ganggebürgen (masses formed of veined rock) and Flötz-Gebürgen (masses formed of stratified rock). These distinctions represented different modes and times of origin, strata being found in historical sequence. The older strata were chemically precipitated out of water, the more recent strata mechanically deposited by the separation of sediment.

Lehmann's work in this direction laid the foundations for *Werner's more refined stratigraphy.   RP

Leonardo da Vinci (1452-1519)

Leonardo's all-round genius brought him face-to-face with problems of understanding the Earth. He saw the Earth undergoing perpetual change, largely occasioned by the forces of weather and water (both marine *erosion of coasts and river erosion of hills). Solid land was perpetually decaying into alluvial plains. The creation by rivers of their own valleys, which they then silted up, fascinated him. Land loss was being compensated for by a steady rise of the continents from the sea (as erosion made them lighter, they were able to rise).

His awareness of the denudatory power of water enabled him to recognize fossils as organic remains buried in strata debris, and he pointed to the similarities between fossil and living specimens. He denied that fossils were due to the Flood and privately speculated on the high antiquity of the Earth. RP

Logan, Sir William Edmond (1798-1875)

Born at Montreal of Scottish descent, Logan was educated at Edinburgh University.

In 1842 the Canadian government set up its own Geological Survey, with Logan as its director. His lifework thereafter was on Canadian geology, up to 1869 for the Survey, and privately after his retirement: he spent much of his personal fortune in promoting the Survey.

Logan's main qualities as a geologist were the accuracy and detail of his descriptive fieldwork. One of his main interpretative achievements was to explain the structural anomaly by which the older Quebec rocks overlie the younger Ordovician beds of the St Lawrence lowlands. He showed this was due to a massive thrust fault, which he traced from Alabama to the Canadian border.   RP

Lyell, Sir Charles (1797-1875)

Born on his father's estate at Kinnordy, Angus, Lyell was educated at Oxford, where his growing appetite for geology was fed by *Buckland. He trained for a career in law, but used his weak eyesight as a convenient pretext to pursue his favorite subject, geology, full-time.

Much of the 1820s Lyell spent geologizing, culminating in his expedition in 1828 with *Murchison through the Auvergne and on his own through Italy and Sicily. These experiences led him to a geological theory bearing strong resemblances to *Hutton's, which he set out in his *Principles of Geology* (3 vols, 1830-33), perhaps the most influential book in the history of geology. He argued for a steady-state, Uniformitarian view of the Earth and of the history of life (Man excluded). Present Earth processes – denudation, land-building, volcanic action – were supposed, given time, to be adequate to explain past changes. He argued that the "catastrophes" then so popular in *Cuvier's directional biostratigraphy were unscientific – and unnecessary.

Lyell argued that living populations became extinct gradually. His examples from recent geological history established the concept of the *Tertiary and its subdivisions.

In writing the *Principles*, Lyell was a powerful enemy of *Lamarck's evolutionary theories. In later years, however, he was won over, somewhat grudgingly, to accept his friend *Darwin's new theory of *evolution. His *Antiquity of man* (1863) assembled the evidence for a high antiquity for Man, and cautiously hinted at the possibility of human evolution from the higher primates.   RP

Mantell, Gideon Algernon (1790-1852)

A man of enormous energies and enthusiasms, Mantell became a successful surgeon, but his hobby of geology steadily grew until it monopolized his life. He was a prolific writer, not least of popular texts. His contemporary fame rested on having identified for the first time fossils of a land

saurian (i.e., dinosaur) – the enormous Mesozoic saurians reconstructed earlier by *Cuvier and others had been aquatic. Among his other work on extinct giant vertebrates was his discovery of armored dinosaurs (*Hylaeosaurus*).   RP

Marsh, Othniel Charles (1831-1899)

Son of a farmer of modest means, Marsh was an important public figure in US science. He acted as vertebrate paleontologist to the US Geological Survey (1882-92), and built up the vast fossil collections of the Peabody Museum at Yale (established by his uncle). His paleontological interpretations depended on the completeness and magnitude of phylogenetic series of fossil specimens housed in his huge collections.

His early work hinged upon four great expeditions through the Western territories between 1870 and 1873. His greatest achievement lay in his remarkable series of fossil horses from the Eocene (*Orohippus*) to the Pleistocene. He showed how European horses were an offshoot of the main American line of evolution. *Huxley used this succession as the best fossil evidence available in his day for Darwinian evolutionary change.   RP

Murchison, Roderick Impey (1792-1871)

A gentleman amateur, Murchison became a "professional" in 1855, succeeding *De la Beche as Director of the Geological Survey. He spent a generation in the field surveying strata according to clear interpretative principles. He believed in a near universal order of deposition, indicated by fossils rather than purely by lithological features. Fossils themselves would show a clear progression in complexity from Azoic (pre-life) times to invertebrates, and only then up to vertebrate forms, Man being created last: this progression was allied to the Earth's cooling.

The great triumph of these principles was to unravel the *Silurian system (i.e., those strata beneath the Old Red Sandstone). For Murchison, the Silurian contained remains of the earliest life (though no fossils of vertebrates or land plants were to be expected). Controversy with De la Beche over the younger end of the Silurian led to Murchison introducing, with *Sedgwick, the fruitful concept of the *Devonian, which incorporated the Old Red Sandstone.

But Murchison also quarreled with Sedgwick over the lower limits of the Silurian, seemingly seeking to incorporate Sedgwick's independent *Cambrian: on this he proved in error. He stubbornly denied there were fossiliferous systems underlying the Silurian.

Late in life, Murchison became highly dogmatic. His growing campaign against *Lyell's Uniformitarianism turned into a rigid denial of Darwinian evolution.   RP

Murray, John (1841-1914)

Born at Cobourg, Ontario, Murray was educated in medicine at Edinburgh. However, after a voyage on an Arctic whaler in

1868 the sea became his great love. Between 1872 and 1876 he was one of C. Wyville-Thomson's assistants on the epoch-making voyage of the *Challenger*. After Thomson's death, Murray edited the 50-volume *Report* of the voyage (published 1880–95), so influential in the establishment of oceanography as an organized science.

Murray's chief scientific work lay in investigating the sedimentary deposits on the ocean floor. He identified the main contributors to organic sediment, and showed they were chiefly surface dwellers. He also traced the extent of inorganic mud, which he believed originated from volcanic dust. His work on the *ocean floor emphasized the slowness of deposition.   RP

D'Orbigny, Alcide Charles Victor des Sallines (1802–1857)

Born at Couëron, near the mouth of the Loire, d'Orbigny obtained his scientific education in Paris.

His career falls into two parts. In 1826 he was commissioned to explore South America. He was away for eight years, making arguably the most thorough natural-history investigation of that continent yet undertaken, publishing his findings in the 10 volumes of his *Travels in South America* (1834–47).

His other chief concern was in paleontology, undertaking two major ventures. From 1840 he worked on the *Paléontologie française*, which was to be a complete account of all known forms of mollusks, echinoderms, brachiopods and bryozoans found in French Jurassic and Cretaceous deposits. An even grander project was his *Introduction to Universal Palaeontology* (1850–52), which sought to divide up all known fossils into 27 successive, and essentially distinct, extinct faunas. Such a view was based upon the Cuvierian notion of successive destructions and creations in Earth history, and so was rather undercut by the subsequent acceptance of *evolution.   RP

Osborn, Henry Fairfield (1857–1935)

Osborn's main work was in vertebrate paleontology. He eagerly accepted evolutionary theory and was concerned to fill out its main trends and details. He continued *Cope's work on the evolution of mammalian molar teeth and wrote an influential textbook, *The Age of Mammals* (1910).

His evolutionary studies focused on the problem of the adaptive diversification of life. He was particularly concerned with the parallel but independent evolution of related lines of descent, and with the explanation of the gradual appearance of new structural units of adaptive value. He always stressed the way evolution results from pressures from four major directions: external environment, internal environment, heredity, selection.

A convinced Christian, he was deeply involved with the interpretation of evolution in religious and moral terms.   RP

Owen, Sir Richard (1804–1892)

Owen's early career was marked by a phenomenal quantity of zoological identification and classification in the style of *Cuvier. He then became progressively more interested in paleontology, his work on the reconstruction of the New Zealand moa and on *Archaeopteryx* being classics of their kind. He published an important *History of British Fossil Reptiles* (1849–84) and a popular textbook, *Palaeontology* (1860).

Owen came into collision with the Darwinians on two important issues. He made Man the single example of a special subclass of Mammalia: *Huxley, in reply, showed plausibly that the anatomical grounds for this classification were illusory. Owen also fiercely attacked Darwin's natural-selection mechanism for evolution.   RP

Peach, Benjamin Neeve (1842–1926)

Much of Peach's childhood was spent in the north of Scotland, near where he was to accomplish his most important work, with *Horne on the question of the succession of strata in the northwest of Scotland. *Murchison, as Director of the Geological Survey, had interpreted the Moine Schists as part of the *Silurian, and asserted they succeeded conformably upon the fossiliferous Durness limestone. Peach was at first inclined to accept this interpretation; but, seeing on the shore of Loch Eireboll Cambrian zones repeated over and over again by thrusting, he started a major reinterpretation. He began to see the remarkable tectonic features which signified the fundamental unconformability between the two orders: overfolds, reversed faults and gigantic lateral thrusts. In 1884 *Geikie, the new Director of the Survey, publicly acknowledged Peach's new assessment, which signalled the yielding of traditional stratigraphy to the new discipline of petrological tectonics.   RP

Penck, Albrecht (1858–1945)

Penck was a leading student of the *Quaternary. Almost all aspects of current relief occupied his attention, and he ranged freely into prehistory, anthropogeography and climatology as well as in the mainstream of geomorphology.

His principal work was on the Alps, and is summed up in *The Alps in Times of Ice Ages* (3 vols., 1901–09), in which he established the basic fourfold division of the Pleistocene glaciation of the Alps. Penck never minimized the complexities of this period, seeking rather to study their causes: glacial isostasy, tectonic movements and changing climatic conditions.   RP

Playfair, John (1748–1819)

Playfair was born near Dundee, son of a Scottish minister of religion. Educated at St Andrews and Edinburgh universities, he followed his father into the ministry. From 1785 to 1805 he was Professor of Mathematics at Edinburgh, vacating the chair for that of Natural Philosophy. He is chiefly remembered, however, as a friend, early supporter and popularizer of the ideas of *Hutton, particularly in his *Illustration of the Huttonian Theory of the Earth* (1802). Almost all 19th-century geologists learned about Hutton through reading Playfair.   RP

Powell, John Wesley (1834–1902)

Powell was intended by his Methodist farmer father for the Methodist ministry, but he early developed a love for natural history. In the 1850s he became secretary of the Illinois Society of Natural History.

In 1870 Congress placed him at the head of an official survey of the resources of the Utah, Colorado, and Arizona area, the fruits of which were published in his *The Exploration of the Colorado River* (1875) and *The Geology of the Eastern Portion of the Uinta Mountains* (1876). This work produced lasting insights on fluvial erosion, volcanism, isostasy and orogeny; but, even more significantly, Powell grasped how geological and climatic causes together produce the essential aridity of the region.

For almost 20 years thereafter he campaigned for massive funds for irrigation projects and dams, and for the geological surveys necessary to work out a water policy. He also argued the need for a change in land policy and farming techniques in the "drylands". Suffering political defeats on these issues, he resigned in 1894 from the Geological Survey, of which he had become director in 1881.   RP

Rosenbusch, Karl Harry Ferdinand (1836–1914)

Born at Einbeck, Hannover, Rosenbusch received his scientific education at Freiburg and Heidelberg.

He graduated at a time when the study of rocks in thin section by microscopic means was in its infancy. It was clearly necessary to correlate all the available information relating to the optical properties of minerals as exhibited in thin sections. This was done by Rosenbusch in 1873 in *Microscopic Structure of the Petrographically Important Minerals*, a work which became a standard text in optical mineralogy.

Rosenbusch also devoted much effort to the description and classification of rocks, particularly *igneous rocks, and is well known for his *Microscopic Structure of the Bulky Rocks*, which appeared in various editions between 1877 and 1908.

Rosenbusch and *Zirkel stand together as the founders of petrography, the descriptive aspect of the study of rocks.   KGC

Scrope, George Julius Poullett (1797–1876)

Scrope studied at Cambridge, being influenced by *Sedgwick, and for half a dozen years thoroughly explored the volcanic areas of Italy and Sicily, the Auvergne, Vivarais and Velay areas of France, and the Eifel region of Germany. The fruits of this exploration were his *Geology and Extinct Volcanoes of Central France* (1826) and *Considerations upon Volcanoes* (1828).

His interpretations of volcanism followed *Hutton and anticipated *Lyell. He stressed the vast extent of volcanic phenomena and showed the volcanic origin of *basalt and related rocks. He argued that volcanoes had been continuously active through geological time, thus emphasizing the "actualist" conception that nature always acts by the same order of causation. He saw how volcanoes were instrumental in mountain-building. His work on the Auvergne also convinced him of continual massive fluvial *erosion.   RP

Sedgwick, Adam (1785–1873)

Son of the curate of Dent, in North West Yorkshire, Sedgwick attended Trinity College, Cambridge, where he became fellow in 1810. Though knowing no geology, he was appointed Woodwardian professor in 1818, holding the chair for 55 years. He soon made himself one of the foremost British geologists.

Sedgwick combined a highly Baconian approach to geological investigation, seeing facts founded on fieldwork as the essence of the science, with strongly held Christian sentiments. He never fully approved of *Hutton's Uniformitarianism; was suspicious of glacial theory; and set his face completely against all theories of evolution, not least those of his former pupil and friend, Charles *Darwin.

Sedgwick excelled in two fields. He was a foremost student of paleontology, especially of Paleozoic fossils, and he also contributed greatly to understanding the stratigraphy of the British Isles, using fossils as an index of relative time, and assuming relatively distinct fauna and flora for each period. His major work lay in the geology of Wales, and bringing to birth the concept of a *Cambrian system, over which he eventually quarrelled with *Murchison. With Murchison, Sedgwick was instrumental in formulating the idea of a *Devonian system encompassing the Old Red Sandstone.   RP

Smith, William (1769–1839)

"Strata" Smith was a pioneering figure in British stratigraphy.

He received little formal education. Born at Churchill, Oxfordshire, he became skilled in the arts of land drainage and improvement, canal construction and mine surveying and prospecting. He also gained close familiarity with the terrain in a broad swathe of England from Somersetshire through to the northeast. Throughout the 1790s his geological ideas developed, and by 1799 he was able to set out a fairly comprehensive list of the secondary strata of England and had started to construct geological maps.

Smith was not the first geologist to recognize the *principles of stratigraphy, or the usefulness of type fossils. His achievement was to actually determine the succession of English strata from the Carboniferous up to the Cretaceous in greater detail than previously and to establish their fossil specimens.

Beyond this, perhaps, lay his achievements in mapping. Smith rightly saw the map as the perfect medium for presenting stratigraphical knowledge. In developing a form of map which showed outcrops in block, he set the essential pattern for geological mapping throughout the 19th century.

His relations with the main British geological community remained ambiguous

A contemporary caricature of the 19th-century paleontologist Richard Owen, shown here "riding his hobby".

and even strained up to the 1820s. In 1831, however, his work was belatedly recognized by the Geological Society of London in the award to him of the first Wollaston Medal.

Sorby, Henry Clifton (1826–1908)

Sorby may be called the founder of microscopic petrology in Britain. Before Sorby, Sir David Brewster (1781–1868) had explored the molecular structure of minerals by investigating how light passed through them, but Brewster had been limited to the investigation of well crystallized specimens.

Sorby overcame this problem by adapting the art of thin-slicing of hard minerals, analyzing under the microscope specimens treated thus. His early papers met with much hostility amongst contemporaries, but came to be recognized as opening up a new science, though one to be developed

more in Germany – by *Zirkel, *Rosenbusch and Vogelsang – than in Britain.

Sorby's interests spread over into metallurgy, where he employed his microscopic techniques to investigate the structures of iron and steel under stress.   RP

Steno, Nicolaus (1638–1686)

Steno (or Niels Stensen, as he was known in his native Denmark) studied medicine at Leiden in the Dutch Republic, migrated to Paris and then obtained a post in Florence under Duke Ferdinand. In 1666, he was struck by the similarity between shark's teeth and certain objects, found on or near the surface of the Earth, called glossopetrae, "tonguestones". He concluded that the stones were the petrified remains of sharks' teeth. In his *Sample of the Elements of*

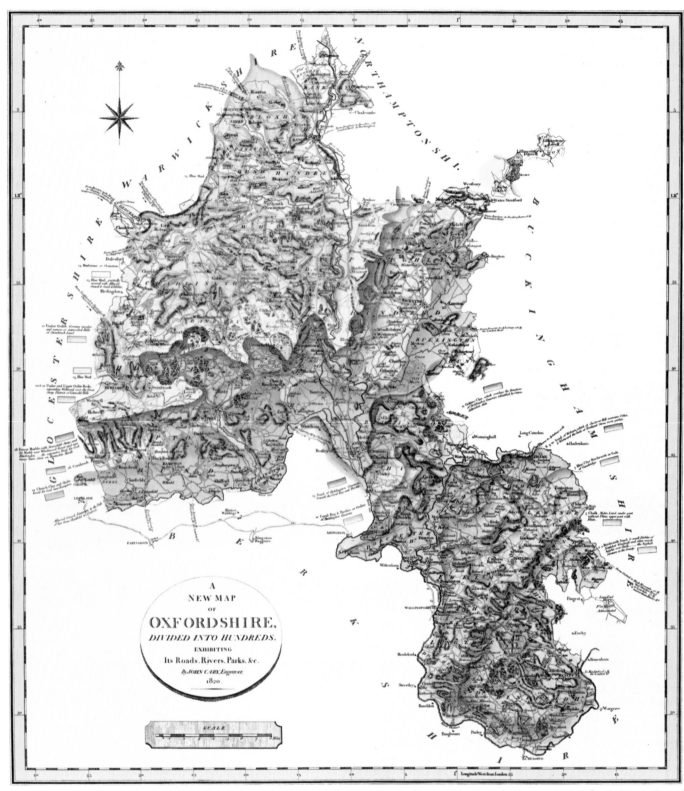

A geological map by William Smith showing the rock types to be found in different parts of Oxfordshire, England.

Mylogy (1667), he demonstrated how they had come to be mineralized.

From there he was led to consider the problem of how such fossils came to be deeply embedded in rocks. He assumed six successive periods of Earth history: first, a period of deposition of non-fossiliferous strata from an ocean; then several peiods of undermining and collapse; then another period of the deposition of strata, this time fossiliferous; followed by further undermining and collapse. This explained why the deepest strata contain no fossils but are

overlain by fossiliferous strata, and also why certain strata are found horizontal while others are tilted to the horizon.

Steno's work is important as one of the earliest directional accounts of both Earth and life history, and it was of considerable influence in the 17th and 18th centuries. RP

Suess, Edward (1831–1914)

Born in London, Suess was educated in Vienna and at the University of Prague. As well as his geological interests, he occupied himself with public affairs.

His geological researches took many di-

rections. As paleontologist, he studied graptolites, brachiopods, ammonites and the fossil mammals of the Danube Basin. He wrote a pioneering text on economic geology. He carried out important research on the structure of the Alps, the tectonic geology of Italy and seismology. He was concerned with a possible former land-

Drawing by Steno showing the effects of folding and faulting (running from 25 back to 20).

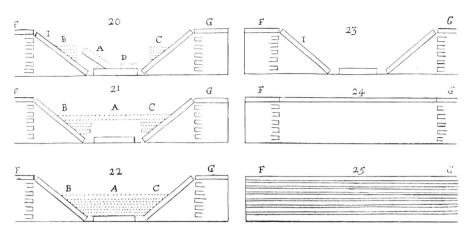

bridge between North Africa and southern Europe.

The fruit of these interests was *The Face of the Earth* (1885–1909), a work devoted to investigating the physical agencies which had determined the Earth's geographical evolution. Suess offered a comprehensive view of crustal movement, of the structure and distribution of mountain chains, of foundered continents, of the history of the oceans; and he rewrote on new lines the structural geology of each continent. This essentially held good until the coming of the theory of ⋆plate tectonics in the 20th century. RP

Ussher, James (1581–1656)

A student of Trinity College Dublin, James Ussher followed a career in the Church of England, and eventually rose to become Archbishop of Dublin. He was an important historical, philological, and Biblical scholar. One of the fields to which he turned was universal chronology, in particular in his posthumously published *Sacred Chronology* (1660).

Contemporary scholars were deeply concerned with the problem of relative and absolute datings of the history of mankind, beginning from Adam. Their methods were to compute backwards, largely using written evidence, and, above all, the various texts of the Bible. Because the Bible pronounced human and earthly history inseparable, and that the Earth had been created only six days before Man, it was widely assumed that the age of the Earth could be calculated from that of Man.

Ussher arrived at a date of creation of the Earth of 4004BC, a figure which (within a few hundred years either way) was widely acceptable in the 17th century; and which has since become famous.

It is often assumed that Ussher's figure was in some way "official" and that not till the 19th century did any Christian dare postulate much higher figures for the Earth's antiquity. This is not true. Several 17th-century British geologists advanced much higher estimates. RP

Walther, Johannes (1860–1938)

Walther was born in 1860 at Neustadt-an-Orla. The first part of his career was chiefly spent on paleontological research into fossil shells, corals and fossil fish. His interests lay less with the reconstruction of the forms of life than with the problems of the fossilization of specimens within sediments on the sea floor.

Walther also became occupied with lithogeny. He took up the wider question of the origin, nature and formation of deserts, and became possibly the world's greatest authority on the geology of deserts, in a series of books beginning with his *Denudation in Deserts and their Geological Meaning* (1891). He is well known also for his important statement of the nature of geology as a science, *Introduction to Geology as a Historical Science* (1890–93). RP

Wegener, Alfred (1880–1930)

Wegener seems at this time to be the most influential geologist of the 20th century. Though by no means the first theorist of ⋆continental drift, Wegener's expositions of the theory, especially his *The Origin of Continents and Oceans* (1929), endowed the hypothesis with scientific plausibility.

Born in Berlin in 1880, Wegener studied at Heidelberg, Innsbruck and Berlin. Before WWI he taught at Marburg. From 1924 until his death on his third expedition to Greenland he held a specially created chair in meteorology and geophysics at Graz, Austria.

From 1910 he began to develop his theory of continental drift, or continental displacement. Empirical evidence for this was the close jigsaw fit between coastlines on either side of the Atlantic, and paleontological similarities between Brazil and Africa. But Wegener had strong convictions that geophysical and geodetical considerations would also support a theory of wandering continents – though he himself was rather unclear about the causes of such displacement, believing partly in tidal forces and partly in a "flight from the poles".

Wegener supposed that the Mesozoic had seen the existence of a united supercontinent, Pangaea. This had developed numerous rifts and had drifted apart. During the Cretaceous, South America and Africa had effectively split, but not until the end of the Quaternary had North America and Europe finally separated, or South America from Antarctica. Australia had been severed from Antarctica during the Eocene.

Wegener's hypothesis met general hostility in its own day. Only with the development of a satisfactory mechanism for displacement, i.e., with the rise of the theory of ⋆plate tectonics since WWII, has the (modified) hypothesis won support. RP

Werner, Abraham Gottlob (1749–1817)

Born in Silesia, Werner studied between 1769 and 1771 at the Mining School at Freiberg, Saxony, and then at Leipzig. In 1775 he was appointed to the Freiberg Akademie, where he continued to teach for the rest of his life. He was the most influential teacher in the history of geology, most of the leading geologists of the next generation having studied under him.

Though wrong on many points, and much attacked (and misunderstood) in the early 19th century, Werner's geology was of fundamental importance in its day for establishing a physically-based stratigraphy. He proposed a general succession of the creation of rocks, beginning with Primary Rocks (precipitated from the water of a universal ocean), then passing through Transition, Flötz (sedimentary), and finally Recent and Volcanic. The oldest rocks were chemically deposited, crystalline and fossilless. Later rocks were mechanically deposited, fossiliferous and superincumbent, formed out of the denuded debris of the first creations.

Werner's approach was particularly important for linking the order of the strata to the history of the Earth, and relating the studies of mineralogy and strata. RP

Woodward, John (1665–1728)

A vain and jealous man, Woodward crossed swords with many of his contemporaries. In his will he established the Woodwardian Chair of Geology at Cambridge, and left to the university his magnificent fossil and mineral collections.

He was a theorist of the Earth, a pioneer of stratigraphy, and an important collector and systematizer of fossils. He asserted that the strata lay in regular order throughout the globe and that fossils were organic remains (contrary to the general view of the time, which saw them as sports of nature). Both phenomena he attributed to the effects of the Flood, which he explained by the action and suspension of the Newtonian force of gravity. RP

Zirkel, Ferdinand (1838–1912)

Ferdinand Zirkel was born and educated in Bonn. He trained as a mining engineer but as a young man acquired an interest in the microscopic study of rocks in thin section, a technique which had recently been developed by ⋆Sorby.

His detailed studies of a great variety of rocks culminated in the publication in 1866 of his *Textbook of Petrography*, which later appeared as an expanded second edition in 1893–94. This work, together with those of ⋆Rosenbusch, marked the founding of the science of petrography, the descriptive and classificatory study of rocks. KGC

ILLUSTRATION CREDITS